THE GREAT NAVAL BATTLE OF OTTAWA

DAVID ZIMMERMAN

The Great Naval Battle
of Ottawa

UNIVERSITY OF TORONTO PRESS
Toronto Buffalo London

© University of Toronto Press 1989
Toronto Buffalo London
Printed in Canada

ISBN 0-8020-2687-7

Printed on acid-free paper

Canadian Cataloguing in Publication Data

Zimmerman, David, 1959–
    The great naval battle of Ottawa

Bibliography: p.
Includes index.
ISBN 0-8020-2687-7

1. Canada. Royal Canadian Navy. 2. World War,
1939–1945 – Technology. 3. Technological
innovations – Government policy – Canada.
I. Title.

D779.C2Z55   1989   940.54'5971   c88-095103-6

This book has been published with the help of a grant from the Social Science
Federation of Canada, using funds provided by the Social Sciences and
Humanities Research Council of Canada, and with block grants from the Canada
Council and the Ontario Arts Council.

In memory of my father, Eugene H. Zimmerman

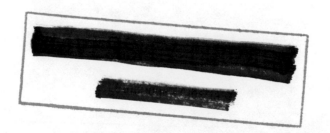

Contents

ACKNOWLEDGMENTS ix
ABBREVIATIONS xi

Introduction 3
1 From Nothing but Possibilities 6
2 Science Found 23
3 The Discovery of Radar 38
4 Nuts and Bolts – Organization 50
5 Liaison 65
6 Shortwave Confusion 72
7 Sound Problems 85
8 Exile and Dissent 98
9 The Ten-Centimetre Débâcle 111
10 One Step Behind 125
11 Confrontation and Dismissal 135
12 The Case of the Missing Scientists 148
Epilogue 161

NOTES 169
BIBLIOGRAPHY 195
PICTURE CREDITS 202
INDEX 203

Acknowledgments

I owe my greatest thanks and appreciation to D.S. 'Toby' Graham, whose unfailing patience and unsurpassed understanding has made this study possible. Marc Milner, the historian of RCN operations whose work and comments have guided me through the maze of Canadian naval history, has been of inestimable assistance. I also owe many thanks to Steven Turner for his introduction to the history of military science, to T.W. Acheson for his course on Canadian business history, and to Ernest Forbes for his insights into the east coast ship repair industry.

Of the many research centres I have worked at I would like to single out for praise the Directorate of History, Department of National Defence, Ottawa. Dr Alec Douglas and his staff have provided me with unfailing support throughout the last three years and five months. Dr Roger Sarty of the Directorate deserves special mention for his assistance both in finding documents and in providing accommodation. I would also like to thank Dr Alfred Tickner for his help; he provided me with vital documentation not seen since the war while I worked at the National Research Council. The Fifth Floor staff of the Harriet Irving Library also deserve special mention for providing a quiet and comfortable place to work during my long sojourn in Fredericton. Thanks are also owed to the staffs of all the various archives I have used, including the National Archives of Canada, the Public Record Office, Churchill College, Cambridge, the National Archives in Waltham and Washington, the Naval Historical Centre in Washington DC, and the Public Archives of Nova Scotia.

The completion of this work was made possible by the editorial staff at the University of Toronto Press. Special thanks to Gerald Hallowell of University of Toronto Press and to my copy-editor, Heather Martin.

I owe thanks to Nancy Burnham of the Tilley Hall Computer Centre, without whose assistance production of this manuscript would have been much more difficult. Also I must thank Karen Braun for her proof-reading of the manuscript. Many have assisted with accommodation during my travels, including Bobbi Milner, Ray Winn, Simon Chenery, my brother Peter Zimmerman and Britt Raphling, Bobbi and Milt Greene-Goldman.

The funding which made this project possible was provided by the graduate school of the University of New Brunswick and the Department of National Defence Post-doctoral Fellowship for Military History.

I would also like to express my gratitude to my many friends and colleagues who have kept me sane, provided a useful sounding board for ideas, and provided some interesting concepts. The list includes Adam Lynde, Brent Wilson, Mike Hennessy, Scot Robertson, David Hall, Martin Hewitt, Robert Tooley, Hurden Hooper, Chris Hull, and Mike Cessford. Finally thanks to my family for their support and assistance during my university years.

Abbreviations

AAAS	American Association for the Advancement of Science
ACNS	Assistant chief of Naval Staff
ADNR	Assistant director, Naval Research
AOR	Advisory Operational Researcher
AORG	Atlantic Oceanographic Research Group
A/S	Anti-submarine
ASE	Admiralty Signals Establishment
ASV	Air-to-Surface Vessel
ASW	Anti-submarine Warfare
BATM	British Admiralty Technical Mission
BCSO	British Central Scientific Office
BT	Bathythermography
C-in-C	Commander-in-Chief
Captain (D)	Captain Destroyers
CAT	Canadian Anti-torpedo
CBC	Canadian Broadcasting Commission
CBO	Chief of Bureau of Ordnance, USN
CCCS	Captain or Commodore Commanding, Canadian Ships (UK)
CD	Coast Defence
CIL	Canadian Industries Limited
CNA	Canadian North-West Atlantic
CNEC	Chief of Naval Engineering and Construction
CNES	Chief of Naval Equipment and Supply
CNO	Chief of Naval Operations USN
CNP	Chief of Naval Personnel
CNS	Chief of Naval Staff

COAC	Commanding officer, Atlantic Coast
COPC	Commanding officer, Pacific Coast
CRDF	Cathode ray direction finding
CSC	Canadian Sea Control – Prototype of SW1C
DA/S	Director, Anti-Submarine
DCNS	Deputy chief of Naval Staff
D/DSD	Deputy Director Signal Directorate
D/DWT	Deputy director of Warfare and Training
DES	Director of Electrical Supply
DHist	Directorate of History, Department of National Defence, Ottawa
DMR	Department of Mines and Resources
DMS	Department of Munitions and Supply
DND	Department of National Defence
DNE	Director of Naval Engineering
DNI	Director of Naval Intelligence
DNS	Director of Naval Stores
DOD	Director of Operation Directorate
DOP	Director of Plans
DOR	Director of Operational Research
DPB	Defence Purchasing Board
DPD	Director of Plans
DRB	Defence Research Board
DRS	Director of Radio Supply
DSD	Director of Signals Division
DTD	Director of Technical Division
DTR	Director of Technical Research
DWT	Director of Warfare and Training
EA	Electrical Artificer
FONF	Flag officer, Newfoundland
GL	Gun Laying
GLC	Gun Laying Canadian
HF/DF	High-frequency direction finding
HMCS	His Majesty's Canadian Ship
HMS	His Majesty's Ship
IEEE	Institute of Electron and Electrical Engineers
IFF	Identify friend or foe
IGS	Imperial General Staff
JCC	Joint Communications (Sub) Committee
LL	Anti-magnetic mine sweep

LONR	Liaison officer for Naval Research
MAP	Ministry of Aircraft Production (British)
MGO	Master General of the Ordnance Office
MIT	Massachusetts Institute of Technology
MOEF	Mid-Ocean Escort Force
MTB	Motor torpedo boat
NA	National Archives, Washington
NAASC	Navy, Army and Air Supply Committee
NA Waltham	National Archives, New England Branch at Waltham, Mass.
NDRC	National Defence Research Committee, USA
NEF	Newfoundland Escort Force
NRC	National Research Council, Ottawa
NRE	Naval Research Establishment, Halifax
NS	Naval Staff
NSHQ	Naval Service Headquarters, Ottawa
OR	Operational Research
OSRD	Office for Scientific Research and Development, USA
PAC	Public Archives of Canada
PANS	Public Archives of Nova Scotia
PPI	Planned Position Indicator
PRO	Public Record Office, London
RCAF	Royal Canadian Air Force
RCN	Royal Canadian Navy
RDF	Radio Direction Finding (term used for radar prior to mid-1943)
RDFO	Radar officer
REL	Research Enterprises Limited
RG	Record Group
RPV	Revised Patrol Vessel
RN	Royal Navy
RX/C	Canadian ten-centimetre radar
RX/U	Canadian/American Hybrid centimetric radar
SCFO	Senior Canadian Flag officer
SCNO	Senior Canadian Naval officer
SG	American ten-centimetre naval radar
SG2C	Canadian gunnery control centimetric radar
SJ	American submarine-based radar, set used in RX/U development
SO	Staff officer

STTD	Senior technician, Technical Division
SU	American three-centimetre radar
SV	Generic term used by USN for centimetric radar
SW1C	Surface Warning One Canadian radar
SW2C	Surface Warning Two Canadian radar
SW3C	Surface Warning Three Canadian radar
USN	United States Navy
VCNS	Vice-chief of Naval Staff
VE	Victory in Europe
WSB	War Supply Board

The River-class frigate HMCS *New Glasgow* off the British Columbia coast, 24 April 1944. She was the most modern anti-submarine vessel in the RCN but mounted the unworkable RX/C radar.

Admiral Percy W. Nelles, chief of Naval Staff, arriving at Naval Service
Headquarters, November 1943

Admiral Nelles (left) with Angus L. Macdonald (centre), the minister for the Naval Service, at a naval exhibition, December 1942. The model is of the corvette HMCS *Halifax*. Note the SW2C antenna on foremast.

C.J. Mackenzie, wartime president of the National Research Council

C.D. Howe, minister for the department of Munitions and Supply. Inscription reads: 'To Prime Minister Mackenzie King with sincere regards C.D. Howe.'

W.E. Phillips at his desk at Research Enterprises Limited, late 1940

The River-class destroyer HMCS *Ottawa* off Halifax, about September 1940. The *Ottawa* and the six other Rivers formed the all-too-small nucleus for the expanding RCN.

HMCS *Chambly* at Halifax, April 1940, just a few weeks before she was used to test the prototype 'CSC' radar. Note absence of anti-aircraft gun in aft gun tub.

HMCS *Battleford* escorting a convoy, November 1941. Note the SW1C antenna on the foremast.

HMCS *Shediac* off the coast of British Columbia, 16 December 1944. Note the extended forecastle, hedgehog, and the 271 radar dome.

Detailed view of HMCS *Fennel*, about May 1945. Note extended forecastle, 271 radar dome, and hedgehog.

sw2c antenna on HMCS *Kelowna*, March 1942

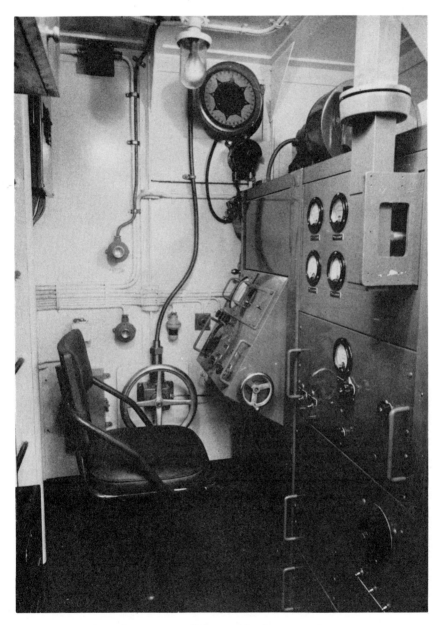

sw2c operator's station on HMCS *Kelowna*, March 1942

Operators' position of the type 127D asdic on HMCS *Rimouski*, 16 August 1943

Sailors loading a hedgehog anti-submarine mortar on HMCS *North Bay* at Halifax, October 1943

The entrance to Canada's top secret radar production installation, Research Enterprises Limited, 1941

THE GREAT NAVAL BATTLE OF OTTAWA

Introduction

It had been an extraordinary trip in a way. Since it was foggy we came round Cape Breton instead of taking the shorter route through the Gut of Canso. We used radar, which was the curiosity that made the voyage extraordinary. It had actually picked out the coast! It was hard to believe but the operator said he was sure it was the coast. Then he reported a vessel ahead and eventually we overtook her. The radar was right! In my ignorance of modern science I had not believed it possible, but who in the summer of 1941 knew much or anything about radar? I became for the first time aware of its possibilities and saw all the danger of fog magically disappearing. Life in the Atlantic, I misguidedly thought, was going to be almost rosy.

Alan Easton, *50 North*

The 'extraordinary' encounter that Alan Easton had with radar was much more than his first experience with a new form of equipment, for it also represented his introduction into a new type of warfare in which success or failure would in large measure be determined in the scientific laboratory. 'World War Two,' wrote the American scientific administrator Vannevar Bush, 'was the first war in human history to be affected decisively by weapons unknown at the outbreak of hostilities.'[1] To conduct such a war successfully required the effective co-operation of the traditional military establishment with science and high-technology industry. Nowhere was this more true than in the lengthy campaign known as the Battle of the Atlantic, the German assault on the ocean trade routes. The wartime development of centimetric radar, which removed the cloak of invisibility granted to U-boat surface night attacks, is just one example of why success in this campaign was due as much to the scientist as to the sailor. Anti-submarine warfare was, and still is, one of the most technically complex and sophisticated forms of military endeavour.

Winston Churchill wrote on the strategic significance of the Battle of the Atlantic: 'Battles might be won or lost, enterprises succeed or miscarry, territories might be gained or quitted, but dominating all our power to carry on the war, or even keep ourselves alive, was our mastery of the ocean routes and the free approach and entry to our ports ... The only thing that really frightened me during the war was the U-boat peril.'[2] Thrust into this vital high-technology campaign was the small and unprepared Royal Canadian Navy. From a force of but eleven ships – six destroyers, four minesweepers and a training vessel – and less than 2,000 all ranks the navy expanded until by 1945 it was the third largest fleet in the world, comprising over 450 vessels and nearly 100,000 men. The RCN's role in the Battle of the Atlantic (including the anti-submarine aircraft of the Royal Canadian Air Force) was perhaps the most vital of all of Canada's contributions to the Allied effort. This was not only the sole theatre of operations that actually involved the nation's territory (with the minor exception of the Aleutian campaign) but also the only one where Canadian officers had a large say in strategic planning and control of Allied forces and where Canadian science and industry made an irreplaceable contribution.

The fact that the Royal Canadian Navy played a role second only to the Royal Navy and far larger than that of the United States in the protection of the vital North Atlantic trade routes meant that it was closely involved in this rapidly evolving and highly sophisticated war of science and technology. Required to act independently because of the nationalistic policies of the government of Mackenzie King, and to provide for its own high-technology needs as a result of the Royal Navy's failure to allocate adequate equipment, the RCN was forced to attempt to develop from an almost non-existent pre-war infrastructure a system for supplying its escort vessels with the necessary advanced electronic detection systems such as radar, asdic, and high-frequency direction finding, as well as new anti-submarine weaponry like the hedgehog ahead-throwing mortar. In attempting to create the organization the navy was brought into close contact with the National Research Council of Canada, the main centre for wartime military science, and industry specializing in advanced technology such as Research Enterprises Limited, a crown corporation created in 1940 to manufacture precision optics and radar.

The account that follows tells the story of how Canadian naval officers, scientists, and politicians tried to come to grips with the harsh realities of this war of advanced technology in the Atlantic. It was a battle fought not on the high seas but in the offices and corridors of power in the nation's capital – this was the Great Naval Battle of Ottawa. It is a story of national failure, for Canada was not able to provide for the timely and adequate supplies of this vital equipment to its escorts. As a result the crews of Canadian warships were called on to escort convoys across the Atlantic knowing that their weapons systems were inferior to those of their Royal Navy counterparts. Nevertheless, Canadian sailors persevered in these conditions, a true indication of their courage, strength, and skill.

The role of the Canadian scientist in the Second World War will be a major theme in this story. Extensive American and British literature shows that there was a major restructuring of the scientist's place in the socio-political structure among the Western allies. Adding to his traditional function of being the mere creator of new types of weaponry, the scientist gained far more power, prestige, and influence assisting with the development of tactics, strategy, and doctrine and in advisory roles at all levels of the political, economic, and military systems.[3] As the dropping of the atomic bombs so chillingly illustrated, scientists in effect become as important to the eventual victory over the Axis powers as any part of the military-industrial complex.

Unlike their colleagues in Britain and the United States, Canadian scientists had minimal influence on military planning. Even in weapon design their efforts were a failure because of the dissimilar priorities of the institutions involved and the inevitable conflict that developed between them. The National Research Council of Canada, the supreme wartime scientific agency, and Naval Service Headquarters did not succeed in resolving their difficulties, the effects of which on the anti-submarine campaign were profound as RCN escorts went to sea with inferior, outdated, or unusable equipment.

1

From Nothing but Possibilities

The organization of the Royal Canadian Navy's scientific and technical program during the Second World War was greatly influenced by the developments of the pre-war era. In peacetime there is usually the opportunity to establish the bureaucracy, management procedures, and interdepartmental relationships which are often difficult, if not impossible, to alter during the hectic pace of war. Paradoxically, while time is available in abundance, money usually is not. Nor is there incentive for radical original thinking; instead, administrators are encouraged to work within the system. Change, when it occurs, often takes years of slow evolutionary progress and is often imperceptible to the participants.

The wartime RCN was haunted by the inescapable ghosts of the pre-war years. Almost scuttled at the height of the Depression, the navy was fortunate in having kept even a minimal fleet intact, and was unprepared for the expansion in size and in technological complexity of naval warfare that would take place in the upcoming struggle. The most senior service in Canada is the army, tracing its ancestry to militia and other irregular units of the eighteenth century. The independent Canadian navy can trace its heritage no further than 1910. It was born amid a political controversy which was one of the factors that led to the fall of the Laurier government in the 1911 election. In the aftermath of the Liberal defeat the RCN consisted of two small and obsolete cruisers which were usually confined to port.[1] Never fully integrated into the imperial naval system, the RCN saw little service in the First World War, and its growth was minute compared to that of the army and the new air service. The navy was confined to providing coastal defence and acquired only patrol craft and a few small submarines. This role provided little opportunity for the RCN to prove itself to the Canadian public, a situation that was exacerbated by the great fame accorded to the Canadian Corps and air aces like Billy Bishop.[2]

The immediate post-war years saw the three services competing for an ever smaller budget, a result of the post-war economic recession and strong pacifist sentiment among the electorate. In 1920 the RCN traded its two obsolete cruisers to the Royal Navy for a modern cruiser and two destroyers, but was forced to dispose of most of its wartime acquisitions. By 1922 the cruiser was withdrawn from service because budgetary reductions prevented its continued service. From this time until 1944 destroyers would constitute the largest true warships in the navy's arsenal. Throughout the twenties Canada's maritime strength consisted of just two destroyers and four minesweepers, equally divided between the coasts.[3] In 1929 the King government contracted with the shipbuilding firm of Thornycroft of England for the construction of two completely new destroyers, the *Saguenay* and *Skeena*. These were the first two vessels to be purpose-built for the RCN and also the first to be equipped to carry asdic, although the devices were not installed until 1939.[4]

The acquisition of these two vessels proved to be the last major expenditures made on the RCN until 1936, for the Depression that followed the Wall Street crash of October 1929 resulted in the coming to power of the Conservative government of R.B. Bennett. Bennett's monetary philosophy revolved around massive government fiscal reductions, and the axe fell hardest on the politically vulnerable military. James Eayrs has written of this period: 'Like the Abbé Sieyes accounting for his record during the terror of the French Revolution, a Canadian officer accounting for his record during the great depression might have answered with no less justifiable pride, "I survived." The depression years were in truth a struggle for survival for the three services. Of the three, the Royal Canadian Navy came closest to losing it.'[5]

After several years of budgetary reductions, the military was finally reduced to desperate measures in 1933 when the Treasury Board demanded a $3,673,023 cut-back in military expenditures. Major-General A.G.L. McNaughton, army chief of staff and close friend and political associate of Bennett, proposed that the money left was insufficient to support all three services. He rationalized that since the RCN was too small for any useful role, it should be scrapped in order to preserve the Royal Canadian Air Force and the army. Commodore Walter Hose, the chief of Naval Staff, waged a successful campaign against McNaughton and a Treasury Board proposal to cut $2,000,000 from a budget of only $2,472,000. Hose was forced to undertake drastic tactics, including threatening to pay off the entire fleet. Faced with the embarrassing prospect of a navy without ships, the government finally relented, settling on an equitable reduction in the budget of all the services.[6]

The election of another Liberal government under Mackenzie King in 1935 marked a turning point in the RCN's history. Although anything but a militarist, King did perceive the growing threat of war in Europe. Limited rearmament was undertaken, and for the navy this meant a doubling in size. From 1936 to 1939 five slightly used RN destroyers were purchased, all of which were equipped with asdic. Allowing for the retirement of the two oldest vessels, this left a reasonably modern half-flotilla of seven fleet destroyers. Added to this were four Canadian-built Fundy-class minesweepers and a naval training vessel.[7]

Although equipped with eleven modern vessels by the end of 1939, the RCN was, in reality, little more than an auxiliary squadron to the RN. Organized along British lines, with copied traditions, ranking, and procedures, an independent Canadian Navy existed only in the minds of its officers and political masters. The RCN was only a shadow of a complete military organization, relying on the British for almost all its logistics support, including weaponry, electronics such as asdics and radios, machinery, all but the most basic training, and all scientific expertise. RCN officers served with the RN to learn skills that could not be gained in Canada, such as large fleet tactics, handling of cruisers and battleships, and staff training.[8] Consisting of only 1,990 men and a small reserve of 683 in September 1939, the RCN could not develop the infrastructure that would be so difficult to create in the war ahead.[9]

The shore establishment of the RCN was tiny. One small and inadequate base on each coast, Halifax and Esquimalt, served the entire fleet. The administrative centre, Naval Service Headquarters, was housed on two floors of the Robinson Building in downtown Ottawa. As late as 1936 only seven officers were stationed at NSHQ; by 1939 that number had barely doubled. There was not one technical or scientific officer, if one excludes the director of Naval Engineering, whose primary concern was ship machinery.[10]

The organizational structure at NSHQ was extremely simple, reflective of its small size and responsibilities. At the top of the pyramid was the minister of National Defence, the civilian administration of the military having been amalgamated in 1922. One deputy minister oversaw the civilian administration of all the services. The key military figure was the chief of Naval Staff, who was responsible for all military functions, liaison with the minister, and with interservice affairs as the naval representative on the Chiefs of Staff Committee. Beneath the CNS were a half-dozen small directorates responsible for the administration of certain specific areas including Naval Intelligence and Plans and Naval Operations and Training. No formal structure existed within NSHQ because the organization was so small that it functioned by informal, personal contact. 'Co-ordination,' wrote the official historian, 'was extremely simple, for in less than a minute the head of a branch could walk to the office of any colleagues in order to discuss a problem.'[11] This was a system destined to collapse under the pressure of wartime expansion.

The effectiveness of NSHQ rested on the shoulders of the CNS. The CNS was a combination of chairman of the board and chief operational officer. Ultimately he was responsible for all Naval Staff decisions, a situation that would not change with wartime reorganization. From July 1934 until his dismissal from his post in January 1944 the CNS was Percy W. Nelles. An enigmatic figure, little is known about him except for the bare outlines of his career. Nelles was born in Brantford, Ontario, in 1892 and joined the fisheries protection service in 1908. He transferred to the RCN in 1910 and for the next twenty-four years served with it and with the RN. His career included First World War service on RN cruisers and sessions at both the Royal Navy Staff College and the Imperial Defence College. He succeeded Commodore Hose as CNS upon the latter's retirement in 1933 and successfully steered the RCN through the last years of the Depression.[12] Nelles's accomplishments have shown him to have been neither brilliant nor incompetent, but somewhere in the middle. Adequate for the pre-war navy, in fact ideally suited for the lethargic pace of peacetime, Nelles was found wanting in wartime. He was particularly unprepared for its technical aspects. Dr D.C. Rose, the first scientific adviser to the RCN, described Nelles as 'a most untechnical man.'[13]

Much blame for the lack of preparation for the coming scientific war lay with the government policies that resulted in inadequate funding. But money was not the only cause of the RCN's unpreparedness; the problem went deeper, into the basic philosophy that permeated the ranks of professional naval officers of the period. In both the RN and the RCN officers believed that the horrors of the First World War submarine campaign would not occur again. Although many naval officers correctly understood the potential of the U-boat, there was an almost pathological need in the naval establishment to believe that warfare in the future would revert to the days of the battleships at Jutland. The report of the RN's Defence of Trade Committee in 1936 optimistically stated:

As compared with the situation in 1915–1917, the problem of dealing with the submarine is more than simplified by the invention of Asdic. This instrument takes the place of the 'eye' and removes from the submarine that cloak of invisibility which was its principal source of strength in the late war ... And in fact it is considered that war experience will show that with adequate defences, the operations of submarines against merchant vessels in convoy can be made unprofitable.

A false, almost mystical belief in the infallibility of asdic and an appreciation of the lack of a viable undersea threat certainly reinforced this view. Germany was not permitted to have submarines until the 1935 naval accord, and even then the U-boat fleet was kept small, allowed no more than 45 per cent of the RN's submarine tonnage. The RN, however, was an institution large enough to survive incorrect premises. Research and development work in anti-submarine warfare continued and a small number of officers devoted themselves to becoming ASW specialists.[14]

For the RCN this intellectual trap would prove both easier to fall into and much more difficult to escape. The RCN, desperately seeking a mission that would provide the publicity needed to prevent a recurrence of the crisis of 1933, perceived its role as being part of the destroyer screen of the imperial battle fleet or as chasing powerful surface raiders around the world's oceans. This belief found expression in the training given its officers and in the type of vessels purchased in the immediate pre-war expansion. Before the war only two officers had received asdic training, both taking a short or basic course in the late 1920s.[15] The majority of the officers had, however, taken one traditional RN long or expert course, which included programs in gunnery, torpedoes, and navigation. These programs were further emphasized in fleet training, at the centre of which were the annual exercises with the British Atlantic and West Indies Squadron.[16] Certainly there was some understanding that a trade-protection role might well befall the service, but since the submarine threat was belittled, it was believed that the main threat would come from armed merchantmen and cruisers, vessels that the navy was well prepared to handle.[17]

Of the three services the RCN was least committed to a program of scientific research conducted at the National Research Council. This conservative attitude to science was reflected in the navy's earliest opinions on radar. Although partially the result of slavishly following RN policy, which in 1939 called for the installation of sets only on ships of cruiser size and above, the small value placed on radar showed a definite lack of the foresight so important in any military service. The RCN saw no practical use in radar and only expressed interest in gaining technical knowledge of the device because it feared that the army and air force might gain a monopoly over it. E.S. Brand, the director of Naval Intelligence and Plans, outlined the RCN's position for the Admiralty in July 1939:

A certain amount has been heard over here regarding RDF developments. I have explained the general situation regarding the matter to the CNS and pointed out to him that it is primarily an air force commitment.

Whilst the CNS agrees with me that the question of fitting Type 79 (or its modern equivalent) in any of our ships hardly arises, he feels that we would like one Canadian Naval Officer to know something of the development and practice of RDF so that we could express our opinion in any subsequent inter-Canadian service discussions regarding the installation of RDF in the Dominion.[18]

The RCN was content to be totally reliant on the RN for all its technical and scientific needs. It was a situation based on mutual convenience but also one that was to fail the RCN miserably when the Admiralty's resources were stretched to the limit trying to fill its own requirements during wartime. There would be very little time or resources left for any of the Commonwealth's navies, particularly one as independent from RN control as the Canadian service was to become.

The RCN, therefore, would be forced to rely largely on indigenous sources for its technical and scientific requirements. Although none existed in the pre-war navy, there was great potential within Canada for the mobilization of the necessary resources. In the field of physics, the scientific discipline that would play the dominant role in the navy's scientific war, there were programs of world standing at both McGill University and the University of Toronto, and smaller ones at schools from coast to coast. Major discoveries had been made at these institutions, including the development of the world's first electron microscope at Toronto in 1937. The centre of the embryonic Canadian physics community, however, lay outside the universities in the National Research Council. NRC's predominance would continue from 1939 to 1945, and essentially the story of wartime science in Canada is that of this one institution.[19]

The NRC was founded in 1916, amid the war clouds of the First World War. In that year the British Secretary of State for the Colonies wrote to the empire's governments suggesting that a committee be established to examine scientific and industrial research and to develop such research to assist the war effort. This, he pointed out, would follow current trends in the United Kingdom. The Borden government responded by creating a voluntary scientific advisory committee consisting of leading scientists, engineers, and a few businessmen. One year later Parliament passed the Research Council Act, which permanently established the committee as an independent government agency controlled by a committee of the Privy Council.[20]

War work by the council was confined to sponsorship of small-scale industrial and agricultural research projects and surveying Canada's scientific resources. In the twenties the council followed two different general policies. The main thrust of the NRC was to finance the education of a new generation of scientists. By 1926 a total of 344 postgraduate scholarships to 199 students had been awarded. Of these people, 155 had completed their studies and 123 were working within Canada. These graduates were employed in expanding industrial and university laboratories, facilities that were growing in part because of extensive NRC research grants. It would be this group of new scholars which would provide the manpower for the NRC during the war ahead.[21]

The second thrust of the NRC during this period was to build permanent facilities for itself. The council believed that a research laboratory financed by the central government would serve to promote science and firmly entrench the NRC in Ottawa. The initial request was lost in the budgetary reductions that followed the armistice and the post-war recession. Numerous other requests for permanent facilities failed. In 1925 the council opened its first laboratory, although it was in temporary quarters financed by short-term grants. In 1924 a full-time chief executive officer, Dr H.M. Tory, was hired to run the council. Tory was able to persuade the Liberal government of Mackenzie King to finance the construction of a large modern research facility on Sussex Drive in Ottawa. This 'temple of science' was just what the NRC needed, and it would be from this building that the nation's wartime scientific potential would be nurtured during the thirties.[22]

Tory's timing of the construction of the new facilities was, in hindsight, exquisite. The project had been approved just before the Wall Street crash, and the new Bennett administration had little choice but to see the project through to its completion. The building was completed in 1932, but by then the NRC too was forced to face the difficult economic conditions of the Depression. The budget was slashed from a high of

$500,000 in 1930 to under $380,000 in 1933. The situation was made more precarious by the increased fixed costs absorbed by the council for the hiring of staff and the purchase of equipment for the new laboratories. This led to the virtual elimination of the scholarship program.[23] Despite the difficult fiscal situation, Tory gradually built a first-class research centre. From 1929 onwards professional staff were hired on a full-time basis. Although the Depression slowed things considerably, enough young scholars were hired to provide a base for future expansion. Tory divided the research responsibilities of the NRC into several major divisions based on basic disciplines of science and engineering. These divisions were further broken down into sections when the area was of sufficient scope to warrant separate supervision.

By far the most important division in the Second World War was that of Physics and Electrical Engineering. The division was formed in 1929 when Dr R.W. Boyle, a senior physicist from the University of Alberta, was hired by Tory. Boyle was an interesting choice, for he was heavily involved with the British research program that led to the invention of asdic in the First World War. As a result of this work one of the first research groups created within the division was the Acoustics Section, which would play an important role in the coming naval war. Boyle spent most of the thirties gradually expanding the division until by 1939 it consisted of twenty-six professional and thirty-seven technical staff members.[24]

During this time the most important section of the Physics Division, the Radio Section, was established. Its origins can be traced to one of the NRC's voluntary advisory panels. On 3 January 1931 the Associate Committee on Radio Research strongly recommended the formation 'of a permanent branch devoted to radio research.'[25] Ten months later Colonel W.A. Steel, formerly head of the army's Royal Canadian Corps of Signals, arrived at NRC to lead the new Radio Branch.[26]

While the NRC research facilities developed, a parallel evolution was taking place in the council's relationship with the military. As early as 1929 very close contacts developed between the NRC and the Department of National Defence, fully three years before the completion of the Sussex Drive facilities. In that year Tory wrote to the cabinet minister responsible for the council: 'I would suggest that the Minister of National Defence be on our Research Committee, as there is no Department for which we will be doing more work in the future. We already have two or three large problems on hand for them at the moment, and I am only awaiting proper technical appointments to get this work started. In the present instance, of course, Colonel Ralston [Minister for DND] would be a tower of strength.'[27]

The completion of the Sussex Drive facilities increased the scope of military research projects, particularly in the fields of aeronautics and surveying. In 1931 Canada's first large wind tunnel was constructed at an NRC annex. The RCAF conducted extensive tests in the aerodynamics of bush aircraft and auxiliary equipment, such as skis and floats. 'Officers of the RCAF,' wrote Mel Thistle, 'were sent to the laboratories for long periods to acquire the experience in aeronautical testing and research, and aircraftsmen were placed in the engine laboratory to everybody's satisfaction and profit.'[28]

The NRC's Meteorological and Allied Measurement Section worked closely with army and air force surveyors developing equipment for the accurate mapping of the vast interior wilderness. This led to Canada's international leadership in surveying equipment, which continues to this day.[29] Noticeably absent from most early DND-NRC co-operation was the RCN.

The budding relationship between the NRC and the military was greatly strengthened by the appointment to the presidency of the council of the army chief of staff, Major-General A.G.L. McNaughton. Tory's term expired in June 1935, and although he desired an extension, his abrasive demeanour, Liberal connections, and age (he was seventy years old) convinced Prime Minister Bennett that a change had to be made. The offering of the nation's premier scientific administrative post to its senior soldier was nothing less than a classic Canadian example of political patronage. McNaughton was selected by Bennett both as a reward for his years of service to the Conservative government and to remove him from the politically sensitive post of chief of staff. It was, after all, an election year. In his role as commander of the army McNaughton had organized the highly unpopular Depression work camps, ostensibly to provide meaningful work for unemployed young men but perceived by many to be nothing more than a thinly disguised government attempt to prevent a revolution.[30]

McNaughton's appointment, however, was one of those rare occasions when political expediency matched ability; this particular patronage appointee was highly qualified for his position at NRC. Before he ever put on a uniform McNaughton was well on his way to a successful scientific career. Born in 1887, he completed his bachelor's and master's degrees in electrical engineering at McGill by 1912. By 1914 he had published a half-dozen scholarly articles mainly on high-voltage electrical transmission lines. The First World War interrupted his academic career, when he joined the Canadian Corps in France. His keen technical abilities and superior leadership skills brought him quick promotion, and by the armistice he commanded the corps' heavy artillery. The corps commander, General Sir Arthur Currie, regarded McNaughton highly and managed to convince him to stay in the army to help guide it through the difficult peacetime years. In the twenties he held a variety of senior staff posts and in January 1929 was appointed army chief of staff by the King government. These years were not completely unproductive scientifically. In 1924 he and W.A. Steel patented the cathode-ray direction finder, a device that allowed accurate navigation by aircraft and ships, a distant technological cousin to radar.[31]

McNaughton brought to the NRC a different sense of mission from that provided by Tory. While the latter saw the development of the council in the abstract terms of the general improvement of Canadian science and technology, the former brought with him a firm practical belief in the need to mobilize Canadian resources for an inevitable future war. As a technical officer in an untechnical army he understood more clearly than most soldiers the role that science could play in developing military capability. As chief of staff he was instrumental in fostering close research ties between the NRC, the army, and the RCAF. From 1935 on wards McNaughton increasingly turned the NRC towards practical military scientific research and prepared it as well as could be expected for the war years ahead. However, McNaughton, having no control over and having lost the respect of the RCN during the budgetary crisis of 1933, could not bring the navy into close contact with the NRC, and this service was therefore the worst prepared for the scientific war.

Under Tory's administration military projects had mainly been confined to civilian aspects of the Department of National Defence's responsibilities, such as surveying. There were notable exceptions to this, including McNaughton's sponsorship of the creation in 1932 of a Ballistics Section in the Physics and Electrical Engineering Division under the leadership of Dr D.C. Rose. Beginning in 1935 the military activities at the council increasingly took a more sinister and ominous role. In 1937 the first overseas military scientific fact-finding mission was conducted when Dr E.A. Flood of the Chemistry Division was sent to the United Kingdom to investigate the latest type of gas masks.[32]

A great deal of the council's efforts during this period revolved around the perfecting of McNaughton's cathode-ray direction finder. CRDF was a device for precision navigation of ships and planes, consisting of an oscilloscope connected to three radio receivers, each of which was in turn connected to a different antenna. The antennae were all placed so as to have different directional responses. 'The output of these receivers, which had identical gain and phase-shifts, is applied to the deflecting electrodes of an oscilloscope in such a way that a radial straight line appears on the screen' in the direction of a fixed transmitter. Another reading is taken from a second transmitter, and by using simple triangulation, the exact position can be determined.[33]

This device, although similar in some respects to radar, is in fact quite different. Radar is self-contained and requires no separate co-operating transmitter. CRDF would prove to have little military value because it required constant transmissions from a fixed ground station, but it is important in this story because it led to the creation of the basic research unit that would spearhead the Canadian radar program. In 1924 McNaughton had developed the theoretical framework for CRDF, and W.A. Steel the first crude, oversized working model. Little was done to perfect the device until work began on it at the council nine years later.[34]

CRDF research at NRC began in 1933 when a young physicist, John T. Henderson, arrived to take over the Radio Section from Steel, who had left the council for pioneer broadcasting work at the CBC. Henderson had taken his bachelor's and master's degrees in physics at McGill in the twenties. In 1929 he went to King's College, London, where he studied for his doctorate under Dr E.V. (later Sir Edward) Appleton. He specialized in the field of radio atmospherics. Included in his doctoral training was a year and a half stay at the Radio Research Station at Slough, the same centre that a few years later would develop the first British radar. Just before his arrival at NRC he conducted brief postgraduate research trips to both the Sorbonne in Paris and the Technische Hochschule at Munich.[35]

Before 1935 Henderson concentrated his CRDF research on a futile attempt to make it a useful detector of weather fronts. Under Mc-Naughton's leadership the Radio Section turned increasingly back to perfecting CRDF as an aid to navigation. This work was jointly sponsored by the Department of Transport and the RCAF. By September 1939 H.R. Smyth, one of Henderson's assistants, was establishing the first practical marine CRDF station just outside Halifax.[36]

McNaughton had originally conceived of CRDF because of its military utility. As Henderson's research team began to have some success, he grew concerned over the device's security. In 1938 the NRC disbanded the Associate Committee on Radio Research so that no one outside of government would have access to CRDF. Established in its place were 'two interdepartmental secret committees on radio,' one to supervise maritime and the other air CRDF research.[37]

These two sections had members from the two sponsoring agencies, the Department of Transport and the RCAF respectively, as well as NRC representatives. The Maritime Section also had a naval member, the only evidence of pre-war RCN-NRC co-operation.[38] To provide day-to-day management control over the Radio Section a small executive committee was created, consisting of McNaughton, R.W. Boyle, head of the division of Physics and Electrical Engineering, Henderson, and the council's secretary-treasurer. Publicity of the work was actively curtailed, and the most minimal mention of the Radio Section's work was made in subsequent annual reports.[39]

One of the reasons for this security clampdown was most likely the growing awareness within the Radio Section of the military potential of such non-traditional radio devices. In the late summer of 1938 preliminary discussions were held between NRC and DND over the use of radio waves to detect aircraft. Although nothing was done to further these basic concepts, it certainly came as no surprise to many Canadian scientists and soldiers when the British decided to reveal the existence of radar.[40]

The detailed history of the early British development of radar need not concern us here. It is necessary to remember, however, that by the spring of 1939 scientists had developed an effective system for the detection and interception of aircraft based on this radically new type of electrical device. Radar was Britain's answer to the formidable power of the Luftwaffe's bomber force and the premier example in the world up to that point of what could be accomplished by close scientific-military co-operation.[41]

In March 1939 the British government, realizing that war was very likely only a matter of months away, decided to share its most closely guarded military secrets with its likely future allies. On 3 March a request was sent to all dominion governments to send a physicist to London to learn of the existence of this greatest secret of all – the development of radar.[42]

When the request reached Ottawa there was little doubt who would be sent. DND had not one physicist but very close relations with the NRC. Choosing a government scientist already used to security arrangements would also satisfy British concerns over the safeguarding of information on radar.[43] It was, therefore, almost inevitable that a Radio Section scientist would be chosen for the mission to the United Kingdom. What no one realized at the time was that, by picking an NRC scientist as its representative, Canada was setting a pattern for military science that would last for at least the next four years. The choice of John Henderson sealed the unofficial bond between the NRC and the DND: it guaranteed that the NRC would play a paramount role in running Canada's wartime scientific expansion and that it would be the main beneficiary of the great increases in government scientific expenditures. This decision also gave the council control of what was to become the country's largest single scientific program. No other scientific institution, such as universities or the few industrial research laboratories, would be able to compete with the power of the NRC. Unlike the United States, there was to be in Canada no massive spending on scientific facilities outside of government or beyond the capital region.

Certainly none of this was apparent to Henderson when he was chosen by McNaughton to be Canada's representative to the secret meeting in London. He arrived in London in early April and was met there by his military assistant, RCAF Squadron Leader F.V. Heakes. The two men were taken on tours of the British radar research centres and to operational stations. They were extensively briefed on both the theoretical and practical aspects of the device, and on its almost limitless future potential. Henderson and Heakes dispatched to Ottawa a series of wildly enthusiastic letters and reports outlining what they had learned and proposing schemes for radar's application to Canadian defence planning. Included were detailed plans for the air defence of the east coast. It was very unusual for a middle-ranked officer and a civilian scientist to propose high-level strategy, but the radical change in warfare created by radar was a powerful incentive to go beyond normal procedures. Their optimism, however, was somewhat clouded when the British firmly and rather bluntly informed the visiting scientists that their countries could expect nothing but basic technical information. It was up to each dominion to develop the technology to suit its own requirements and industrial practices. No supplies would be available from British sources in the foreseeable future, as they were barely able to meet their own needs.[44]

Henderson saw a paramount role in Canadian radar research for the NRC and stressed this in his correspondence to McNaughton.[45] The NRC president realized the importance of Henderson's message even better than did Henderson, for McNaughton understood the tremendous impact radar would have on the face of the battlefield. He also saw the great ramifications that a large, highly secret military project might have on the NRC itself. McNaughton was determined to establish for the first time a formal working relationship with DND. Being an expert on military organization and management, he knew that there were great dangers in entering into such a undertaking without a clear delineation of responsibilities and duties. In July a meeting was arranged with the chief of Air Staff, Air Vice-Marshall Croil. McNaughton later summarized his ideas to Henderson:

I had reached the conclusion that the part which the National Research Council might usefully play in aid to the Department of National Defence was in the organization and training of a small nucleus staff to the point that they could be available to the Defence Department to undertake research work required to fit the English proposal to Canadian conditions; that this staff would act as a consultant to the Defence Department, undertaking research on problems as they developed. This staff could also assist the Defence Department in the installation of the apparatus when received from England.[46]

Croil accepted McNaughton's premises and asked that they be presented in a formal report. The NRC staff, following their president's lead, submitted this report on 25 July. This document, 'Co-operation of NRC in RDF Programme of the Defence Department,' became the basis of all DND-NRC relations during the war.[47]

The five-month head start that the NRC received in creating a Canadian radar program was unfortunately wasted by the still restricted monetary policy of the King government. Several attempts to acquire funds were defeated in Cabinet, and in fact no money would be available until September 1939.[48] Subsequent trips to the United Kingdom by Boyle and McNaughton, combined with Henderson's information, did, however, provide a theoretical basis for future research and development.

While McNaughton was able at least partially to prepare the NRC for war, and the RCN was completing its late-thirties expansion program, much less was being done to prepare Canadian industry for the upcoming struggle. In the First World War Canada, like all the dominions, was utilized by the British Empire mainly as a provider of raw materials, including foodstuffs, minerals, fossil fuels, and, most important, manpower. The industrial resources of the country were meagre in comparison to European or American standards, but even most of this went unused. The only weapon built in any number was the infamous Ross Rifle, which proved almost useless in combat. Artillery-shell production was the only other major manufacturing endeavour conducted within the country. Even this small manufacturing commitment was found hard to control, and the serious scandal over war profiteering was second only to conscription as the most difficult wartime political problem. Virtually no naval construction was carried out in the nation's shipyards as the RCN remained a coastal-defence fleet.[49]

The 1920s had marked a period of tremendous growth in the manufacturing sector of the economy. This development was primarily a result of large-scale American capital investment, and was enhanced by high tariff barriers, which forced American investors wishing to compete in the Canadian market to build subsidiary factories north of the border. Of particular note was the dramatic growth in automobile, aluminum, electronic, and radio industries.[50]

The large industrial growth of the twenties resulted in the creation of great military manufacturing potential within Canada. This potential was not exploited to any large extent before 1936 because the small military budgets precluded any investment in manufacturing. All the wartime munitions concerns either went out of business or converted to manufacture of civilian products. By the mid-thirties only the Dominion Arsenal at Quebec City, which produced .303 rifle ammunition, manufactured any military material.[51]

The initial impetus for mobilizing industry came not from the Canadian military but from a 1936 request by the British defence planners. In April the Imperial General Staff made inquiries to both Canada and Australia about their industrial capacity and its military potential. Although the IGS found that Canada could provide an important imperial industrial reserve, it also found the King government extremely reluctant to invest in weapons and munitions manufacturing without considerable British orders. The British, for their part, still had ample industrial reserves of their own and were equally unprepared to order goods in Canada that would undoubtedly cost substantially more than the home-made product. The Imperial Conference of May 1937 led to a compromise between the two positions. The British agreed to place small educational orders, matched by equal dominion commitments, with Canadian manufacturers. By September 1939 progress had been made in establishing munitions, small arms, artillery, and aircraft production.[52]

The pre-war industrial developments had little direct effect on the RCN. Except for the building of the four small Fundy-class minesweepers in yards in Ontario, Quebec, and British Columbia, all immediate pre-war expansion was undertaken by direct purchase from the RN. On the whole the navy was less fortunate than the army or air force in the effort made to develop war industry before the commencement of hostilities.

Nowhere was this more obvious than in the electronics and radio industries, which would be vital in producing the equipment for the highly technological warfare against U-boats. These industries would be totally insufficient for wartime requirements, not because of their size but because of their internal structure. Like much of Canada's branch-plant economy, these industries would be hampered by their attachment to American industrial techniques and standards, which precluded the direct adoption of British equipment. The military would also demand rigorous quality control, something almost unheard of in factories geared to mass production of consumer goods. The most difficult problem in wartime, however, was the almost complete lack of technical expertise and industrial laboratories. The subsidiaries relied on their American parents for most of their engineering requirements. The description of the pre-war electronics industry provided by British naval experts is typical:

[The companies] tend to be manufacturing units only, dependent for their engineering and design on their American principals. Frequently they are dependent on them for components, and in some cases they only manufacture in Canada sufficient of the product to evade the import duties on the complete item.

This lack of design engineering was a serious handicap to some of the firms, since most of their staff were essentially sales engineers out of touch with design work. The Canadian General Electric Company, Cemco Electrical Manufacturing Company, and the Electric Tamper and Equipment Company of Montreal were the only firms which could handle the whole process of production inside their own organization, i.e. development, design, engineering and manufacture. The others were dependent on their principals in one way or another.[53]

While there were few direct measures to mobilize industry, there were at least some attempts to establish the organizational framework needed to control it in wartime. In 1936 DND established the Navy, Army and Air Supply Committee under the chairmanship of the Master General of the Ordnance, which conducted a survey of the nation's industrial resources. DND control of armament procurement did not survive for long, however, because the first major contract, for the production of Bren light machine guns, resulted in a tremendous political scandal. DND did not call for tenders but gave the order to the John Inglis Company and guaranteed a minimum 5 per cent profit. The opposition seized on these features and revived memories of the last war's profiteering controversy. Much public attention was focused on the seemingly incongruous situation of having a washing-machine manufacturer produce machine guns. The King government was forced not only to appoint a royal commission but, unusually, actually to follow its findings.[54]

The commission headed by Henry H. Davis, a Supreme Court judge, recommended that the military be removed from managing supply. To replace DND 'the negotiations leading up to and making of contract between the government and private manufacturers either for the purchase or production of ... munitions or armaments should be put into the hands of an expert advisory group of competent businessmen.'[55] In July 1939 Davis's findings were put into effect when the Defence Purchasing Board was established. To ensure no further scandal the board was placed under severe restrictions that were to hamper its early wartime operations greatly. Tendering was made mandatory for most contracts, and a limit of 5 per cent net contract worth was established on profits on any untendered work.[56]

These early developments in industrial organization, coupled with the developments in the RCN and the NRC, were in September 1939 disjointed and not destined to begin to come together as a recognizable military-scientific-industrial system until well after the declaration of war. There existed nothing but possibilities for future evolution, but already certain vital elements of the RCN's wartime high-technology war were in place. Throughout the war the failures of peacetime would severely impede the utilization of advanced equipment by Canada's escort ships. Many must share the blame for the unpreparedness in 1939, from politicians to sailors to the Canadian public at large. It is clear that Canadians had the type of navy they wanted. The full cost of the inadequate pre-war navy is impossible to measure, but certainly it was a major factor in the poor performance of the navy in the highly technological war against the U-boat.

2

Science Found

In the first twenty months of the Second World War the RCN entered
the new age of military science and advanced technology. The naval war
began as a series of unplanned forays to provide for unexpected con-
tingencies, to thwart the first of the Nazi secret weapons, and to fulfil
the navy's role of coastal and harbour defence. By the end of the twenty
months the navy was attempting to impose an organizational structure
on its growing scientific program. In many ways this was the period of
the most rapid evolution in navy thinking and of its greatest technological
successes, but it was also a time when problems that would haunt the
service for most of the war began to emerge.

The naval war from September 1939 to January 1941 was a dynamic,
rapidly changing series of campaigns. From the first day of the war when
the British liner *Athenia* was sunk by U30 there was no 'Phony War,' and
losses in men and ships were heavy on both sides. The commerce war,
not unexpectedly, was initially dominated by surface raiders, either warships such as the armoured ship *Graf Spee* or converted merchant cruisers. Losses from submarines, although greater than from surface ships,
were rare in properly established convoys until the late summer of 1940.
By then the famous wolf pack tactics had been perfected and made all
merchantmen vulnerable to attack. In the first year of the war minefields
laid by U-boats, surface vessels, and aircraft were a greater menace to
properly escorted trade than was the submarine-launched torpedo.

The new electronic detection devices, asdic and radar, had their first
successes and failures. The asdic myth was shattered on 17 September
1939 when the aircraft carrier *Courageous* was sunk in broad daylight
through her destroyer screen by U29. The submarine escaped shaken
but unharmed. Yet asdic also led to many successful attacks on U-boats

and was shown to work given a high amount of skill, luck, and daring in the hunter. Radar was also used operationally for the first time and proved its worth in several early engagements, particularly in its ability to give early warning of air attack. Radar became the most important electronic detection equipment, and research on it throughout the world was given the highest priority.[1]

The RCN's role in these early naval campaigns was small. Most of this period was taken up with the first RCN wartime expansion program, the beginning of a tremendous period of growth that saw the navy increase by a staggering 450 per cent. Several of the early organizational changes and policy decisions had a profound effect on the future course of this highly technological war. By January 1940 the simple and casual running of NSHQ was replaced by regular weekly meetings of the Naval Staff. The first meeting took place on 22 January; although its exact composition is unknown, its minutes were distributed to most of the senior staff officers.[2] The Naval Staff Committee covered a great variety of topics involving operations, administration, and supply and was intended both as an informative and a decision-making body. Ultimate authority continued, however, to rest with the Chief of Naval Staff (CNS).

The civilian administration of the navy also went through some important changes designed to deal with the increasing amount of detail. Early in the war a second deputy minister of National Defence was appointed to serve the navy and air force. In April 1940 the air force received its own deputy minister. Finally, in July, the Department of National Defence was divided along traditional service lines, and Angus L. Macdonald, the former premier of Nova Scotia, was appointed naval minister. Interchange between the expanding civilian and military bureaucracy of Naval Service Headquarters was enhanced soon after by the creation of the Naval Council, designed to ease the burden of liaison on the CNS. It consisted of the minister, deputy minister, CNS, DCNS, DNI, and a secretary, and held its first meeting on 9 September. For the rest of the year monthly meetings were held; the frequency gradually increased in 1941, until by March the council met weekly.[3]

Details of the early expansion and combat activities of the RCN need not concern us here except for two important developments that directly affected the technological war. In September 1939 the King government thwarted the RCN's long-cherished dream of becoming part of the imperial fleet. Rather than accede to the Admiralty request to place its destroyers under British control, the Cabinet, against Nelles's expressed wishes, decided to authorize only full co-operation between the two navies. This decision, wrote C.P. Stacey, 'was clearly a fundamental one, which had the effect of reserving to the Canadian government the right to decide whether or not to commit its naval forces to any specific theatre or operation.'[4]

The independence of the RCN had its price, and certainly one of the greatest costs incurred was that it influenced the Admiralty's decision to treat the RCN as being outside its normal logistical responsibilities. The Canadian service, if it was to retain autonomy, was also expected by the British to fend for itself in finding the equipment necessary for its warships. Certainly the nationalist policy of the the King government was not the only factor in determining British treatment of Canadian requests for equipment; there were, for instance, legitimate limitations on Admiralty resources under the increasing stress of war. However, the Royal Navy was far less responsive to the needs of an independent Canadian service than it was to Allied navies directly under Admiralty control. The RCN would be forced to turn increasingly to developing indigenous sources of supply, a nearly impossible task for a country whose pre-war military-industrial complex was almost non-existent.

The lack of even one Canadian shipyard capable of building vessels to naval specifications would, paradoxically, increase the number of electronic systems required by the RCN. The navy had hoped to use money allocated for expansion to acquire a small number of destroyers and sloops, but, cut off from British suppliers, who were fully occupied with Admiralty orders, the service was forced to change its plans. In February 1940 the navy ordered a large number of small escorts to be built by Canadian yards to mercantile standards. A total of sixty-four corvettes and twenty-four Bangor-class minesweepers were authorized to be used as coastal escorts, patrol vessels, or minesweepers and as barter for RN destroyers. Both classes of ship were compromises, the best types that Canada could build at any useful rate. As such they sacrificed almost every desirable quality of a warship. The corvette was a small vessel of only 950 tons, based on the design of a civilian whale catcher. The offensive armament consisted of only one obsolete First World War–vintage four-inch gun and a few anti-aircraft weapons. Its old-fashioned steam reciprocating engines could only generate the very slow maximum speed of sixteen knots. Each ship, moreover, would require a relatively sophisticated asdic, but in February 1940 there was no consideration given to the availability of these sets from the Admiralty. The difficulty of supplying this large number of ships was exacerbated during the summer of 1940 by the unlooked for acquisition of six of the American flush-deck destroyers exchanged in the famous bases-for-ships deal and ten corvettes being built in Canada for the RN.[5]

Throughout this period of rapid growth and reorganization the war of advanced technology slowly and quite unexpectedly took over the centre stage of Canadian naval planning. At first NSHQ, believing that the war would last at most two years, was as non-committal concerning Canadian-based research projects as before the war. In September 1939 it was the only service to fail to provide funding for the NRC's first foray into radar research and even declined to be involved in the project's management committee. In October the first meeting of Section III of the Radio Branch, the new unit created for the program, was attended by senior members of both the RCAF and the Royal Canadian Corps of Signals, but the RCN did not send a representative. When McNaughton asked for information on future naval requirements, the director of Naval Intelligence, Commander F.L. Houghton, laconically replied, 'I have no comments from the naval point of view.'[6] This position, with one exception, would remain unaltered through the rest of 1939 and all of 1940.

The navy did, however, begin contacts with NRC in other fields such as medicine in the closing months of 1939. One of the possible stumbling blocks to RCN-NRC co-operation was removed in October when McNaughton was recalled to military service. Although some in the navy may have approved of the departure of the man who had led the campaign to scuttle the navy in the early thirties, McNaughton took with him a very special talent in both the scientific and military worlds that would prove irreplaceable.

His successor at NRC was C.J. Mackenzie, formerly the dean of engineering at the University of Saskatchewan. He was no stranger to the NRC, having been a member of the council and on several advisory committees. He had impressed McNaughton at council meetings with his tough but low-key approach to management. As the most important of Canada's wartime scientific administrators Mackenzie would emerge as one of the most controversial figures in the disappointing tale of Canadian naval-scientific co-operation. His main goal throughout the war was to increase the power and prestige of the research council, something that would often put him in direct conflict with the RCN's requirements. Mackenzie was a poor administrator, unable to divest himself of day-to-day detail and concentrate on larger questions of policy. As a result there was both administrative confusion and a lack of planning, something that he was honest enough to admit in the post-war period when he created the post of vice-president of Administration. He also lacked the vision of senior wartime scientific administrators in both the United States and Great Britain, men such as James Conant and Henry Tizard, who understood the special effort required to ensure that effective use was made of the scientist's skills and knowledge.[7]

The RCN's first encounter with the war of advanced technology did not take place until February 1940, when the Admiralty requested help in defeating the first of Hitler's secret weapons – the magnetic mine. The mine operated by detecting the magnetic field of ships as they passed near by, and the resulting explosion was usually fatal. Traditional minesweeping techniques were not only ineffective, but the minesweepers were actually at great risk of being sunk themselves. From the beginning of the war German cruisers, destroyers, and aircraft laid small numbers of the mines in British coastal waters and inflicted casualties out of all proportion to the numbers employed. Although devices of this type were known to the Admiralty (an unsuccessful version had been used experimentally in the First World War), solutions to the German mines could not be discovered until one mine, accidentally dropped by an aircraft on the Shoeburyness mud flats, was found. The mine was disarmed and examined by the scientists and engineers of HMS *Vernon*, and by the end of 1939 effective countermeasures were developed, involving degaussing, 'the partial or complete neutralization of the permanent and induced magnetism in ships.'[8]

Coiling, the preferred method of degaussing, was a permanently placed system of cables running along the hull of a ship; when powered, the system generated the necessary neutralizing field. Wiping was a temporary measure in which results were 'obtained by raising a surrounding, energized coil, from about the turn of the bilge to a level a few feet above the waterline.' This 'sets up a strong field that magnetizes the ship in a direction opposite to the magnetism induced by the earth's magnetic field.' The effects of wiping lasted, on average, three weeks, and were effective only for a given magnetic latitude. Deperming complemented both of the above methods, as it neutralized the permanent fore and aft magnetism by 'heavily energizing for a short period of time, a helical coil wound around the ship from stem to stern.' Its effects lasted about one year and greatly decreased the power needed to shield coiled vessels as well as improving 'the magnetic characteristics of all ships.'[9]

The Admiralty request of February 1940 to the RCN involved the establishment of a degaussing station in Halifax, the main concentration centre for convoys in the first two years of the war. This was a sensible expedient to safeguard vessels before they entered the dangerous waters around Britain. Unfortunately for the commanding officer, Atlantic Coast, Captain H.E. Reid, the Admiralty request was accompanied by no offer of scientific assistance and very few technical specifications. Reid turned to two Dalhousie University professors of physics, G.H. Henderson and J.H.L. Johnstone, who, armed with the most basic information on degaussing, set about developing their own methods and equipment. They adapted a magnetometre in a watertight box to measure ships' magnetic fields so that suitable cables could be designed and installed. Other developments soon followed, and by late spring a fully operational degaussing range was installed in Halifax harbour.[10]

The project quickly grew beyond the limited research and administrative facilities of Dalhousie, and by the end of February Nelles met with Mackenzie to find a 'scientist to direct their special investigations in Nova Scotia and elsewhere.' This person would have 'direct contact with the research council and all its facilities and at the same time work on naval problems.'[11] On 11 March it was decided to transfer Henderson and Johnstone to the NRC payroll and to 'make them in charge of all scientific work for the navy.'[12] This solved the immediate problems by giving the Halifax team access to NRC funding, administration, and staff, but it did not provide NSHQ with a scientific adviser, as both men remained on the east coast.

NRC was involved with degaussing as early as February, when an electrical engineer, B.G. Ballard, began designing procedures to test the degaussing cable. By May the methods had been finalized and the work farmed out to the electrical engineering departments at McGill and the University of Toronto.[13] Ballard then moved to Halifax, where he undertook to design and build from scanty British specifications LL sweeps, the final solution to the safe detection and destruction of magnetic mines. The LL sweep consisted of two unequal lengths of buoyant cable trailing behind a minesweeper. The cables were powered by a series of pulsating electrical charges which in turn induced a magnetic field strong enough to fire the mine.[14]

Throughout 1940 the Halifax station of the NRC continued to be the major scientific facility of the RCN, but by June the NRC's headquarters in Ottawa were once again becoming the centre of these scientific activities. This trend began as the scope of the Canadian involvement in the naval war broadened to include industrial development. The King government discriminated against the Maritime provinces, to the benefit of Central Canada; even shipbuilding and repair work was concentrated in the winter-ice-choked Great Lakes and St Lawrence River areas. Only 3 corvettes of an eventual 121 were constructed in east coast shipyards.[15] Investment in scientific facilities in this region was even more unlikely, particularly since the NRC confined its activities whenever possible to the capital region. Also, it was inevitable that NSHQ would like to have close contact with its scientific staff.

The first major high-technology industrial program of the navy reflects the renewed emphasis being given to Ottawa, and it is ironic that the initial impetus for it came from Halifax. On 29 May 1940 Captain Reid, the commanding officer, Atlantic Coast, submitted a plan to NSHQ for the production of asdic sets within Canada. Unfortunately no details of Reid's plan have survived, but undoubtedly they were inspired by a severe shortage of submarine detection sets for his motley collection of requisitioned vessels used for coastal patrols. In April Reid had complained of a shortage of asdic spares, and it appears likely that few of his vessels had any way of locating a submerged U-boat.[16] The new Naval Staff handling of Reid's proposal was by all standards quick and positive. On 3 June the staff decided that the director of Naval Stores and director of Plans should examine the matter and put 'the whole scheme to the Admiralty.'[17] By the middle of June the Admiralty had not only been informed but had given its own wholehearted endorsement and a promise for full technical assistance.[18]

This rapid decision making, which would be so unlike future events, stemmed from the urgency of the matter and from the unusual events of the late spring and early summer of 1940. The German Blitzkrieg into the low countries and France which culminated in the British expulsion from the continent at Dunkirk had completely altered Canada's wartime role. Thrust suddenly into the role of senior ally to a beleaguered Britain, Canada found itself faced with mobilizing for total war. Since September 1939 the industrial and manpower resources of the country had barely been utilized. Although representatives from the British services and Ministry of Supply had arrived to place industrial orders soon after the outbreak of hostilities, in total only $81 million in contracts had been issued in the first eight months of the conflict. This was a result of continuing dollar shortages and a belief that the war would be of too short duration to utilize Canadian industry effectively. The Canadian government had also shown an understandable reluctance to abandon pre-war financial constraints and to invest in industries that no one wanted.[19]

The fall of France suddenly changed everything. The United States was still neutral, and until the passage of the Lend-Lease Act in March 1941 access to American industry was very limited. The war, if it was to be won at all, was to be a long and costly struggle which would only be successful if every resource in the empire were mobilized. Not only would the productive resources of the dominions be needed to augment British capacity, but they would be used to provide an alternative source of supply to vulnerable United Kingdom factories. It is no coincidence that on the same day that Reid's proposal reached Ottawa, NSHQ requested that the Admiralty lodge copies of all specifications, technical drawings, and samples of all vital naval equipment in Canada.[20] Another motivation for NSHQ's request was to provide sets for the large number of escort vessels ordered in February. The Admiralty had proved unable or unwilling to supply the RCN with the thirteen sets for Reid's small flotilla of requisitioned patrol vessels, let alone the eighty-one asdics required for the new corvettes and minesweepers.

As soon as Admiralty approval was received to build asdic sets in Canada, the RCN approached the NRC for technical assistance. On 17 June the deputy minister, Colonel K.S. Maclachlan, asked Mackenzie if the NRC could provide space for the assembly of oscillators and for developing techniques for the cutting of quartz crystals. Although space was at a premium at NRC, which had grown out of its Sussex Drive building, Mackenzie acceded to the navy's request.[21] This was to be the limit of the NRC's role in the initial stages of the program. The asdic story is one of technological adaptation rather than scientific innovation, and the key role was played by an Admiralty production expert, A.E.H. Pew.

Pew arrived in Canada in July 1940 not only with eight tons of specifications, drawings, and samples but, more important, with over twenty years of experience in asdic development and production.[2] He was one of the members of the initial asdic group at HM Signal School in 1919, and by 1927 was in charge of production and design at HMS *Osprey*, the Admiralty's underwater sound and asdic research and development establishment.[23]

Pew joined the staff of the British Admiralty Technical Mission, in charge of Section 9 and responsible for asdic production. The BATM was established in July 1940 when the British Purchasing Mission was disbanded in favour of the new Canadian Department of Munitions and Supply. DMS had been created in April by the King government to act as the sole agency responsible for placing contracts with civilian manufacturers. BATM was responsible for technical liaison with Canadian industry working on Admiralty contracts.[24] It should be emphasized that assisting the RCN was not BATM's primary responsibility. The Admiralty sent Pew to Canada because it wished substantial supplies of Canadian-built asdic sets; assisting the RCN was almost incidental. As the case of radar would later make clear, the Admiralty would not supply experts of the calibre of Pew if it was not interested in Canadian production for RN needs.

Pew's expert eyes quickly saw the 'resources for A/S [asdic] production most promising'; he was particularly impressed by the facilities for oscillator assembly at NRC.[25] He was assigned a RCNR lieutenant, F.W.R. Angus, who was to learn the details of asdic manufacturing. They were joined in September by another *Osprey* member, A.W. Miller.[26] Armed with a mandate to construct 193 sets by 1 March 1941, the three men set out to establish this new industry almost from scratch.[27] They began by visiting manufacturers that were to build the components: 'Over 150 firms were contacted and the specifications gone into in detail. The articles required had to be described by the aid of samples. Then, further explanation invariably had to be made before firms could tender satisfactorily ... Seventy major components and at least double that number of minor components had to be ordered. These components, in themselves, sometimes are made up of another twenty or more items.'[28]

In August the first contract for components were tendered, and by October the program was far enough advanced to establish an agency for managing production. An order-in-council established the Equipment Division, to be run as part of the navy under the director of Naval Stores with Angus as the production manager. The division was to be run as a company and given an initial working capital of $4 million. Staff was hired with some difficulty, and included inspectors, technicians, storekeepers, and office staff.[29] For security reasons only Pew, Angus, and Miller were to know the full details of the sets. Technicians, contractors, and inspectors were actively discouraged from gaining knowledge of equipment outside their specialty. The sets were to be assembled only when the components arrived at the ship for installation.[30]

The organization of the Equipment Division was contrary to the existing pre-war practice of having civilians control industrial production, a policy which had been reinforced by the replacement of the Defence Purchasing Board on 1 November 1939 by the more powerful War Supply Board. The WSB was in turn succeeded by the Department of Munitions and Supply by June 1940. After the disbandment of the British Purchasing Mission in July, DMS had almost complete control over the issuing of contracts and allocation of supplies. Its power was greatly enhanced by the appointment as minister of C.D. Howe, who, after King, was probably the most powerful member of the war Cabinet. He controlled DMS as his own fiefdom and became the wartime czar of Canadian industry.[31] The independence of the Equipment Division from DMS control stemmed from a little-used section of the Department of Munitions and Supply Act which allowed for other departments to run government-owned and -operated industry.[32] However, its separation from DMS was not complete. Contracts for components made by non-government concerns had to go through the DMS, but it acted only as a clearing house, for Angus and the DNS had full control over the contents of these contracts.[33]

Although the scheduled March 1941 date for the completion of the first set was missed by four months, the establishment of an entirely new industry in a year was a remarkable accomplishment.[34] By March 1941 progress was far enough advanced to allow the Naval Staff to decide that all future RCN requirements could be met within Canada.[35] By December, 274 sets were to be completed, with additional orders to follow. These were broken down as follows:[36]

Type	Britain	Canada	Netherlands	Total
123A	47	63		110
128	32	52		84
134A	21	50	9	80
Total	100	165	9	274

The immediate success of the asdic program is in direct contrast with the difficulties encountered with radar. We have already seen how the RCN refused to get involved in the early research work at Section III, but it is necessary to follow the radar story in some detail until the navy finally discovered the device in the winter of 1941. The initial funding provided in September 1939 from the army, air force, and NRC combined was only $18,600. From this money a small team of Radio Branch personnel led by John Henderson was asked to begin development work on an ASV (air-to-surface vessel) set for the RCAF and a CD (coastal defence) set for the army.[37] Initial progress was slow, as funds and British co-operation were lacking. On 21 November 1939 Henderson requested an additional fiscal allowance of $57,740, but was turned down by the Cabinet. No more funding was provided until May 1940, when $60,000 was allocated. The failure to fund radar research adequately was another result of the Phony War period.

As the British had warned John Henderson in April 1939, they could provide little material aid to Canadian radar development. This was understandable given the pressing need within Britain to secure its own, much more vulnerable, defences. The difficulty in obtaining technical data, drawings, and reports was far less understandable. G.H. Henderson, after visiting England in July 1940, said that the dearth of written information was a result of excessive 'secrecy' and of the lack of 'time to write it up.'[38] Undoubtedly, another factor was British ignorance of Canadian scientific potential. It was not until the spring of 1940, when A.V. Hill, a Nobel Prize–winning physiologist, made two trips to Ottawa, that this oversight was noted in Britain; it would be several years before fully satisfactory Anglo-Canadian scientific co-operation was achieved, and this, as we shall see, was only the result of action taken on the western side of the Atlantic.[39]

With these inadequate resources, therefore, NRC scientists were forced to reinvent radar, using civilian tubes and circuitry. By June 1940 flight tests were commenced on an experimental ASV set, operating at sixty-seven-centimetre wavelength, but it never progressed beyond the prototype phase.[40] Ironically, the only naval project instigated before 1941 led to the first operational set developed in Canada.

The first interest expressed by the RCN in radar involved the securing of the approaches to Halifax harbour. In March 1940 Commander Houghton, director of Naval Intelligence, requested Section III to construct a simple set to be used in conjunction with the Halifax guard loop. Requirements were finalized in June, and by the end of July the set known as 'Night Watchman' was in operation at Sleepy Cove just outside the city. The rapid completion of the set resulted from the progress made at NRC in basic research, the increased funding provided in May, and the simplicity of the requirements. No great accuracy or range was necessary, and it was often referred to as a burglar alarm, as it gave only the most basic warning of the passing of a vessel.[41] 'Operating on a wavelength of 150 cm. with a fixed directional antenna, it serves to patrol the narrow entrance across to MacNab's Island. A submarine loop is used in conjunction with this equipment. Range and bearing measurements are only approximate. The maximum range used is about 300 yards, which is the width of the channel at that point.'[42]

Within its limited parameters Night Watchman was a success, but only three more were constructed (one as a back-up to the first and two additional sets for the United States Army for the defence of the Panama Canal). As a step in Canadian radar development its importance is obvious, but in terms of naval radar, hereafter confined to shipboard sets, it was insignificant. After the completion of Night Watchman the RCN once again reverted to its position of indifference.

Understandably, the RCN believed that the RN would provide for its small requirements, since in the summer of 1940 only destroyers seemed likely to be fitted. It did not help that the Admiralty was having difficulty in deciding its own priorities. G.H. Henderson reported in July 1940 that within the RN 'there had been two conflicting schools of thought, one insisting that RDF sets should be used for gunnery purposes and the other that it be used for detection, and the actual use has swayed violently back and forth between them.'[43] Also, it was at this time that the RCN came closest to fulfilling its pre-war goal of becoming an integral part of the imperial fleet. The destroyer force was assigned to anti-invasion patrols in the English Channel. 'This fleeting foray into traditional naval warfare,' writes Marc Milner, 'assuredly whet the navy's appetite for more of the same and, at the same time, firmly established the policy of full aid to the RN.'[44] This aid included the seconding to the RN of virtually every qualified physics, mathematics, and engineering student that the navy could enlist to be trained as radar officers. The Canadian service would later find it impossible to retrieve them despite a severe shortage of qualified personnel.[45]

The radar program, despite the RCN's attitude, prospered through the rest of 1940. The NRC, with full support of the other services and adequate fiscal resources, pushed on to develop world-class research and production facilities. The radar funding was greatly enhanced by a $60,000 allocation in May, and in August by the turning over to the NRC of a million-dollar fund established by some of the country's most prominent businessmen.[46] British co-operation gradually improved, and the arrival in July of two GL (gun-laying) Mark I sets only heralded an increasing flow of overseas contacts.

The Tizard mission of August 1940 began a flood of visits from British scientists that was to continue for the duration of the war. Although his mission was primarily to establish Anglo-American co-operation, Sir Henry Tizard heeded Hill's advice and began his visit with a one-week stay in Ottawa. He spent most of that time with Mackenzie, and invited the NRC president to accompany the mission to Washington. NRC scientists had their first chance to see much of the British radar technology, including a cursory two-day examination of the first practical ASV set to reach North America, before it was sent to the United States for demonstration. Canadian scientists also received their first glance at the ultra-secret cavity magnetron valve, which would shortly revolutionize radar technology by making possible very short-wave, high-powered sets.[47]

The Tizard mission, however, did not solve the problem of Anglo-Canadian co-operation, and the program continued to be hampered by a lack of sensitivity to Canadian requirements. As late as January 1941 no other ASV set had arrived, and only one-third to one-half of the technical information needed to adapt the set for Canadian production was available.[48] NRC representatives in London could not convince officials of the Ministry of Aircraft Production of Canada's ability to produce radar equipment; as a result MAP refused to allocate the necessary sets. Even the help of some of the returning members of the Tizard mission, in particular J.D. Cockcroft, could not sway MAP, and only the personal intervention of C.D. Howe, coincidentally in England, solved the problem. Howe contacted the Canadian-born minister of MAP, Lord Beaverbrook, who saw to it that three ASVs were air shipped to Ottawa in the second week of January 1941.[49]

The reluctance of MAP to co-operate with NRC stemmed from its appreciation of Canada's manufacturing situation. Members of the British Purchasing Mission had reassessed the industrial potential in the first few months of the war and had found the electronics and radio industry sadly lacking in its ability to produce modern equipment. What little capacity existed, such as at Marconi Canada, was quickly utilized to construct radio sets. In July 1940, however, the Canadian government took steps to establish a radar manufacturer because of the unreliability of British supplies and to provide an imperial industrial reserve.[50] On 16 July representatives of the NRC, DMS, and the services met to discuss the organization of the new company. With the exception of the naval member, a non-commissioned officer, all were senior officials or officers. W.C. Woodward, the DMS representative, outlined the plan that was accepted as the basis of this new scheme. Woodward emphasized the need 'to preserve the secrecy of the equipment.' Most radar components would be subcontracted to private industry but 'the assembly of these units together with the construction of such secret parts as aerials, should be done at a central plant under government supervision.' The new concern would be organized as a government-owned Crown corporation with its own independent board of directors.[51]

In September 1940 the scheme was slightly modified when the responsibility for radar production was given to a new Crown corporation, Research Enterprises Limited. REL had been formed in July 1940 to produce precision optical equipment, and the next logical step was to add radar because of the high-technology and top secret aspects of both items. In the autumn of 1940 the sod had only just been turned for REL's huge new facilities in Leaside (now the borough of East York, Toronto), but it had a board of directors and senior executives already in place to begin planning for the new 'radio' factory. On 8 January 1941 construction was started on the new plant, and production was scheduled to begin in the summer of 1941.[52]

The technological upheaval in defence and industry that commenced in 1940 did not go unnoticed by NSHQ, although it found itself completely unprepared to deal with it. Although the Naval Staff had acquitted itself well in its handling of asdic and magnetic mines, it had failed to appreciate the importance of radar and of long-term planning for research and development; NSHQ was aware of the shortcomings of not having permanent scientific advisers, and by the end of 1940 steps were taken to rectify the situation. On 31 October 1940 Mackenzie lunched with Colonel Maclachlan at the Rideau Club to 'discuss coordination between operations and research in the navy.'[53] The two men agreed that the navy needed scientific staff similar to the Admiralty research establishments, but came to no firm decisions. One month later Maclachlan attempted to recruit Dr Forest F. Musgrave, a researcher with Imperial Oil, but was refused because Musgrave was undertaking vital war work for the company. Imperial Oil suggested that Maclachlan try to obtain one of their former staff members, Major Gordon McIntyre, then serving with the Royal Canadian Engineers, but here too he was rebuffed, this time by the army.[54]

The slow pace of establishing an RCN scientific office was, however, hindering the work of the Equipment Division. On 26 November Maclachlan, Pew, and Commander Angus met with Mackenzie and Boyle and agreed that Boyle would 'act as general consultant and liaison' for asdics.[55] This limited arrangement was not satisfactory, and by the end of December it was apparent to Mackenzie and Nelles that 'some sort of scientific officer at [Naval] Headquarters seems to be necessary'; the problem was in finding a suitable candidate.[56] On 30 December Nelles, Maclachlan, and Reid, now the deputy chief of the Naval Staff, met with Mackenzie. They decided to make council the official scientific establishment of the navy, responsible for all research development and scientific liaison.[57] Co-operation between the council and navy was to be administered by a 'liaison officer to be selected and retained by [NRC] and attached to the personnel staff of the Deputy Chief of the Naval Staff.'[58]

Mackenzie found his first two choices for the liaison post, Professor Johnstone and naval Lieutenant J.R. Millard, occupied with research at Halifax.[59] He then turned to an NRC physicist, D.C. Rose, only to discover that Millard was on his way to Ottawa after all.[60] Unwilling to disappoint either man, Mackenzie decided to employ both in council-navy liaison. Not until 19 February were the respective roles of Millard and Rose established, the former being responsible for developing 'contact with all phases of naval operations and bring to Dr. Rose's attention whatever operating problems appear to require scientific work.' Rose was to bring to Millard's attention any council 'developments which would appear to have an application on naval problems.' Neither 'would be restricted in [his] activities.'[61]

It was not an auspicious beginning for NRC-RCN formal relations, but the appointment indicated that a dramatic change in naval attitudes towards science had occurred since the beginning of the war. On 17 January 1941 J.O. Cossette, the naval secretary, informed the commanding officers on both coasts of the adoption of NRC as the navy's scientific research establishment, and asked them to give full co-operation to the scientists because 'the value of [the] scientific knowledge of these gentlemen cannot be over-estimated and can be cultivated with great advantage to the service.'[62] Unfortunately, it was advice that would not be fully heeded.

3

The Discovery of Radar

The year 1941 was one of discovery for the rapidly growing but still immature Royal Canadian Navy. In May the first strategic operational command under Canadian control, the Newfoundland Escort Force, was formed under the auspices of Commodore L.W. Murray. Canadian escorts entered the mid-Atlantic convoy routes in large numbers and learned through first-hand experience of the trials, tribulations, boredom, and dangers of escort work. The skill and numbers of the U-boats increased throughout the year, something which was brought home to the RCN in September, when its defence of convoy sc 42 ended as a tragic defeat for the Canadian escort: sixteen merchantmen were never to see home again. The action, however, did see the first Canadian naval success against the Kriegsmarine's underwater arm when u501 was destroyed by the combined efforts of the corvettes HMCS *Chambly* and *Moose Jaw*. The lesson of 1941 was that the new Canadian fleet was still not ready to be entrusted with the defence of a convoy against sustained attacks from U-boat wolf packs. There was an acute need to improve training, co-ordination, seamanship, and equipment, but no quick solution to any of these problems was possible.[1]

The operational problems of 1941 were caused in part by the still embryonic state of equipment development within Canada. In 1940 the RCN had laboured with some success to establish the scientific and technical organization vital for equipping its ships with the new weapon systems so integral to ASW. Degaussing facilities had been established, asdic production was tooling up, and the research council had become the scientific research and development directorate. Except for asdic none would have a direct impact on the convoy actions of 1941. The

Naval Staff had failed, however, to come to grip with the most important of the new technologies – radar.

As late as 9 January 1941 the RCN's official representative on the Interservice Electrical Methods of Fire Control [Radar] Committee, Engineer Commander J.F. Bell, denied any requirement for a Canadian-built, ship-borne radar, but instead stated quite emphatically 'that all Naval requirements were being looked after in England.'[2] Bell was following the long-established Naval Staff position on radar, and by refusing to participate scuttled this early attempt to create a unified Canadian interservice policy on the device. The navy blindly relied on the paternal instincts of the Royal Navy to provide for all Canadian needs and keep the Naval Staff well informed on both policy and new technological developments.

In January 1941, however, the Naval Staff was made aware that Canadian destroyers serving with Western Approaches Command were being equipped with the first small-ship set, the type 286. The 286 was adapted from the Royal Air Force's ASV Mark II and went into production in the summer of 1940. The set operated at 214 megacycles, with a wavelength of 1.4 metres. Its greatest fault was a fixed-antenna system which consisted of 'two yagi aerials with six radiator-reflector dipoles sets, paired vertically to produce three broad fixed beams.'[3] With this fixed antenna it was only possible to receive rather inexact bearings, an accuracy of no greater than 10 degrees, and a set that could search for targets no more than 120 degrees from the bow of the ship. Test results indicated that the set could detect a cruiser at six to eight miles, a destroyer from four to seven miles, and a trimmed-down submarine at one to one and a half miles.[4] Although inferior to daytime optical detection, the 286 improved detection tremendously in inclement weather or at night.

These performance figures were a theoretical norm; in operations, particularly against submarines, they were rarely achieved. Long-wave or metric radar could not, unless under optimum conditions and with the best trained operators, detect a trimmed-down U-boat – a fact already admitted by the Admiralty Signals Establishment in January 1941, when it was well on in the development of far superior centimetric surface-warning radar. But 286 was the best available in the summer of 1940, and was fitted as a stopgap measure to provide some form of radar to detect surfaced U-boats at night, assist with station keeping, coastal navigation, and aircraft warning for destroyers and eventually for sloops and corvettes. The set was by no means a complete failure; in all roles other than submarine detection it performed admirably.

The equipping of RCN destroyers in the United Kingdom with 286 caught the Naval Staff by surprise, as they were kept in the dark by the Admiralty over its radar-fitting policy. Concern began to mount at NSHQ that the RCN would be asked to supply radar sets for its growing fleet of escort vessels. At the Naval Staff meeting of 14 January Commander F.L. Houghton, now director of the Plans Division, outlined the current radar policy, which relied on Admiralty directives and supplies. He also reported on the situation in the other services and on the workings of the Electrical Methods of Fire Control (Radar) Committee. After some discussion no decision was reached concerning future policy; instead the Naval Staff turned to the old sage for advice: 'The Naval Staff considers that Admiralty should be asked as to present Admiralty policy regarding types of sets fitted and what ships are being fitted. If corvettes are being fitted then RCN corvettes should also.'[5]

At least one officer at NSHQ was not content to wait for the Admiralty, and before 23 January, when the British were actually queried, Commander A.R. Pressey, the director Anti-Submarine, discussed with John Henderson at the Radio Branch the feasibility of building a set for the 'detection of surfaced submarines.'[6] The motivation behind Pressey's action is unclear, but it is entirely possible that he was well aware that the British would be unable to supply enough sets for the RCN's escorts and, therefore, that indigenous production would be necessary.

Henderson told Pressey that he thought a modified British ASV, having then only just arrived in Canada, could be used for this purpose. Henderson was asked to consider the matter further and to treat it with some urgency.[7] One week later Henderson concluded that the best the Radio Branch could do in the immediate future was to develop a set in which the main purpose would be to assist in preventing collisions. He anticipated that such a set would have a 200– to 2,000–yard range, be low powered to avoid detection, and be able to change frequencies periodically in order to avoid enemy jamming.[8] Evidently Henderson intended to use components from both the Night Watchman and the ASV. The concept of low power and frequency changing were advanced, as Henderson had some concept of the possibilities of electronic countermeasures, but the limited utility of a collision-avoidance set did not inspire confidence.

A rare insight into the Naval Staff's reaction to Henderson's proposal and their technical knowledge has been found in two marginal notations on a memo circulated by Houghton. The first, written by the director of Operations, Commander R.E.S. Bidwell, demonstrates a good understanding of the limited value of Henderson's idea as well as some grasp of the hydrophone effect using asdic: 'I am not convinced that it would be worthwhile to install an RD/F merely for the purpose of avoiding collision, though it would be extremely useful – Asdic incidentally can be used for this purpose ... If the set had a range of 5 or 6 miles, perhaps it could be used to detect the approach of a submarine on the surface. Is this a practical suggestion?'[9] While Bidwell had at least some concept of the potential worth of radar to an escort, the candid comments of the DCNS, Captain H.E. Reid, are much more revealing of the true state of technical knowledge in the Naval Staff: 'I am *completely in the dark* as regards the ways and capabilities of sets already fitted in some of our destroyers serving in the U.K. The ASV set [probably 286] appears to be fitted in one or two ships. Can you enlighten me as regards to function?'[10]

In the face of such ignorance February became a month of learning for the Naval Staff as it struggled to create a radar policy. Prior to the receipt of any information from the Admiralty it was decided that Henderson's limited-function set was inadequate; only a much more complex and costly submarine-detector set would fill the requirements of the RCN's escorts.[11]

It was not until 18 February that information was finally received from the Admiralty outlining its current naval radar policy. It came as quite a shock to NSHQ: 'So far destroyers and sloops are the smallest types fitted with RD/F but it is the policy to fit corvettes as soon as the gear is available.'[12] The Naval Staff suddenly realized what Pressey had already guessed a month earlier, that they would be required provide radar sets for its most numerous class of escorts. Quick action was necessary, and within a week the research council was authorized to begin work on a prototype submarine-detector set to be based on the British ASV Mark II. The set was scheduled for completion in May; further pre-production models were targeted for June, and manufacturing was to commence at Research Enterprises in August.[13] One cautionary note to the program came from a now informed Reid, who warned that the RCN and NRC 'should be certain that the sets embody all the latest improvements.'[14]

Unfortunately, Reid and the rest of the Naval Staff were unaware that the set to be built by NRC was already a full generation behind the latest developments of the Royal Navy. Poor technical liaison had left both council and navy uninformed of the rapid progress being made at the Admiralty Signals Establishment on sets using the cavity magnetron valve, which enabled them to operate at a much shorter wavelength than ASV, an important factor in detecting a trimmed-down U-boat. Although the first Canadian prototype magnetrons had been completed by Northern Electric Company in February 1940, it appears that no one considered the technology would be available for operational use for some time to come. The decision to build a long-wave radar would be much regretted in the years head. It remains unclear whether or not Naval Staff advised the Admiralty of its plans and, if so, what information was contained in any reply. Whatever the case, Naval Staff remained ignorant of the British development of short-wave radar until June 1941.[15]

It was not until 11 March that the Naval Staff came to a final policy on radar, one that apparently followed Admiralty guidelines to the letter. The immediate problem was seen as the need to fit corvettes, to be followed at a later date by equipment for minesweepers and smaller patrol craft.[16] The corvettes, which had been thrust into the role of ocean-going escorts in late 1940, desperately needed the new equipment.

More than radar sets was necessary. In March a beginning was also made in providing the operators, artificers, and officers required to man the new sets. By mid-March a basic course for fifty radar officers had been organized at the University of Western Ontario, with plans to train eventually four hundred men.[17] Courses for advanced officer and enlisted personnel training were established at the new 'RDF School' located at the Halifax Signal School. The school was to consist of four lecture and two demonstration rooms staffed by only two instructors.[18]

Despite the desperate need to acquire trained radar officers there were no plans at this time to end the scheme of lending personnel to the RN; in fact, the director of Plans proposed an increase in this scheme if so required.[19] As a result, throughout the rest of the war a large number of RCN Volunteer Reserve officers, well trained in radar, would serve with the Royal Navy. At first the Admiralty reciprocated by sending a handful of instructors to the new training establishments, but these remained only until they could be replaced by Canadian officers.

To co-ordinate and control the new operational, research, and training establishments a major reorganization took place at NSHQ. Radar policy, until now loosely under the control of Commander Houghton as the director of the Plans Division, was transferred to A.R. Pressey, the director Anti-Submarine. One of Pressey's first actions was to create a separate RDF branch run by the RDF officer (RDFO).[20]

The officer appointed to be the first RDFO was Lieutenant J.V. Argyle. Argyle had long-term affiliation with radio engineering and the navy and had been with Marconi of Canada since before the First World War. During that war he had served with the fledgling RCN as a chief petty officer, telegraphy, serving in the Gulf of St Lawrence and on the Atlantic coast. By 1918 he was assigned to the Radio Direction Finding Station at Newcastle, New Brunswick. He rejoined the Marconi Company as a radio engineer between the wars and by 1940 was the traffic manager at Halifax. He did not re-enter naval service until March 1941, although he had been acting as an informal technical adviser as early as August 1940.[21]

Although he had much practical experience with radio, Argyle lacked the theoretical knowledge to appreciate all of the intricacies of the new, rapidly changing technology. He was, however, a good manager. He capably guided both the introduction of the first generation of radar equipment into the RCN and the rapidly expanding technical staff. C.J. Mackenzie cited Argyle's excellent contribution to the successful working of the Radar Committee. He saw him as having 'the age and experience in the field, [and] a broad gaze,' that always kept 'discussion on a sensible footing.'[22] Argyle served as RDFO until June 1942, when he joined the Directorate of Radio Supply, and although his last five months in the position were marred by growing exhaustion, he was nevertheless responsible for the successful wide-scale introduction of radar into the RCN.[23]

As the navy was getting its own house in order, the NRC began the task of designing the new naval radar. In mid-March Dr D.W.R. McKinley was sent to Halifax to examine a 286 radar set on a destroyer.[24] It was the first examination of a small-ship naval set by an NRC scientist, and it led to the realization that the Canadian radar would be similar to the 286 in that it too would be an adaptation of the Canadian version of the ASV Mark II, only then being developed from British models received in January. A design team was created under the leadership of H.R. Smyth, another Radio Branch member. Smyth, who was destined to lead the naval radar program at NRC for the rest of the war, was a self-taught radio expert. He possessed an uncanny ability to perceive the solution to a problem by intuition rather than by scientific equation. He was one of the last of the breed of gifted amateurs who had taught science so much about radio in the 1920s and 1930s.[25]

Smyth's team forged ahead with the design of the new radar throughout March. Great progress was made, but despite this, towards the end of the month, the Naval Staff began expressing doubts concerning the NRC's ability to finish the first prototype on time. On 18 March, during a routine visit to Pressey's office, McKinley discovered that the navy was giving serious consideration to ordering fifty or a hundred unmodified Canadian-built ASVs. The Canadian version of the ASV was already in an advanced stage of development, the major delay being that the REL 'Radio' factory complex was still incomplete. McKinley persuaded Pressey to delay implementation of this plan until the Radio Branch had a chance to present the case for its new set before the full Naval Staff. Unwilling to delay the decision any longer, Pressey arranged to have Henderson, Smyth, and McKinley attend the next day's Naval Staff meeting.[26]

The meeting of the Naval Staff on 19 March was one of the few in which NRC scientists had direct input, and their impact on the wavering commitment to the council's radar set was decisive. The Radio Branch members convinced the Naval Staff that it would be a grave error to proceed with the purchase of the ASV when a prototype of the purpose-built set was but three weeks away. Since the Canadian version of the British ASV Mark II, on order for the Royal Canadian Air Force, would not be in production at Research Enterprises until the summer, the small delay to test the new set was more than justified. The Naval Staff agreed to proceed with the new set, provided that the timetable was accurate and the test proved its superiority to ASV.[27] The navy, however, hedged its bets on the success of the council project by informing REL four days later that the RCN would be ordering three hundred to four hundred sets but refusing to say which set, one based on the Night Watchman, or ASV, or the new CSC (Canadian Sea Control) type.[28]

From this point onwards Smyth's team worked at considerable speed to produce a final design and working model of the set, now officially dubbed the CSC. Within four weeks both were complete and preliminary tests were undertaken in Ottawa. These early tests convinced the navy to proceed with the CSC program, and on 17 April one hundred sets were ordered from REL.[29] By 24 April REL was informed that the design for the CSC was considered final and that production should begin 'as soon as possible.'[30] All this occurred more than two weeks before the first sea-going tests had been carried out and when CSC was still an uncertain commodity.

The prototype CSC set was to be the basis for the production model known as SW1C (Surface Warning One Canadian). Fortunately, this prototype possessed few major technical faults, as future testing would prove. As completed, CSC consisted of two separate cabinets. The first contained 'the transmitter ... and power supply,' the second, the receiver and a five-inch, cathode-ray tube 'scanning chassis' which presented information in A-scope form.[31] It operated at two hundred megacycles or a wavelength of 1.5 metres, a frequency chosen specifically to avoid interference with 286 sets.[32]

Two major design compromises were made in order to get the prototype to sea on schedule; one of them was the use of a lower-powered transmitter than designed, incorporated because of the unavailability of micropup valves. This valve shortage would not be resolved until production began in Canada at the end of the year. The second compromise was the use of a fixed-antenna system similar to that of the 286, which was recognized as inadequate. A rotatable antenna design, which would provide 360 degree as opposed to 120 degree coverage and allow for more accurate bearings, was well advanced but would not be ready until the summer.[33]

Sea trials of the prototype CSC set began on 12 May on board the corvette HMCS *Chambly*, J.D. 'Chummy' Prentice commanding, and continued until the 26 May. The account of the test of 13 May is worth quoting in some detail:

The weather was very foggy and visibility about 1/4 mile or less ... a corvette and a Dutch submarine accompanied us to sea for routine tests. The other corvette stood guard over the submarine at a distance of about one mile while we steamed away from them. The submarine gave an indication up to 2.7 miles, and we continued an additional mile, turned and the Captain headed in the general direction of the submarine. At 2.7 miles we again detected the submarine and gave bearing to the Captain. He insisted that the submarine should be 28 degrees from the bearing we gave him. Nevertheless we continued by RDF bearing giving the range to the Captain at intervals of 1/10 of a mile.

We sighted the submarine absolutely dead ahead at 1/4 mile range. The Captain was delighted with these results, and we repeated the tests for him a second and third time.

During these operations we reported ships at five miles and kept a record of their ranges and bearing and in every case we approached them through the fog with such accuracy that collision contact would have been made if we had continued on the bearing.[34]

Further tests continued, including a simulated defence of a convoy on 16 May.[35] By 20 May the Naval Staff met with Argyle, whose enthusiastic report of the test results convinced them that their April gamble was about to pay off. They agreed to 'proceed with the fitting in all ships,' and in consequence space was allocated 'in present and future construction.'[36] The tests were flawed, however, a situation which would have been predictable in May 1941 if proper knowledge of U-boat tactics had existed in Halifax or Ottawa, as it did in London and Liverpool.

The test results on the Dutch submarine 0-15 provided the Naval Staff with a false sense of accomplishment. The 0-15 was almost certainly fully surfaced and running in calm waters in order to be spotted at 2.7 miles. The May tests were a very poor simulation of U-boat tactics, since the German submarines usually operated in a trim-down mode, with only their conning towers appearing above the surface. In addition U-boats operated in the North Atlantic, where even the calmest swell would make it almost impossible for long-wave, ship-mounted radar to differentiate a submarine from waves. Admiralty tests of the 286 conducted in the summer of 1940 had involved a trimmed-down submarine, and the greatest range recorded in this case was but 1.5 miles.

That this major difference in the testing procedure had gone unnoticed by Prentice, who, although he had just been posted to the Chambly, his first anti-submarine command, was one of the most experienced captains, and by Argyle, the navy's RDFO, reveals the dearth of knowledge of ASW tactics which existed in the RCN. The Naval Staff, guided by the results and the enthusiastic endorsement of the naval officers present, put its complete faith in the swic, a misguided trust that would hamper the later centimetric radar program.

The error in proceeding with the swic, however, was understandable. First, we must remember the revolutionary nature of the device; it was such an advance over night or bad-weather optical sighting that any set at all was rightly seen as a tremendous improvement in the navy's ASW capabilities. Secondly, there is the question of whether Canadian science and industry could have handled a more advanced radar. Since complete technical information on British centimetric development was unavailable until January 1942, the question is almost academic because an independent design was clearly beyond the nation's capabilities at this time.

Whatever the negative consequences of the test result, it nevertheless had the positive effect of plunging the navy headlong into the age of radar. The RDF branch and training facilities were greatly expanded throughout 1941 as the navy geared up for the anticipated mass arrival of the swic. By the end of June seven officers were assigned to the RDF branch, five of whom had been recruited from private industry and two returned from the Royal Navy 'with approximately one year's experience in Admiralty RDF fitting and operation.'[37] By September this number had grown to fourteen officers and thirteen electrical artificers, distributed thinly throughout the navy, with an officer and eight EAS on loan to the NRC and two officers assigned to the British Admiralty Repair Mission to maintain radar sets of RN vessels in the United States.[38] By the end of the year installation facilities were established at Halifax, and a repair depot was set up at St John's. The presence of radar at NRC was made permanent by the establishment of a 'naval experimental group,' ostensibly to assist the Radio Branch but in reality to provide training and manpower for naval radar projects. Also by January 1942 the radar training establishment housed in the Practical Building at the Signal School, located on Hill 100, Herring Cove, overlooking Halifax harbour, was in operation training operators to work the new sets.[39]

Meanwhile, work continued on SW1C development. The prototype on the *Chambly* was removed by the end of May, but testing at sea continued on board the yacht HMCS *Beaver*. The prototype of the yagi rotatable antenna was completed by the end of June and tested on the *Beaver* during the summer. The yagi, which looked similar to a modern television antenna, was 'fitted at the head of a steel tube which, in turn, is mounted vertically along the masting guide bearings.' Rotation was provided by a rather cumbersome and primitive mechanism composed of 'a horizontal steel shaft connected to a sprocket and chain reduction gear which in turn, is rotated with a hand wheel mounted in the RDF office.'[40] Accuracy was provided up to 5 degrees, and more importantly, bearings were possible over a 360 degree arc, a major improvement over the Admiralty's 286 whose accuracy and directional search was limited by its fixed antenna.[41] Signals were carried to and from the set by a coaxial cable, insulated with nitrogen gas, a cumbersome arrangement which was destined to cause much trouble in service.[42]

The expected entry of the SW1C into widespread service in August was delayed until early 1942 by a series of nagging production delays. REL, only then just finishing its new factory complex, could only deliver thirteen sets by 20 December.[43] Problems in acquiring major component parts, including a supply of small motor generators and micropup valves, also hampered efforts to mass-manufacture the sets.[44] These delays occurred despite the fact that the project, along with the RCAF's ASV development, had been given the highest Canadian priority rating.[45] With all these problems, by the last week of 1941 only fifteen corvettes and three armed merchant cruisers had been fitted with CSC and SW1C.[46]

The new year saw the final fruition of the SW1C production program.

Ships were being fitted at a much faster rate, and by August almost all RCN corvettes had a radar set.[47] With the introduction of the SW1C into operational service during the month of January the first information on the production models' performance began to come to light. On 23 January 1942 the Captain (D), Newfoundland reported that 'corvettes find the SW1C invaluable for station-keeping on convoy.'[48] Ranges of up to three miles were the norm for this purpose. The set, however, even at this early date began to suffer from a defect that was to haunt its use up to the end of 1943. This was the failure of the seal of the coaxial cable, which allowed the cable frequently to become exposed to sea water; the result of this was a dramatic reduction in the transmission and reception efficiency, which rendered the unit almost useless. Dockyard repairs were necessary to correct the fault.[49] Other faults were also found but were usually more easily resolved. These included the repeated failure of the main rectifier tube, which was later replaced with an improved model.[50]

Despite these early teething problems, development of the sets continued throughout 1942. The first major model change was the conversion of the SW1C to 214 megacycles, compatible with Identify Friend or Foe (IFF) sets. IFF-equipped ships could automatically send and receive coded identification signals that clearly separated them from any possible enemy. This redesigned radar, known as the SW2C, formed the bulk of those fitted on corvettes and minesweepers. The primary difference from SW1C was a modified yagi antenna. The SW2C began to enter service in February 1942.[51]

One other major development of the set which began in late 1941 was the modification of the SW2C for small-ship use, particularly on Fairmile patrol craft and motor torpedo boats. This set, known as the SW3C, differed mainly from the SW2C in its antenna, which was considerably lighter and used a slightly different yagi design. The SW3C began entering service in mid-1942.[52]

The SW sets failed in their primary role of submarine detection, a fact that cannot be ignored when assessing the success of the program. There is but one recorded case of a Canadian long-wave, ship-borne set detecting a U-boat prior to visual sighting. In August 1942, while defending convoy ON 115, HMCS *Sackville* sighted two U-boats in poor-visibility conditions using its SW2C. Unfortunately, the limited range of the radar did not give the corvette time to manoeuvre into a good attack position, and both submarines escaped. It was a situation, stated one senior British officer, in which a ship equipped with centimetric radar would have found both targets a 'gift.'[53] Unquestionably, as we shall see when looking into the unhappy tale of Canadian ten-centimetre development, work on the sw series delayed the introduction of superior radar, which involved using the cavity magnetron valve. The set was also a maintenance headache, with the coaxial-cable problem proving unsolvable until the whole antenna system was redesigned in early 1944.

Nevertheless, the sw series gave invaluable service in station keeping and aircraft detection. Until ten-centimetre equipment became available in large numbers in mid-1943, it was the only radar available to the RCN in quantity. Milner is correct in his assertion that the main value of the sw series was that it provided the experience necessary in radar technology to allow the smooth entry of centimetric sets starting in mid-1942.[54]

Long after the Admiralty had removed the 286 from its corvettes, the sw2c was retained by the RCN for aircraft detection and as a reserve set. In the autumn of 1943, when centimetric radar finally entered widespread use in Canadian service, the RN's Western Approaches Command, tired of maintaining the set, which they considered a bothersome orphan, tried to have the RCN remove it from its vessels. sw2c was defended with spirit by most Canadian operational commanders, and the Naval Staff decided not only to retain them but to continue to improve them.[5] This led to the sw2c/P and sw3c/P, which had a defect-free antenna system and a plan-position indicator display.[56] The sets continued in service to the end of the war, a remarkable feat which perhaps best indicates the true measure of the project.

4

Nuts and Bolts – Organization

By the end of 1941 the RCN had made substantial efforts to acquire the latest equipment and to develop a system for administering it. Details of this organization have been touched on in previous chapters, but now an overview of the entire system is necessary in order to understand many of the problems that would soon develop in the RCN's highly technological and scientific war. Although the accomplishments up to January 1941 were impressive – the commencement of asdic production and the development and introduction of the new long-wave radar being the best examples – there were administrative faults that would by the end of 1942 lead the navy into what historians have dubbed the 'equipment crisis,' when RN and USN officers believed that poorly equipped Canadian warships were a liability on the mid-ocean convoy routes.

By the end of 1941 the RCN had some internal structure for dealing with advanced equipment research, development, and procurement. The creation of the Equipment Division and the RDFO's office are the two best examples. By March 1941 most scientific and technical sections had been placed under the control of one naval staff officer, the director of the Technical Division. In practice, however, the DTD did not provide the leadership necessary to ensure that the RCN developed equipment policy which kept pace with British technical developments. Part of the reason for this failure can be seen in the schizophrenic nature of the DTD's responsibilities. The DTD was in charge of everything from new vessel inspection to degaussing; his divisions included the director Anti-Submarine and, therefore, the RDFO and liaison with the NRC. Such diverse responsibilities meant the DTD was a jack of all trades and master of none. He left most administrative and planning functions to his junior divisional heads, and therefore did not provide the strong voice at the senior levels of the naval staff that was required.¹ Recognition at senior levels of the need to plan equipment research and development well in the advance of an actual need was in its most elementary stages at NSHQ. The csc/sw1c program only came about because it fitted an Admiralty policy. Independent equipment policy development was still beyond the capability of the Naval Staff and council.

The problem that the navy had in establishing advanced planning for equipment procurement can be linked to the failure to develop management skills at the same pace as the growth in numbers of warships and men. By November 1942, when NSHQ moved into a new, temporary building on Cartier Square in Ottawa, the administration of the navy was undertaken in seventeen separate buildings – a far cry from thirty months before when the entire organization was comfortably housed in two floors of the Robinson Building.² With this growth had come the end of the close personal men's club atmosphere and, therefore, of the simple pre-war management system. Prior to late 1941 reforms of the organization of NSHQ, such as the formation of the Technical Directorate, had been haphazard and piecemeal. This had important ramifications for all areas of administration as the navy found itself increasingly unable to keep pace with the rapidly changing technology.

The first systematic reforms of NSHQ began in late 1941, when a careful study of the problem of organization was done by naval officers and civilian officials, 'including experienced businessmen who were brought into the Department as special assistants to the Deputy Minister.' This group soon realized that the administration of the navy was close to collapse. The growth in business, for instance, had swamped the naval secretary, who was responsible for co-ordination. He was said to have signed twelve hundred letters a day, 'an average of two a minute for ten working hours.'³ There was an immediate need to reform even the most senior reaches of the administration. Both the Naval Council and Staff had been operating without any legal authority, and neither body was working smoothly. One of the major difficulties was the failure to differentiate between operational and support components of the organization. The CNS was swamped with the details of naval personnel, ship building, and supply, and little time was left for his primary functions of providing operational leadership and ensuring liaison with the naval minister.⁴

The investigations began in late 1941 and culminated in a series of major structural changes to NSHQ in the first six months of 1942. In January 1942 the support functions were brought together under the authority of three new super-directors – the chief of Naval Personnel (CNP), the chief of Naval Equipment and Supply (CNES), and the chief of Naval Engineering and Construction (CNEC). The CNS continued to be responsible for operational decisions and the deputy minister for financial and civil administration.[5]

All five, plus the vice-chief of Naval Staff (VCNS, formerly the DCNS) and the head of a newly enlarged naval secretariat, were appointed to the Naval Board, which was designed to replace the Naval Council. Modelled on the board of the Admiralty, with some reference to Australian experience, 'the powers of the Board were limited to giving of advice to the minister on matters relating exclusively to the Naval Service or referred to it by the Minister.' The minister, although technically not a member, attended many and in some periods most of the meetings and when in attendance took the chair.[6]

The Naval Staff was also reformed and given legal status by naval order. The order stated: 'The Naval Staff will consider in detail matters of Naval Policy, either originated by it or referred to it by the Naval Board and will submit proposals to the Naval Board *in their complete form*. Its relation to the Naval Board parallels that of the Navy Board to the Minister. In effect, the Naval Staff constitutes the Naval Board's brain trust.'[7] The new Naval Staff consisted of an expanded and reorganized operational section consisting of the CNS, VCNS, director of Naval Intelligence (DNI), director of Plans (DPD), director of Trade (DTD), director of Operations (DOD), and the director of Signals (DSD).[8]

While the theory behind this reorganization was sound, it did not work in practice. The Naval Board was never an effective policy adviser to Angus Macdonald but rather tended to deal with trivial issues that 'could have been settled by some Lieutenant-Commander in Halifax or Esquimalt.'[9] Few major policy decisions were undertaken by this body, and Macdonald was not kept fully informed by it. The reasons for this are uncertain but seem to stem from the personalities of both Macdonald and Nelles. It appears that Macdonald, unwilling or unable to learn its intricate details, was content to keep solely to the political side of the administration of the Naval Service. He intervened only when an issue verged on becoming a public and therefore a politically damaging scandal. This is reflected in Macdonald's papers in the Public Archives of Nova Scotia, which contain only two major groups of documents on his wartime activities – on Nelles's dismissal and on conscription. Like any senior officer, Nelles was quite content with this absence of political interference and made most major policy decisions within the confines of the Naval Staff or by his personal authority as CNS. By doing so he made himself responsible for the entire non-financial administration of the service. Uniformed members of the Naval Board frequently attended Naval Staff meetings, and as a result the careful differentiation between operational and support directorates was never achieved in practice.[10]

The 1942 reorganization also affected in detail the day-to-day administration of advanced technology and science within the navy. In April 1942 the administration of radar was divided among three new directorates. The director of Signals Division was made responsible for policy and technical developments, the director of Ship Building, under the authority of the CNEC, was made responsible for wiring radar to machines and instruments of new construction, and the CNES was placed in charge of production of equipment. The DSD took overall control of the RDFO and his organization.[11] The placement of the RDFO's office in an operational directorate is a reflection of NSHQ's view of the unit as being primarily responsible for planning operational radar policy and for providing technical personnel to maintain sets at sea. The RDFO's responsibility for research and development was a secondary concern, and the main channel of communication with NRC remained the Technical Division.

The new DSD was Commander G.A. Worth, an original member of the RCN who had retired in 1931 and rejoined the service in 1940. His previous service was typical of that of Canadian officers of the period and marked with no particular distinction. It is rumoured that after his retirement he had assisted rum runners to establish elaborate communication networks, and this is borne out by his appointment in 1940 as the chief signals officer on the COAC's staff when there is no indication of previous naval signals experience. It was here that he first became acquainted with radar. A tough individual, Worth was an indifferent administrator but an uncompromising defender of his small empire. He was no diplomat, and his tendency to engage in bureaucratic infighting would eventually lead to the most serious confrontation between the RCN and the NRC of the entire war.[12]

Other technical and scientific areas were the responsibilities of the new senior technician of the Technical Division (STTD) and the director Anti-Submarine, both under the authority of the CNES. The STTD took over the much-reduced Technical Division, which was now responsible for liaison with the NRC, magnetic and acoustic minesweeping, chemical warfare, and inventions. The DA/S retained responsibilities for asdic research and development and took over administration of production in June 1942 after the closing of the Equipment Division.[13]

The reforms of 1942 were not particularly effective in providing the navy with the means to plan and administer its advanced technology requirements. The reorganization turned out to be a stopgap measure which would require major restructuring again in 1943. It was the best the RCN could do given the service's limited resources, rapid growth, and the constant need to deal with operational demands, which quite correctly had to be given top priority. Some of the difficulties that were not solved by these reforms had a direct impact on the looming equipment crisis. Of these, two are of particular significance, obvious when seen from the advantage of hindsight but only dimly perceived during the tumult of war.

Nowhere was the failure of the 1942 reforms more apparent than in the navy's inability to keep current information on the types of equipment mounted on its warships. Without this information and the corresponding data on equipment mounted on RN vessels, it was very difficult for the staff officer to appreciate the growing disparity in equipment on the two navies' warships. No central registry of equipment existed until February 1944. Prior to this official publications listing shipboard systems were filled with inaccurate and incomplete information. Typical are the first five years of the semi-annual publication *Particulars of Canadian War Vessels*, the only documentary source that covers the entire war. Early issues fail to specify the type of much of the equipment listed, including radar and asdic, and do not report at all on many other categories. Inaccuracies abound, such as the listing of corvette armament in the February 1942. It states that all vessels of the class had been equipped with two-pounder pom pom anti-aircraft guns, but the weapon was not in general issue on Canadian warships until mid-1943.[14]

It was not until November 1942 that the navy made its first attempt to get an accurate picture of the state of equipment on Canadian warships. At that time NSHQ requested that ships report on twenty-five different categories ranging from main armament and asdics to gyrocompasses and searchlights. Interestingly, although the vessels were not required to report on radar over a quarter of the vessels did, and of these over 80 per cent carried fully modern type 271 ten-centimetre equipment.[15] This report was a one time effort, and it was not until February 1944, after Nelles's dismissal, that a central registry file listing ships' equipment was established and maintained.[16]

Effective communication between operational units and the laboratory, which might have prevented many equipment problems, was conspicuously lacking. These communication difficulties were aggravated by the physical distance of the capital from the nearest major naval base at Halifax over fourteen hundred kilometres away. Naval headquarters became more concerned to avoid duplication than to encourage field innovation, which could have led to more accurate evaluations of equipment reaching the council. For example, in late 1941 naval headquarters severely chastised the commanding officer, Atlantic Coast, by then Admiral G.C. Jones, for allowing the Halifax dockyard staff to duplicate NRC efforts to design a flexible rotation device for the SW1C antenna. Jones spiritedly defended his staff because 'while development and general policy is unquestionably a Headquarters responsibility, *it is clear that a certain amount of development work must, or should be carried out in actual ships.*'[17] Ottawa insisted, however, that it be kept informed and that it approve any field innovation to ensure 'the prevention of uncontrolled development.'[18]

While discouraging field innovation, NSHQ did not open other ways of communicating with operational units. Very few officers at NSHQ had recent wartime sea-going experience. In his memoirs H.N. Lay stated that in June 1941, when he was appointed director of Operations from the destroyer *Restigouche*, he was 'the only officer at Naval Headquarters who had been at sea during World War II.'[19] There was very little interchange between administrators and scientists in Ottawa and officers with combat experience. Those officers and electrical artificers who were assigned to the NRC did not have battlefield expertise to bring to the scientist. The reason for this situation was the extremely limited resources available to the RCN, and the effects were unfortunately as serious as they were unavoidable. NRC was uninformed on operational as opposed to strictly technical requirements. This led to the introduction of the highly complex and cumbersome coaxial-cable system that nearly ruined the SW1/2C series. It was designed as the best technical solution, but no consideration was given to keeping it in working order at sea with radar staff that barely knew how to run the sets, let alone do complicated and costly maintenance. More serious complications were to follow.

The RCN's policy of sending mainly inexperienced personnel to its scientific laboratory was directly opposite to Admiralty practice. At the Admiralty research establishment all projects were carefully guided by officers with recent sea-going experience. They ensured that a piece of equipment would work and could be maintained at sea.[20] At the American Naval Research Laboratory similar guidance was provided by scientists who had up to twenty years of experience building electronic equipment for warships.[21] No such pool of expertise existed in Canada.

Men such as Argyle and Pew were very scarce and simply could not do everything. The real tragedy was that the Canadian navy was far less capable of handling temperamental devices than was the RN or USN. No vessel smaller than a destroyer had artificers, and therefore only very limited on-board maintenance could be done. Dockyard staff were equally limited, particularly in St John's. In the end much Canadian repair work was undertaken by the British at Londonderry. It was here that the sw1/2c received its deserved reputation for being a maintenance head-ache and convinced the Admiralty that it should be scrapped.[22]

The decision to appoint the research council as the official Research and Experimental Division was made at a time when the navy had few options. It was soon realized that it was far from a perfect solution. The NRC, while not given official status by the army and air force until 27 March 1943, was at least as interested in serving the other services.[23] After all it was the army and RCAF that had sponsored the early devel-opment of the Radio Section while the navy vacillated from mild interest to outright indifference on the sidelines.

An added problem was that Mackenzie's loyalties were divided between being the senior administrator of the NRC and the mandarin of all war-time science. He could do what was best for Canadian military science or for the NRC, the two not necessarily being the same thing. Mackenzie's loyalty was to the council, and his goal was to give its laboratories an international reputation, without peer in Canada. This attitude is re-flected in his diary entry of 7 March 1941 concerning the possible ad-dition to the NRC of certain research functions from the army's Master General of the Ordnance Office: 'I am not sure whether it is a wise move as I now have more than I can do. However it is difficult to shirk re-sponsibility at a time like this. If it works it would *add greatly to the prestige of the Council and give us very powerful friends*. The danger is that if there is a blow-up in Munitions and Supply [concerning the disbanding of the MGO's office] we might be involved in the general criticism.'[24]

In the United States, Vannevar Bush had already perceived the need to divest himself of the day-to-day management responsibilities of the National Defence Research Committee. This led to the formation in June 1941 of the planning and advisory body of the Office of Scientific Research and Development. This was despite the fact that NDRC was only a contract allocation and clearing agency with no direct control of work-ing laboratories.[25]

The Naval Staff did not fully appreciate these problems for some time and went to absurd lengths to ensure the integration of the NRC within the naval establishment. After adding the council to the naval list in March 1941, NSHQ requested that the NRC organization conform to that of the Admiralty's research establishments.[26] The NRC, at a loss over how to accomplish this, simply took a pre-existing organizational chart, added a new title, put some lines connecting the division heads to Rose, as the liaison officer for Naval Research, who was then connected to Millard, the Research liaison officer.[27]

The most telling effect of the multitude of roles undertaken by the NRC and its officials was the lack of guidance to senior-level naval planning. Mackenzie had only nominal charge of a naval directorate because he was not involved with RCN business on a daily basis. A multi-hatted individual, much more than the director of a department, he had more responsibilities than any one officer at NSHQ with the exception of Admiral Nelles. Moreover, even if Mackenzie or Rose had had the time or inclination to assist in naval planning, neither were members of the Naval Staff Committee and could only be present when invited by the CNS.

This situation was not enhanced by the centralizing attitude of the NRC. Mackenzie had led the council to a dominant position in military science, the concentration of responsibility in its hands exceeding that of any single institution in either the United States or Great Britain. Universities and industrial laboratories were quickly relegated to doing mainly secondary work such as testing and basic training. While major investments were made in the Ottawa area on new facilities for the NRC, such as the new complex on Montreal Road and the radar testing station on Metcalfe Road, some outside facilities were underused. The best example of this was the availability of new laboratories at the University of Montreal to house the Anglo-Canadian atomic energy program; these facilities lay unused while the NRC continued to build new laboratories in Ottawa.[28]

The NRC's reluctance to house any research unit outside of the national capital region had a direct impact on the RCN. Originally the navy believed that its research facilities should be located on the coasts. This was the intention behind approaching Dalhousie University to establish the Halifax station in the winter of 1940.[29] When the NRC took the facility over soon after, it made little effort to undertake scientific projects at Halifax. Instead the Halifax station was allowed gradually to degenerate, until by August 1942 Mackenzie saw it as nothing more than an applied engineering establishment: 'On the whole the Halifax Station does not impress one as a research station but rather as an engineering affair. Most of the work is pretty much routine now. Of course the analysis is on a high level and everything that is done is done very well indeed. Also Johnstone and Henderson give a great deal of advice on innumerable subjects to the officers of the Navy.'[30]

Many areas of research, such as underwater acoustics, that should have been undertaken in salt water were conducted primarily in Ottawa. This led to such incongruities as a barge furnished with the latest in asdic, hydrophone, and other related equipment being tested on the Ottawa River![31] There was no incentive to establish field units at Halifax or St John's, and therefore no scientist monitored existing equipment or developed the expertise needed to design the next generation of weapons systems. Visiting scientists were occasionally sent to investigate a particular problem or to test new apparatus, but these trips were neither coordinated nor frequent and thus played little role in establishing the type of liaison needed to maintain pace with the rapidly changing technologies of anti-submarine warfare.

It could be argued that this was a naval responsibility and that the NRC should not be held at fault. In both the United Kingdom and the United States, however, it was scientists like P.M.S. Blackett, R.V. Jones, and James Conant who ensured that intimate and constant liaison was established between the front line and the laboratory. Neither Mackenzie nor anyone else at NRC shared this vision, or if they did, they were unwilling to take on the entrenched conservatism of the defence establishment.[32]

One example of Mackenzie's growing influence within military science was his emergence as the premier administrator of the radar program. The first attempt to establish a central co-ordinating agency for the program took place in the summer of 1940, when the first concrete results of NRC radar research began to emerge. The Radio Section found that it required some system to establish priorities and co-ordinate requests made to its still limited research facilities. The army chief of staff, General Crerar, proposed the creation of an interservice subcommittee with representatives of the services and NRC. This committee, the Interservice Committee of Electrical Fire Control (Radar), did not meet until 16 November 1940. It was composed of junior level officers and acted as a purely co-ordinating agency. Further, it had no executive authority and could only operate by consensus.[33]

Nevertheless, the Fire Control Committee functioned adequately until the production element of the program, the REL Radio Factory, neared completion in the spring of 1941. The company required the services to reach agreement on production priority and material compatibility.

By the beginning of April 1941 – not coincidentally, when the SW1C program was coming on stream – the Fire Control Committee was paralysed by indecision. 'The three services,' wrote the air minister C.G. Power, 'were placing orders for practically the same equipment but with slightly different specifications.'[34]

On 19 April REL's president, W.E. Phillips, met with E.P. Taylor, C.D. Howe's assistant at the Department of Munitions and Supply, to discuss the situation. Taylor requested a formal report, and only four days later REL submitted their proposal to reorganize the management of the program with a new, more powerful committee controlled by a powerful civilian chairman. The company warned that the issue of management organization 'must be solved *before we can produce.*'[35] Phillips, in his covering letter, nominated O.M. Biggar, a member of the REL board, for the chairmanship of the restructured committee. This was an undisguised attempt by the company to gain control over the program.[36]

The memo was passed directly to C.D. Howe, the minister of DMS and, with the exception of Prime Minister King, the most influential member of the war Cabinet. As the czar of the wartime economy Howe had direct responsibility for the Crown corporation. His managerial style was such that he did not get involved with the day-to-day operations of any one concern, but when a problem was brought to his attention, he ensured quick resolution as long as it was politically expedient to do so. On 29 April 1941 Howe wrote to the minister of National Defence, J.L. Ralston, expressing his strong approval of both REL's recommendation and Phillips's nomination.[37]

Ralston consulted with his colleagues in the air and naval service. Angus Macdonald agreed to have NSHQ study the matter, and on 4 May Captain G.M. Hibbard, the director of the Technical Division, submitted an extensive memorandum which denied any naval involvement in the breakdown of the Fire Control Committee. He did agree, however, that there was a need for 'a co-ordinating committee to knit closely together the production requirements, and to deal with the priority between the services.'[38]

Macdonald, after consulting with Ralston, ordered the Chiefs of Staff Committee to reform radar management along the lines suggested by REL. Ralston, for some unknown reason, recommended that Mackenzie be given the chairmanship. This act confirmed NRC dominance in science and high technology in the Second World War. It also ended REL's brief attempt to gain some control over senior-level planning in the radar program. The company had to acquiesce to an NRC-dominated committee dictating production priority. Phillips was not initially displeased by Mackenzie's nomination because it appeared to solve REL major problems and the company at that time seemed to have developed an excellent working relationship with the research council. Howe and Mackenzie had been friends since before the First World War, and the service chiefs were satisfied with a man with whom they already had extensive experience.[39]

On 6 May the chiefs of staff approved a restructuring of radar management under the auspices of a new RDF[40] Committee, with Mackenzie as chairman. Each service, REL, and NRC were to appoint a senior-level administrative officer to the committee. Its power as outlined was extensive: 'Co-ordination of development, design requirements and production of RDF apparatus for the fighting services. This to include the determination of types, quantities and future requirements, and the preparation of all necessary production specifications.'[41] Both the committee and, 'in case of fundamental differences of opinion,' the chairman were empowered to consult directly with the chiefs of staff.[42] Direct access to the chiefs of staff meant that Mackenzie, who was completely supported by the service chiefs during the war, had absolute power over radar research, development, and production.

Here was the crucial centre of the power of the NRC. By having the acting president placed in charge of the biggest scientific and one of the largest technologically sophisticated industrial programs in Canada, the council ensured that there would be no competition with its control of military science in the first half of the war. This was only one of Mackenzie's many roles that conflicted with his naval responsibilities. He could not represent navy interests while acting as chairman, nor could he be a neutral chairman while NRC president. Thus, the problems with the RCN-NRC agreement were growing almost from its inception, a situation that would become increasingly serious as the need for high-technology equipment became more pressing in the intensifying Battle of the Atlantic.

The RCN was represented on the RDF Committee by its new technical staff officers. The original naval member was the director Anti-Submarine, A.R. Pressey; he was joined after the second meeting by Argyle acting as a technical assistant.[43] In subsequent meetings the navy was usually only represented by the RDFO, although the senior staff officer responsible for radar retained the right to attend.

The RCN's lack of control over the radar program can be illustrated by the restructuring of the Radio Branch that took place between July 1941 and January 1942. As early as the spring of 1941 it was apparent that the NRC's radar research centre had serious administrative problems. They centred on the inability of John Henderson to adapt to the role of full-time administrator. Henderson, a good practical scientist, did not possess the skill or temperament required of a manager.

To assist Henderson in the spring of 1941 Mackenzie appointed Colonel F.C. Wallace as an administrative assistant. A British army officer and industrialist, Wallace had arrived in Canada with the Tizard mission in the summer of 1940 and stayed on to assist and observe the Canadian economic mobilization.[44] In June 1941 Wallace was made the secretary of the RDF Committee, responsible for co-ordinating all radar specifications. By the summer of 1941 it was clear to Mackenzie that Wallace was a superior administrator and had earned a greater role with the Radio Branch. The need was certainly pressing, for by mid-summer between 125 and 150 civilians plus assigned military personnel worked at the NRC on radar. At this time the Radio Branch was undertaking projects for all three services as well as advanced research of its own. The RCAF's ASV and the navy's SW1C held top priority, but the NRC was already committed to building its first ten-centimetre radar, the army anti-aircraft control set that would be known as the GLC Mark III. The navy alone had approximately a dozen projects under way at the council, most relating to the SW1C.[45] Although the RDF Committee established overall priority, a mechanism to allocate laboratory resources was found to be necessary. On 15 August 1941 Wallace was placed in charge of Radio Branch administration, while Henderson was made chief scientific officer. This date also marked the creation of a new internal committee, called the Heads of Groups Committee, consisting of project leaders. In all, twelve different scientists were present.[46]

The system set up in August did not completely solve the problem. Henderson still proved incapable of managing his much more limited areas of responsibilities. Other difficulties centred on R.W. Boyle, the head of the Physics and Electrical Engineering Division, who did not approve of the growing independence of the Radio Branch, which by this time was only nominally under his control. The organization of the Heads of Groups Committee also proved unwieldy as its membership constantly changed when new projects were added to old ones.

By the end of November these problems led certain members to stage what W.E.K. Middleton has called a 'palace revolution.'[47] They insisted that changes be made, and they appear to have directed their anger at Henderson. Throughout December Mackenzie and Wallace extensively studied the situation, and in mid-January 1942 a new structure emerged.

At its top for policy decisions was the Radio Control Board, consisting of Wallace, Mackenzie, and Boyle, although the last was only nominally involved. Wallace was appointed managing director and chaired the new Co-ordinating and Management Committee. Unlike the Heads of Groups, the new committee consisted of heads of sections newly created by the compartmentalization of the branch. The division of the laboratory was undertaken according to both service and research functions. The sections included one each for the army, air force, and navy, as well as Microwave, Special Research and Development, Mechanical Engineering, and Workshop groups. The head of the naval section was H.R. Smyth. Henderson remained chief scientific officer, but he was given no clear responsibility and was soon aware that he was an unnecessary appendage. By April 1942 he transferred to the RCAF to conduct operational research.[48]

The navy attached a liaison person to the Navy Section, generally a junior-level officer reporting to the RDFO.[49] But in the organization of the Radio Branch there was little place for direct input by any of the services. The navy would increasingly find its limited control over radar research a serious problem and one that would eventually see a complete split between the branch and the RCN.

The NRC's central role in the navy's scientific and technological war was further enhanced by its control over major portions of industry, particularly the largest concern, Research Enterprises Limited. In the first week of October 1940, Professor E.F. Burton, a University of Toronto physicist and REL director, met with John Henderson to settle operational procedures between the two organizations. They agreed on the basic feature of REL-NRC co-ordination. The former was to have exclusive control over manufacturing, the latter over research, with a sharing of responsibilities for development. Burton, however, secretly confided in his report of the meeting that the manufacturer should 'be in the position to foresee future trends and should recommend to the authorities of NRC lines along which REL thinks research should be directed.'[50] Clearly, Burton wished REL to be the senior partner in the relationship, a theme that Phillips would echo in his unsuccessful attempt of May 1941 to have an REL director appointed chairman of the RDF Committee.

Relations between REL and NRC were not always smooth. There were numerous skirmishes between the head of REL's Radio Division, R.A. Hackbusch, and his staff, and Wallace and the Radio Branch. Often outside mediation was necessary, and the Howe papers record several occasions on which the Department of Munitions and Supply chief had to intervene.[51] The argument between the two centred on two points. First was the responsibility for the slow pace of getting a set from the completed research stage into mass production. We have already seen the delays associated with the sw1c program, and more serious incidents were to follow. Second was the NRC's intrusion into the manufacturing role by hand-building large numbers of sets while REL was still tooling up for production.

After the formation of the RDF Committee in May 1941 there was never any doubt that the NRC was the senior partner in the relationship. Infighting between the two organizations only ended when they were united at the most senior level by the appointment of Wallace to replace Hackbusch at REL in September 1943. Since Wallace retained his position at NRC, in effect REL became the manufacturing division of NRC's Radio Branch.[52]

At REL the navy maintained only a junior-level officer, who was mainly concerned with keeping the navy informed on production rates and ensuring that equipment was properly packaged and shipped. Technical liaison was generally carried out through the NRC.

Given these problems, including the failure to integrate the scientist and the sailor at senior level, the growing power of the council, and Mackenzie's clear conflict of interest with what the navy perceived as his naval role, there was bound to be growing dissatisfaction within the RCN over the terms of the December 1940 agreement with NRC.

The first person to voice this dissatisfaction with the council was J.R. Millard, the navy's Research liaison officer. Born in 1905 in Toronto, Millard graduated from the University of Toronto in 1930 with a bachelor's degree in electrical and mechanical engineering. He then spent nine months at NRC, followed by a year of unsuccessful graduate studies. From 1932 he was a self-employed radio and electrical engineer, and in 1937 he became the chief engineer at Burlec Company, a manufacturer of electrical equipment, including switchboards. He joined the navy in 1940 and served in Halifax before coming to Ottawa in early 1941 to take up the NRC liaison post.[53]

By February 1942 Millard saw that the shortcomings of the NRC-RCN agreement far outweighed any advantages because the council was a 'public institution' established to do research for all government departments and commercial organizations. As a result, he believed, the NRC could 'never be a perfectly satisfactory Naval research organization, since it is not under naval control.' He complained that the agreement with the council, which was the only formal arrangement between it and any of the services, should have given the navy priority, but that occasionally there was 'a difficulty in getting naval projects underway if the personnel of the NRC Division involved happened to be occupied with work for the other services.' The NRC was also accused of not allowing research work to be carried out by other laboratories which may have been 'more capable' in certain areas.

Millard made wide-ranging recommendations, including the reappointment of the Research liaison officer as the officer in charge of research and development. This officer would take over much of Mackenzie's and Rose's duties, including 'the authority to select the organization most suitable to carry out a given research project' and the power to 'overcome the difficulties experienced with priorities and methods of conduct of a given project being carried out by the NRC.'

As a second stage Millard proposed a more radical change, calling for the replacement of the NRC laboratories by a naval research and experimental department. To this end he asked that steps be taken to recruit 'a group of scientists and engineers to form the nucleus for the formation of such an organization.'[54]

Although none of Millard's proposals were to be immediately acted upon, they were to be the basis of the navy's future strategy for managing its scientific and advanced technological effort. But this would have to wait until it became apparent at more senior levels at NSHQ that there were serious problems with the navy's scientific war.

5

Liaison

Throughout the war Canada remained reliant on technological development from Great Britain and the United States. While major strides had been made by the end of 1941 in developing an industrial, scientific, and military infrastructure within Canada, the nation was nowhere near a point of self-sufficiency where it could pursue independent development with a reasonable chance of success. The navy still relied almost entirely on basic British designs for equipment and on Admiralty scientific and policy decisions. Advanced scientific research was still in its infancy at NRC and in most areas had been purposely superseded by work to adapt British designs to Canadian and, therefore, American standards. All asdic sets built by the Equipment Division were close copies of Admiralty designs, interchangeable with their British-built counterparts. The SWIC was an adaptation of the British ASV guided by the examination of an RN type 286 set. As a result close co-operation and liaison between Canada and Great Britain was vital if the RCN was to have any chance of providing modern ASW equipment to its growing escort fleet.

The Admiralty had realized the importance of permanent liaison personnel in Canada quite early on in the war. It was one of the major reasons for the establishment of the British Admiralty Technical Mission in July 1940 (see Chapter 2). The formation of the BATM led to the most successful Canadian project involving advanced technology to date – the building of asdic sets. But the BATM was intended to serve the Admiralty and was not designed to provide the RCN with technical expertise and information. Since the Admiralty expressed little interest in the Canadian naval radar program, the BATM gave no major assistance to the project. Also, British representatives tended to lose touch with the latest technical developments back home after a few months in Canada. What was required was a Canadian office or offices in London to look after Canadian interests in such areas as radar and asdic technology; unfortunately there was no pre-war base from which to build.

Until the summer 1940 Canadian naval liaison with the Admiralty was maintained through letters, annual staff meetings with the Commander-in-Chief (C-in-C) of the Atlantic and West Indies squadron, and through the office of one civilian employee at Canada House in London. From 16 January 1941 naval liaison was taken over by the Captain Commanding Canadian Ships (CCCS), an office that developed from the placement of RCN destroyers in United Kingdom waters after the fall of France. In March 1941 the CCCS was transferred from his destroyer to Canada House in London, and his primary responsibility became liaison with the Admiralty, but he had virtually no staff to deal with technical and scientific liaison. In fact, until the middle of 1943 only one person, the Staff Officer (Material), looked after all technical liaison, from ship engines to radar.[1]

The lack of technical staff within the RCN was the reason for the minimum staff in London. As with other scientific manpower problems, NRC was asked to provide the solution. The RCN-NRC agreement of December 1940 had given the council control over the exchange of technical and scientific information and equipment. By then the research council was already heavily involved in working out procedures for scientific cooperation with both the United Kingdom and the United States; however, no real solutions had been found. The problem of establishing good interchange of information on the ASV has already been examined, but it should be remembered that NRC scientists visiting the United Kingdom could not convince officials of the Ministry of Aircraft Production of Canada's legitimate need for prototypes of the set. The MAP bureaucrats simply could not believe that Canada was capable of producing radar. It was only the coincidental arrival in London of C.D. Howe and his personal intervention with Lord Beaverbrook that assured delivery of two sets in January 1941.

Part of the difficulty was NRC's failure until August 1941 to establish a permanent liaison office at Canada House in London. Mackenzie resisted requests made by the British as early as 1940 to establish a full-time office in the United Kingdom. He argued that periodic visits by experts was sufficient for liaison, that NRC did not have the staff to spare for a permanent office in London, and that continuous exchange of information could be handled by the permanent British representative,

Professor R.H. Fowler, who had arrived in July 1940.[2] Mackenzie had some support for his position. G.H. Henderson, after his summer 1940 visit to the United Kingdom, had stated that he 'would deprecate the idea of having a sort of general scientific attaché permanently attached to Canada House in London and would recommend having a series of overlapping visits to England.'[3]

Mackenzie's reasons for delay are nevertheless unsatisfactory; in fact, by the beginning of 1941 Canada was the only Dominion without a permanent scientific office in London. If the council could not provide suitable liaison officers, then it is surprising that no attempt was made to recruit a candidate from the universities or industry. Mackenzie was, after all, a dean from a small prairie university and was seen to be quite capable of running the NRC. If Mackenzie required further proof of the usefulness of university personnel, then he only had to go to the next office, where Fowler, a Cambridge professor, worked. But Mackenzie showed great reluctance to create a unit of the council that was too far away for his direct personal supervision.[4]

Mackenzie also believed that Fowler could act in a liaison capacity for Canada. Fowler's primary duty up to March 1941, however, was to administer Anglo-American scientific co-operation. Canada's interests were, at best, a secondary concern, and even if he had had the time his immediate superior was with the Ministry of Supply, which constituted only a small part of the diverse British scientific community.[5] The Admiralty considered Mackenzie, in his role as director of Naval Research, and not Fowler, to be their scientific contact in Ottawa.[6]

With no liaison office there was no one to guarantee a free and rapid exchange of information with Great Britain. As the ASV problem illustrates, the British lacked knowledge of Canada's scientific and industrial potential. As a result, the British were reluctant to slow down in any way their own scientific developments in order to assist Canadian work. Often Canadian projects that had little immediate potential for fulfilling British requirements received only marginal assistance. The CSC project was given almost no technical help beyond the delivery of the original ASVs. While it was being developed, it is doubtful that anyone in Canada knew of the advanced state of the far superior 271 ten-centimetre set which was tested at sea almost at the same time as the CSC. Had they been informed, NRC scientists would undoubtedly have understood the ramifications of this work and may very well have advised the Naval Staff quite differently.

A visiting Canadian scientist could not come to an understanding of the complex and seemingly haphazard British scientific system. The Admiralty had two, sometimes competitive, research organizations, the permanent research establishments such as ASE and the wartime Miscellaneous Weapon Development Department. The latter was specifically created to rapidly develop devices whose introduction into the service would have been delayed by the conservative research establishments. Its most famous device was the ahead-throwing ASW mortar, the hedgehog.[7] Radar in Britain was under development at no less than five different research centres under four different departments.[8] No central scientific co-ordinating body existed. To even the most educated occasional visitor, such as the American scientific administrator Vannevar Bush, the British system seemed incomprehensible.[9] Only after a prolonged stay could any individual come to an understanding of its intricacies.

The first permanent NRC presence in London developed from one of the trips to Great Britain made by a Canadian scientist. In March 1941 A.H.R Smith, a junior member of the Radio Branch staff, went to the United Kingdom to examine recent radar developments. By May he had been seconded to Canada House in order to assist with the transfer of scientific information between London and Ottawa. He soon developed into much more than a clerk, as the British considered him to be the long-awaited NRC liaison officer. Uncomfortable with the role the British had given him, Smith felt that a more senior liaison officer was required in order to be 'able to make minor policy decisions with some expectation of being upheld by Council.' Smith found himself 'constantly being asked questions which can be answer [sic] only very vaguely if at all.' This led to a natural 'lack of confidence' in his efforts.[10]

Pressure mounted on Mackenzie to establish a senior-level liaison officer in London. In Ottawa Dr G.S. Fields, head of the Acoustic Division, who had recently returned from Britain, reported on the need for an expanded effort at Canada House.[11] In England McNaughton, Fowler (who had only recently returned), and Smith urged action.[12] On 13 June 1941 Smith wrote to Boyle:

The question of Canada's intention with respect to the establishment of a permanent scientific liaison office here has again been brought to the fore ... I understand that General McNaughton is convinced that it is necessary to make permanent provision in London for the interchange of scientific information of all sorts, and to its proper distribution both here and in Canada. The bureau established by the NDRC at the United States Embassy here is under the direction of Hovde, who is permanent secretary. Their staff is being augmented daily by men sent from United States [sic] ... I am continually being mistaken for one of their representatives.[13]

Two weeks later Smith also warned that 'so long as Canada feels that the best men cannot be spared from Ottawa, we may expect to be snubbed on this side.' He warned of Canada being excluded from scientific information and contracts by the presence of the Americans with their far more effective liaison staff.[14]

By 19 June 1941, before Smith's last letter was written, Mackenzie had tentatively agreed to improve liaison in the United Kingdom but was still unable to find a suitable candidate.[15] It was not until August 1941 that Mackenzie finally decided to appoint Dr L.E. Howlett, head of the Optics Section, to be the first scientific officer.[16]

Howlett's arrival in the United Kingdom noticeably improved Anglo-Canadian scientific and technical co-operation, but he could not solve all of the problems overnight. There was a continuing insensitivity toward Canadian requirements and abilities, and this often had a extremely negative impact on the RCN. One recurring problem was the British failure to draw up blueprints and written specifications for equipment still under development. They often insisted on waiting until a radar or asdic set was already in mass production before providing technical information. This meant that the RCN, reliant on British designs and Canadian production, could not help but be behind the RN since adaptation of equipment to North American industrial standards and the tooling up of factories resulted in considerable delay before production actually commenced. We shall see several examples of just how damaging this practice was in subsequent chapters.

Howlett was also incapable of providing the navy with the information needed to plan for future requirements. His primary responsibility was to provide technical and scientific information to the NRC, not to keep the RCN informed about Admiralty equipment policy. The December 1940 NRC-RCN agreement was ambiguous on this point, and eventually by default the CCCS's staff was placed in charge of scientific and technical policy liaison with the Admiralty. Unfortunately, there was insufficient manpower for effective co-operation until the general expansion of the RCN's London staff, which began in the summer of 1943. As a result the RCN, as it was with the decision to place radar on corvettes, would continue to experience some nasty technical surprises, some of which could not be resolved in a reasonable period of time.[17]

American scientific liaison was of increasing importance by the end of

1941. The American entry into the war in December only increased the pace of scientific and technical interchange between the United States and Canada. The United States Navy provided little of direct value in terms of complete equipment to the British-dominated RCN. In terms of component parts, however, the value of American information and hardware was immense. Canadian industry, including REL, operated using American standards and parts. The main job of NRC in adapting the ASV design for the CSC and REL production of ASVs was to duplicate component performance using completely different parts. Fortunately Canadian scientists and engineers between the wars had established close professional ties with their American counterparts. Much of this took place in memberships in professional organizations such as the IEEE and AAAS or through North American scientific periodicals. The ease of communication compared with that of the trans-Atlantic crossing also meant much closer and more intimate connections between American and Canadian scientists. As a result, for most of the war the NRC and the American Office for Scientific Research and Development operated together quite well without a permanent presence in each other's capital.[18]

Direct official contact between the United States and Canada did not begin until the Tizard mission in the summer of 1940. Fowler's office at NRC was established to run Anglo-American scientific co-operation at a time when it was politically unacceptable to establish a permanent office in the still-neutral capital. He was assisted at NRC by Canadian-born Princeton University professor A.G. Shenstone, who also undertook to look after Canadian interests. By the spring of 1941 American-Canadian scientific co-operation was well established. Visits between individual research centres or corporations were frequent, as was the exchange of letters and technical data. Senior-level interchange was kept up via frequent exchanges of letters between Shenstone or Fowler and the OSRD's liaison officer Carol Wilson.[19]

In March 1941 the British decided that it was politically possible and more efficient to establish a permanent liaison presence in Washington. The new organization, the British Central Scientific Office, was charged with the power to administer all scientific liaison between the United States and the entire British Empire. This unilateral decision came as no surprise to Mackenzie; he had been informed of the British intentions by Fowler in January. His stated opposition then went unheeded and resulted in much trouble later on: 'I told Fowler that we would not waive our right to negotiate or exchange information directly with the Americans, as we had built up contacts over many years which we did not propose to drop, and that we would not accept the position that our dealings with the Americans had to be through any British organization!'[20]

When the BCSO was established in March, Mackenzie simply refused to co-operate with it and continued on as if the British office did not exist. The BCSO complained to Carol Wilson, who refused to be drawn into the argument between the Commonwealth partners. In the end the BCSO had to acquiesce to Mackenzie's insistence on maintaining NRC's special relationship with the Americans.[21]

6

Shortwave Confusion

While the prototype sw1c was being fitted in HMCS *Chambly*, on the other side of the Atlantic a completely new radar, the 271, was being tested in HMS *Orchis*. The 271, using a radically new technology operated at ten-centimetre wavelength, while the sw1c merely used pre-existing techniques to operate at a wavelength of 1.5 metres. The advantage of sets operating at a centimetric wavelength in ASW during the Second World War was that their finer, narrower, and more distinct beam permitted escorts to detect at long ranges trimmed-down submarines consistently and accurately. Thus, U-boats would be deprived of their cloak of invisibility when making surface attacks on a convoy at night – their most effective offensive tactic.

The secret behind the development of the 271 was the cavity magnetron valve invented in February 1940 by a team of physicists at the University of Birmingham. The valve allowed the transmission of high-powered short-wave radio signals, thereby increasing the power available in the centimetric range by a thousandfold. Canadian scientists were made aware of the magnetron shortly after it was perfected in the summer of 1940 when NRC representatives with the Tizard mission saw it unveiled to an amazed American audience in Washington. Aware from this early date of the significance of microwave radar, Canadians were caught off guard by the rapid progress of the 271 program.

The development of the 271 has been rightly called by the British official historians 'one of the outstanding examples of a crash program' undertaken in the Second World War.[1] After a demonstration of an experimental centimetric set in November 1940 by the Telecommunications Research Establishment, the Admiralty Signals Establishment began development work on a small ship set. By February 1941 ASE was ready to build its first prototype, and in a bold step indicative of the importance placed on the work, component parts were ordered for the first 150 sets. This meant that modifications that would in any way delay production were unacceptable. In May the 271 prototype was successfully tested on *Orchis*. Tests included the detection at up to 3,500 yards of a trimmed-down submarine, in sharp contrast to the unrealistic trials of the SW1C on a fully surfaced submersible. By the end of June twenty-five RN vessels were equipped with 271s.[2]

Neither the Naval Staff nor NRC were fully informed of these developments, again the result both of the failure to establish a permanent scientific and technical liaison office in London and of continuing British insensitivity to Canadian interests. As a result, SW1C was obsolete in its primary role as a submarine detector *before it entered production*, and the RCN was committed to it for at least a year after 271 entered Royal Naval service. This situation was understandable, but, because of it, the RCN would for the rest of the war remain unable to provide for the timely supply of sufficient centimetric sets for its growing escort fleet.

The origins of Canadian ten-centimetre naval radar development can be traced to a memorandum sent to NRC by NSHQ on 21 June 1941 stating that 'it was essential to increase the maximum range [at] which surfaced submarines could be detected.'[3] It is uncertain where or why this request originated, but it seems likely that it was the result of rumours reaching NSHQ concerning the shortcomings of the 286 and of the excellent test results obtained with the 271. In July and August Radio Branch scientists conducted a series of tests in Halifax with an experimental ten-centimetre set borrowed from the Radiation Laboratory at the Massachusetts Institute of Technology. The experimental set proved to be more than twice as effective as SW1C. While in Halifax the council scientists also had their first cursory ninety-minute examination of a 271 on board a British warship.[4]

On 25 August 1941 Radio Section scientists held a meeting at the Metcalfe Road Field Station to discuss the ramifications of the summer tests. They agreed that the navy had to be convinced of the superiority of ten-centimetre radar and 'since no naval specifications were available, the meeting drew up what seemed like reasonable performance characteristics, to be checked later with naval authorities.'[5] In September the Radio Section and the RDFO's office met and hammered out the details of the next stage of Canadian naval radar development. They agreed to begin research into two centimetric sets – a general-purpose, surface-warning radar that would eventually be known as the RX/C,[6] and a gunnery control type code-named SG2C.[7]

The NRC had begun work on short-wave radar in late 1940, because members of the Tizard mission had advised the Canadians that Britain was in desperate need of a ten-centimetre anti-aircraft radar. The development of this radar, known as the GLC (gun-laying Canadian) Mark III, had led to the establishment of magnetron production by the Northern Electric Company. The first Canadian-built magnetron was completed in February 1941. Thus when development work commenced in September 1941 on the short-wave naval radars, the NRC design team was already a step ahead.[8]

On 4 October Argyle told Henderson that he expected the new sets to include the best design features of both the GLC and the 271, and urged the rapid completion of the prototypes so that production could commence in the summer of 1942. Although no 271 had yet been delivered to Ottawa, Argyle had been mistakenly assured by NRC that one was in transit, and clearly the naval officer wanted this already proven design examined before major design work was undertaken. Argyle further encouraged Henderson to keep REL updated on components needed for production and offered naval personnel to work in NRC machine shops. Henderson's reply, five days later, indicates that he misunderstood the magnitude of the project. He called the provision of equipment for the new radars relatively simple following the work done on the GLC. On 24 October Henderson optimistically stated that a complete prototype of both RX/C and SG2C would be ready by May.[9]

Henderson's optimism was soon found to be misplaced, for the naval radar program development took far longer and proved much more complicated than he had originally anticipated. Several factors hampered development, including the long delay in the delivery of a 271 set to the council. The Admiralty bureaucracy was partly to blame, as was the inexperience of Howlett, the Canadian scientific liaison officer. Howlett, who, it must be remembered, had only arrived in England in mid-August, had requested a 271 in early September which the Admiralty immediately agreed to supply. Howlett assumed the set would automatically be shipped to Canada, but in mid-October he learned that he was expected to arrange delivery. As a result the 271 was dispatched only in November, to arrive at the council in early January 1942, shortly after the first crude working model of the RX/C was completed.[10]

While the SW1C had been an adaptation of the British ASV, the absence of more than a scanty knowledge of 271 meant that the initial RX/C design was an independent Canadian creation. Development of a new design was a much more complicated procedure than closely duplicating an already existing set, and one that was much more prone to serious difficulties. Unlike the SW1C, which went directly from the drawing-board to ship-borne testing, the RX/C had to pass through several stages before it was ready for anything approaching operational conditions. The first set completed in early January was a cumbersome experimental model that had to be completely revamped before it was ready for sea trials. An independent design also meant that for the first time council scientists were not relying on British expertise, and by the time a 271 arrived in Ottawa, there was general reluctance to make major design changes.

The Radio Branch team stuck primarily to this independent design, even when a 271 became available, a fact that would eventually have fatal consequences for the entire Canadian naval radar program. Henderson was over-optimistic about the council's ability to see the project through to a successful conclusion. Understandably, the apparent success of the SW1C, which did not enter widespread service until early 1942, led to this overconfidence. Unquestionably the Radio Branch staff were technically competent, but they lacked the intuitive knowledge that comes only from experience in what will or will not work under operational conditions.

RX/C development was also slowed by competition with other projects for scarce Radio Branch resources. At least two other developments, the army's GLC and modifications of the SW1C to SW2C and SW3C, were given higher priority than the naval ten-centimetric radar program. There were also numerous other projects at various stages of research and development for all three services that kept the now over 150 personnel involved in radar work at the council fully occupied.

Although NSHQ may have appreciated the council's difficulties, it felt intense pressure to find a quick solution to the problem of its centimetric radar supply. The navy unrealistically compared the rate of progress on the RX/C to the far less complicated SW1C. On 12 November Cossette asked Henderson 'to speed up the development and production' of the project and also requested answers to twenty-one highly technical questions on the proposed sets. These questions were asked because the naval representative at the Radio Branch, Lieutenant J. Carlisle, had 'formed the impression that the navy requirement may not be clearly understood.'[11] Henderson's answers did not satisfy the navy, and NSHQ began to explore alternative sources of supply for its ten-centimetre requirements.

The matter came to a head at a special meeting of the RDF Committee held on 4 December. A.R. Pressey and J.V. Argyle, the naval representatives, began the meeting by explaining that the RCN had examined three sources of centimetric radar supply including a United States Navy set called the 'ssv' (likely the SG) to be built in Canada by Research Enterprises, British-built 271s, and the NRC's RX/C. Both the RCN and the REL came out strongly in favour of the American set, as production drawings were immediately available and a pre-production model was promised in February by its American manufacturer, Raytheon. This would have allowed REL to begin production as early as July 1942. RX/C development was to continue 'as a not too long-time distance project, aiming at a set of greater accuracy than the other sets.' No one expected British supplies to be adequate or on schedule, a feeling prompted by the failure to deliver a prototype 271 to the NRC.[12]

The results of this meeting, while not a condemnation of the council's efforts, saw the lowering of the priority of the RX/C for the next six months and caused the cancellation of the SG2C.[13] The council was understandably reluctant to commit resources to a project that looked unlikely to go into production, as all signs it received from the navy until May 1942 strongly indicated.[14]

The navy's hope of quickly adopting American radar designs for Canadian production never materialized. Unfortunately details of American-Canadian negotiations on the subject have not been found, but it is safe to assume that the initial attempt to build the 'ssv' collapsed when the USN found itself desperately short of all radar equipment after the Pearl Harbor disaster of 7 December 1941. Negotiations between the Americans and the RDFO's office continued, however, and on 24 February 1942 Argyle was optimistic enough to tell H.R. Smyth, head of the Naval section of the Radio Branch, that 'due to the probability of supply of 10 cm. RDF from American sources ... it is doubtful whether it is desirable that [RX/C] reach the production stage.' The American radar then under consideration was the submarine-based SJ currently under development at Westinghouse. Even though it appeared unlikely that RX/C would ever enter production, Argyle advised Smyth to have his scientists 'retain keen interest in centimetre RDF as the experience will doubtless be drawn upon by the service frequently during the whole course of the war.'[15]

It was not until 13 March that Argyle secured from the Americans a firm commitment to supply twenty-five SJs and a tentative agreement for more if required. The choice of this set was an unusual one, and was probably forced on Argyle by the USN because it required that

Canadians design a new antenna system to make sj suitable for mounting on escort vessels. The American submarine antenna did not have enough resolution to locate a trimmed-down U-boat at reasonable range. This was not a minor modification, as we have already seen with the sw1c, because the antenna was one of the most complicated and vital pieces of equipment of a radar set. On the same day that the agreement with the Americans was signed, Argyle requested the Radio Branch to begin work on the antenna forthwith, and to ensure rapid completion he asked that the rx/c be given an even lower priority.[16] This American-Canadian hybrid was to be known as the rx/u.

Argyle expected the rx/u to be ready for operational deployment by the late summer of 1942 but was once again far too optimistic. It became apparent in May that the set would not be available until late 1942 or early 1943. The sj would not enter production until June 1942 and the usn would not deliver to Canada until its immediate requirements were filled. This compares unfavourably with rcn action in promptly filling an American request in May for twenty-five sw2cs. Admittedly the sw2cs sets were not immediately required by the rcn, but it is just one more example of Canadians bending over backwards to help an ally when it in turn did not receive the same treatment.[17] Because more serious delays were experienced with the rx/u's antenna system, nrc did not complete research and development work until June 1942 and rel did not complete delivery until March 1943.[18]

The net effect of this attempt to find an American miracle cure to the rcn's ten-centimetre radar woes was that in May 1942, a year after 271 entered British service, the navy was not much closer to finding an adequate supplier. Except for a few 271s mounted mainly on British-owned but Canadian-manned corvettes, and the twenty-five rx/us on order, there was no firm commitment to provide rcn escorts with this vital weapons system. There was other fall-out from this period, particularly in the distinct cooling of nrc-rcn relations. Mackenzie, who in 1941 felt Argyle to be an excellent technical officer, now believed him to be an incompetent liability. Unquestionably Argyle was under intense pressure, as he was carrying the main burden of responsibility for establishing the rcn's radar policies, and it seems likely that his transfer to the Directorate of Radio Supply in June 1942 was associated with the ill-health that forced his retirement from the service in October 1944.[19]

The fact that Argyle, a middle-management level staff officer, was given such major planning responsibility is indicative of the low priority given by the Naval Staff to high-technology equipment issues. Until

August 1942 the Naval Staff completely misunderstood the importance of setting radar and other advanced technology policy. It comprehended neither the operational necessity for this equipment nor how long it would take to fit it once it had been supplied. RCN convoy disasters in the fall of 1942 would be caused, in part, by the staff's failure to take action on the new weapons systems in the spring. Indeed NSHQ's failure to plan ahead doomed RCN escorts always to remain behind in the mounting of the latest electronic hardware.

Evidence of the Naval Staff's lack of interest is the fact that discussions on centimetric radar fitting and supply policy did not commence until 2 March 1942 and lasted until 1 October. The meetings that concerned centimetric radar were marked by continual indecision and show that the RCN was still unable to make technical policy without Admiralty assistance. They also demonstrate the failure to integrate NRC expertise into the Naval Staff, for at none of the meetings in 1942 was a council scientist present to represent the views of what was supposed to be the navy's research laboratory.

The first meeting in which centimetric radar policy was discussed attempted to deal with the difficult issue of fitting RX/C or an equivalent system in River-class destroyers. This topic, which would also be the last issue decided nearly seven months later, focused on the utility of centimetric radar versus central gunnery directory controls and range finders. The Naval Staff agreed that none of the existing centimetric radars which could be fitted in destroyers were sufficiently accurate to be used to direct long-range gunnery, and that their placement on the Rivers might force the removal of the optical gear carried for this purpose. The replacement of the range finder and directory equipment would preclude the use of the destroyers in a fleet support role, thereby restricting them exclusively to ASW work.

Many senior officers upheld the pre-war view that the only proper function for the professional navy was in support of the battlefleet, and believed that the placement of centimetric radar on the Rivers was the last step in accepting the secondary escort role. Discussions in March left the issue undecided, for although Nelles stated quite clearly that the main function of the destroyers was to be 'North Atlantic escorts,' the Naval Staff agreed only to fit the British type 290 – an updated version of the already fitted 286. The superintendent anti-submarine argued for equipping the Rivers at a later date with the RX/C rather than the 271 because 'he felt that the Canadian set was probably better in that it would be easier to fit and that it be designed on information available a year later; the drawback to the Canadian set being that it would be difficult to get replacements in the United Kingdom.'[20] It was agreed that RX/C or RX/U could be fitted 'if and when available,' but no authorization was given to land the gunnery control gear which would be required if the sets were to be effectively mounted.[21]

The Naval Staff did take quick action, however, on centimetric radar policy for escorts other than the River-class destroyers. By 16 March it had decided to mount a centimetric set on all corvettes and frigates, the next generation of escort vessels then being laid down, though the question remained as to the type of set and how they would be obtained.[22]

It was not until 11 May that the Naval Staff finally held a meeting to discuss the source of supply of the one hundred radar sets immediately required. Argyle, an invited participant at this meeting, argued against ordering RX/C until 'a delivery schedule could be ascertained' and 'results of further experiments as to the efficacy of this equipment are available.' R.E.S. Bidwell, the director of Operations, stated that he had reports from the Captain (D), Halifax that indicated that the SW1C had proven a disappointment while 271s in service on RN vessels of Western Local Escort Force had proven 'extremely satisfactory.' A.R. Pressey, the director Anti-Submarine, defended the Canadian set as an improvement over the 286, although he did agree that 271 was superior to both. Worth then suggested that an Admiralty radar expert currently in Ottawa should be consulted; the Naval Staff, again unable to make an independent decision, deferred to British advice.

The Admiralty radar representative was in Canada to discuss the use by the Royal Navy of the NRC and REL to build another new type of set that was to operate at three-centimetre wavelength. The British request to use these facilities was immediately approved by NSHQ, NRC, and the Department of Munitions and Supply. It was typical of Canadian generosity since the RCN had no immediate requirement for this type of set and the offer was only partially reciprocated by the British.[23]

Worth, who by the end of May was beginning to take over control of RCN radar policy from the soon-to-be-replaced Argyle, held a series of detailed conversations with the British expert concerning the Canadian naval radar situation. He reported the results to the Naval Staff meeting of 14 May, stating that the Admiralty representative had advised 'that the National Research Council should take steps to develop a Canadian 10 cm. set, as the Admiralty type 271 would probably not be available for delivery in Canada, and delivery of the U.S. set looked most improbable in view of the need for this equipment for American new construction.' Argyle, however, remained against ordering RX/C until sea trials were carried out in June. He was strongly supported by Pressey who correctly stated that it would still take at least a year to tool up for production and unfairly warned that the set would be an 'orphan' for which it would be impossible to supply spare parts outside Canada.

It was again decided to delay making a firm commitment to RX/C but instead to approach the Admiralty concerning possible 271 supplies. Nine days later the Admiralty offered to provide ten 271s per month for fitting in Canada. Although this offer was quickly accepted by NSHQ, Worth recommended that the British be asked to provide as many as possible of these sets until Canadian sources of supply became available.[24] Worth's request, if it was ever sent, fell on deaf ears, for by the end of 1942 only forty 271s had been fitted in Canadian warships.[25]

In May the Naval Staff had commenced discussion on yet another invaluable piece of advanced electronic equipment – the ship-based, high-frequency direction finder. Shore-based HF/DF had been developed before the war and had long proven invaluable in providing intelligence on U-boat activities. The German submarines used short-wave radio to keep their command centre informed as to convoy sightings and weather conditions. A ship-based HF/DF – the FH3 – was developed by July 1941 to supply immediate tactical intelligence to escort groups.

The FH3 was a crude device which relied on operators manually scanning suspected U-boat frequencies. Detection was through audio signals supplied via a headphone, while direction was determined by turning the antenna to where the signal was strongest. Distance was impossible to determine accurately, but operators soon learned to distinguish high-frequency radio ground waves from sky waves. Since ground waves could only be detected twelve to fourteen miles from the transmission source, FH3 operators knew when an intercepted signal represented a dangerously close U-boat.

Although the Royal Navy began mounting FH3 on at least one destroyer per escort group by the beginning of 1942, by May only one such set was fitted in the RCN. This set had been mounted during the winter on HMCS *Restigouche*, not because of any staff action, but because the captain of the destroyer, on his own initiative and against headquarter policy, convinced a British officer in Londonderry to fit the set.[26]

Staff discussions on HF/DF also took considerable time to get started, and early discussions reveal a complete misunderstanding of the importance of FH3. On 28 May 1942 Worth, also responsible for the technical aspects of HF/DF, and Commander J.M.B.P. de Marbois, the director of the Foreign Intelligence Section and responsible for shore-based radio direction finding, reported on the fitting of FH3 in River-class destroyers. They questioned the suitability of the set, citing its inability to give accurate distances, and thus discounted the limited range of ground waves and the possibility of triangulation with two or more sets. They asked that no decision be made on acquiring FH3 until more information came available; the Naval Staff, ignorant of the tactical value of this equipment, agreed. Further discussions on the topic would not take place until August.[27]

While the Naval Staff grappled with centimetric radar supply and fitting policy, slow progress was made at the research council with the RX/C, although at some time in this period the development of the gunnery-control set SG2C was terminated. In January and February 1942 the first crude RX/C was tested alongside the first 271 to reach the council at the Metcalfe Road Field Station. After extensive reworking, including the adaptation of several 271 design features, a sea-going version of the RX/C was ready for testing in late April.

Preliminary testing was conducted at the field station followed by experiments in late May and early June at Portuguese Cove just outside Halifax. Ranges obtained from this series of tests showed the set to be more than twice as effective as the SW1C, capable of spotting freighters at 29,000 yards, corvettes at 20,000, and buoys at 3,500. Following this the set was mounted on HMCS *Port Arthur* with similar results. A grateful secretary of the Navy Board commenting on these results wrote to Smyth to say that they indicated 'that the project has been very worthwhile and the RCN are assured of an efficient centimetre equipment.'[28] With the basic research and development work completed the next stage of the project would involve adapting NRC's design to mass production by Research Enterprises, a task that would prove at least as difficult as all of the previous work done on the project.

Before RX/C could go into production, however, the navy had to order it, and it took another series of Naval Staff discussions on centimetric radar policy from early August to early October to decide the matter. The impetus for the series of discussions leading to decisions on radar, HF/DF, and asdic policy stems from a series of convoy defences from early June to August by Canadian mid-ocean escort groups. The defence of convoy ONS 100 in early June by group C 1, ONS 102 a few weeks later by the predominantly Canadian group A 3, ON 115 in late July by C 3, and of SC 94 in late August, all pointed to the necessity of modern equipment. Although none of these actions were disasters, neither were they unqualified successes. These actions were contrasted with the extremely successful defence in mid-August of ONS 122 by the Anglo-Norwegian group B 6. By effectively using 271 radar and FH3 HF/DF the group was able to prevent a large group of U-boats from inflicting more than minimal damage.

The reports of these convoy actions were sent to NSHQ with strong requests that the Naval Staff make equipment policy decisions and improve the supply situation.[29] The first discussion on radar policy in August was directly motivated by the 4 August request of Captain E.R. Mainguy, the Captain (D), Newfoundland, which was strongly supported by Rear Admiral Murray, the Flag officer, Newfoundland, for permission to fit the River-class destroyers *Saguenay* and *Skeena* with 271s during their periodic layovers in Londonderry.

Mainguy's request was discussed at the Naval Staff meeting of 10 August and the central issue, as the director of Naval Construction pointed out, was that 271 'cannot be fitted on the bridge with the existing range finder.' Worth, who was now completely responsible for radar policy, insisted that no other position was suitable and that the range finders be removed. Other staff members were not convinced, and were still unwilling to preclude the use of the destroyers in a fleet role. They did not trust the advise of their own operational commanders but instead, on the suggestion of Reid, the vice-chief of Naval Staff, the matter was deferred to the Admiralty.

The debate over fitting the 271s on the Rivers continued until 1 October when the Naval Staff, following the Admiralty's sage words of wisdom, finally agreed, only seven months after the issue was first discussed, to mount the British centimetric set. Even when the issue was settled by Nelles's concurrence with Admiralty advice, one die-hard traditionalist still felt strongly enough to point out 'that the proposed changes will mean that the class of vessel cannot be used as an attacking force.'[30]

Virtually every staff meeting between 10 August and 1 October dealt with some issue of radar policy and supply, and even the purposely unemotional minutes give an indication that the debates were heated ones. On 8 September there was a lengthy discussion about making a firm order to REL for RX/CS. Worth argued strongly for ordering one hundred sets to supply the requirements for 1943 but Captain H.N. Lay, the director of the Operations Directorate and perhaps the only staff officer with recent sea-going experience, called for more experimentation at sea under the supervision of the Captain (D), Halifax. Lay may have wanted this because of his personal knowledge of early and continuing problems with the sw1c series but, whatever his reasoning, he was persuasive enough to carry the meeting.

Worth was not one to accept defeat lightly and two weeks later he once again requested that the radar be ordered. This time Worth came prepared to defeat Lay. He distributed a copy of the report of the test conducted on the *Port Arthur* in June and a signal from Captain (D), Halifax that confirmed that the set had already performed adequately in sea-going experiments. Worth won the rematch and was given authorization to order the first one hundred rx/cs; he would live to regret the decision.[31]

During the course of these discussions on radar, the Naval Staff was also finally convinced of the growing need to solve the centimetric supply problem. Responding to a request by Murray of 16 September, the Naval Staff agreed to allow all mid-ocean escorts to fit 271s in the United Kingdom during turnaround periods. Prior to this ships had to wait until normal refit schedules which could delay mounting by up to a year.[32] The Admiralty agreed to supply the Canadian mid-ocean escorts, but warned that these sets might be provided in lieu of the 271s already earmarked for Canada.[33]

During this period the Staff also made some policy decisions on HF/DF, albeit timid and tentative ones. On 10 August Worth requested that any decision on HF/DF policy be further delayed until the FH3 mounted on HMCS *Restigouche* had been given an adequate trial and until an RN signal expert, Captain F.J. Wylie, arrived in Ottawa at the end of the month. The Naval Staff agreed, despite the fact that the FH3 on the *Restigouche* had already been fitted for over six months and had proven its value in the defence of ONS 102 six weeks earlier.[34]

Wylie was present at the meeting of 31 August and was finally able to persuade the Canadian Naval Staff of the necessity for HF/DF. However, Wylie also cast further doubt on the suitability of FH3, since he informed them of the development of the much improved FH4. The new set automatically tracked signals and displayed them on a cathode-ray tube, which enabled accurate distance and direction determination for the first time. Worth expressed concern about acquiring an obsolete set but reiterated that the RCN should follow the long-established Admiralty minimal requirement of providing one FH3 per escort group.

The results of the Naval Staff discussions from August to September was that, by the end of 1942, the RCN had finally established a definitive centimetric radar and HF/DF policy. The fact that it had taken over fifteen months since the first request was made to the council to begin work on the RX/C shows that the RCN was incapable of making timely decisions in advanced technology fields. As we shall see, radar and HF/DF were not the only technologies whose introduction was delayed by the procrastination of NSHQ. It was not that Canada lacked technical expertise, but that there was a dearth of talent that could link operations, staff and the scientist. For that the navy was to suffer.

Worth, however, not gifted with an historian's hindsight, was well pleased by the decisions of the Naval Staff and looked forward to 1943 when all major escort vessels would be equipped with a centimetric set. He saw the future equipment of the RCN assured mainly from Canadian sources, as he outlined in detail to the chief of Naval Engineering and Construction on 29 October:[35]

Class	RX/U	RX/C	271
River Destroyers			5
Town Destroyers			7
Frigates		99	
Corvettes	22	60	32
Algerine Minesweepers		16	
Bangor Minesweepers		54	
Trawlers		8	
Training Vessels		2	
Total	22	239	44

Certainly Worth was anticipating a better year than 1942, when only six destroyers and thirty-four corvettes were fitted with the 271, while the remaining four and forty-two respectively had to be content with ineffective long-wave sets such as the SW2C. This does not include smaller vessels like the Bangors, none of which had a centimetric radar.[36]

The Admiralty, however, was not satisfied with future possibilities and was increasingly concerned with the actual combat ability of Canadian escorts. The seriousness of the situation in late 1942 can perhaps best be understood in comparison with British escorts. An Admiralty report of 6 December 1942 warned that of the fifty-seven warships that still required a 271 or equivalent set forty-five, or approximately 75 per cent, were Canadian.[37]

7

Sound Problems

The failure to manufacture centimetric radar or to find an adequate substitute from the Americans or the British stands in sharp contrast to the successful Anglo-Canadian co-operative effort to produce asdic sets in Canada. Paradoxically, despite this industrial triumph the warships of the RCN remained at least one generation behind in the fitting of asdic and related weapons systems in comparison to their RN counterparts.

To trace the roots of the difficulties in providing fully modern asdic to the fleet we must look beyond the industrial system developed by British production expert A.E.H Pew (see Chapter 3). The 'History of the British Admiralty Technical Mission' proudly boasted that 'no record of a single Canadian built [asdic] set has been found unserviceable on issue.' Nothing has yet been uncovered to discredit this statement or the impressive production statistics that can safely label the asdic program as the single most successful Canadian advanced industrial endeavour. By the end of the war twenty-one different types of asdic, in total nearly 2,600 sets, were produced in Canada for the RCN, RN, USN, and other Allied navies.[1]

So effectively did the program function that it went through little of the fluctuations in personnel, organization, or institutional relationships that marked the centimetric radar program. In fact only a minor re-structuring of senior management organization occurred, and this was more the result of factors external to asdic manufacturing.

When asdic production was established from late 1940 through 1941 it was viewed as an experimental project of such a super-secret and sophisticated technical nature as to be beyond the capabilities of the still-fledgling staff of the Department of Munitions and Supply to adequately control. In the spring of 1942 the unusual arrangement which saw the

RCN's Equipment Division issuing contracts was changed to conform to the principle of civilian control of all wartime industry. The DMS's Naval Armament and Equipment Branch assumed responsibility for managing asdic-manufacturing. The Equipment Division remained in charge of the drawing up of naval specifications and requirements, and of the supervision of the final assembly of the sets on the slipways or in refit dockyards, while the BATM's staff, under Pew, continued to be the principal technical advisers and supervised the large Admiralty contracts which composed approximately half the orders.[2]

If the production of asdic was assured by early 1942, why was the RCN unable to keep abreast of the relatively slow advance of asdic technology? Partly the answer is that few understood the technology in the first place, and no one was the master of its practical use on the heaving deck of a corvette. Furthermore, asdic was a system, and components were often initially unavailable in Canada. The fact that Canada only produced sets instead of manufacturing complete systems led to a number of problems, the first of which became apparent during the introduction of the 123A asdic.

As early as 1940 the Naval Staff decided to mount the 123A asdic sets in corvettes instead of the superior 127 fitted on British vessels. The former differed from the 127 in that it utilized a magnetic compass to establish the direction of a contact, while the latter used a far more reliable gyro-compass. At the best of times magnetic compasses are inaccurate and subject to wild fluctuations in battle due to the ship's manoeuvering or to the shock of depth charges and gunnery. The 123A also had only one compass and indicating position, in the asdic hut located above the wheelhouse, and it was almost impossible for a captain to keep one eye on the information from the asdic hut while controlling the ship from the bridge.

The decision to mount the inferior set was inevitable since gyro-compasses were not manufactured in Canada and the Admiralty refused to provide an adequate supply. Some were available from Sperry Corporation, a private American manufacturer, but only sufficient for mounting in Bangors. Priority was given to the smaller vessels because it was originally intended that their primary role was to be minesweeping, a task which required accurate navigation to mark swept channels. Corvettes, which were to be coastal jack-of-all trades – escort, minesweeper, and patrol craft – would have to make do with the less-accurate magnetic compasses. As a result, the Bangors were able to fit the superior 128 asdic, the retractable-dome version of the 127.[3] When both classes of vessels were transferred into ocean escort from the spring of 1941 onwards, it was the larger corvette, suffering from an inferior asdic, that served with the more vital mid-ocean escort groups, while the Bangors served with the less important Western Local groups.[4]

Starting one step behind in asdic technology was not in itself as great a handicap as it was with radar. Asdic development in the Second World War was not subject to the same radical advances in technology, and, in fact, all but one new set introduced during the course of the conflict were added simply by modifying the pre-existing model. The 128s on Bangors and the 124 mounted on River-class destroyers initially were fully modern, and only the shortages of gyro-compasses in the corvettes left them inferior to their British cousins. But as the RCN did not keep up with subsequent asdic improvements or with new anti-submarine weapons systems, the gap widened to a point where the technical incapacity of Canadian vessels to track and destroy a submerged U-boat became unacceptable to the British.

The progress made in the first three years of the war in simply expanding the number of asdic-equipped ships, supplying the trained personnel needed to man them, and developing manufacturing capability was, nevertheless, in itself a creditable accomplishment. The number of asdic-equipped ships grew from the four River-class destroyers of September 1939 to ninety-two vessels just two years later. In another twelve months even this number would increase more than two-fold to 194.[5]

To keep pace with this growth, training facilities were established at Halifax and Esquimalt to provide basic training for the large numbers of officers and men required to man the sets. By the end of 1941 Halifax had three attack teachers, one mass-procedure teacher, a procedure teacher, four sets of demonstration apparatus and a mobile training unit. Esquimalt's facilities were only slightly smaller. Basic training courses had been established at the University of Toronto and were transferred in early 1942 to the Westdale Technical School in Hamilton, Ontario. In 1941 alone the number of trained submarine-detection ratings and artificers soared from 283 to 507; three months later this figure had increased to nearly 700, and still there were not enough. Considering that the still-minuscule technical staff was wrestling with its training commitment, it is not surprising that it did not keep itself informed on asdic and related research going on in the United Kingdom, nor apply itself to upgrading the corvettes, just coming into service, by mounting the 127.[6]

In 1942, however, the introduction into the Royal Navy of a radically new anti-submarine weapon, the ahead-throwing mortar whimsically dubbed the hedgehog, and two new asdic sets to work with it, forced Naval Service Headquarters to consider modernizing its escort fleet's equipment. The origins of the hedgehog can be traced to the early 1930s when Admiralty scientists began to realize that the current method of attacking a submerged submarine by dropping or throwing depth charges off the stern of a ship was hopelessly inadequate. The problem was that asdic projected its beam in a cone shape ahead of the escort at an angle of 10 degrees from the horizontal. This meant that there was a considerable dead space when a target would dip under the cone of the asdic, and from that point on depth charges had to be dropped by estimating the target's position. Wartime experience showed that this dead zone was even larger than anticipated because U-boats could dive far deeper than was originally thought possible, and as a result, a clever submarine commander could often manoeuvre out of harm's way. It was also found that, once lost, contact was difficult to reestablish when approaching for an attack.[7]

Admiralty scientists realized before the war that the solution lay in developing a weapon that could fire sufficiently ahead of the ship before a submarine entered the dead zone, and by the beginning of 1940 they were working on several experimental devices. The first to enter service was the hedgehog, which was developed by the Department of Miscellaneous Weapon Development, an ad hoc research group specifically created by Sir James Somerville in the summer of 1940 to cut through Whitehall red tape and get the new systems into service as quickly as possible. After only twelve months of work under the leadership of Commander (later Sir) Charles Goodeve, an expatriate Canadian sailor-scientist, the scientists had hedgehog ready to enter into service in January 1942. The device consisted of twenty-four small contact bombs fired by a recoilless spigot-mortar system at a fixed distance 300 yards ahead of the ship.[8]

Meanwhile, scientists at HMS *Fairlie* (the new name for the asdic development centre) designed two new asdic sets, the 144 and 145, to work in conjunction with hedgehog. These sets, wrote Willem Hackmann, 'heralded a new chapter in asdic thinking and was the first attempt to an integrated weapon system with a certain degree of automation.'[9] Special features included automatic training, improved indicating equipment such as new bearing and range recorders which showed the correct course to steer, and a 'time to fire' device which automatically rang buzzers at the hedgehog and depth-charge stations when firing should commence. The 144 and 145 differed mainly in that the former worked in ships equipped with retractable asdic domes, the latter with those fitted with a fixed dome.[10]

Information on the new sets and on hedgehog began to trickle into Naval Staff Headquarters in the spring of 1942. As with centimetric radar, these sets provoked impressive discussion leading to indecision and lengthy delays. An untechnical staff in Ottawa handling policy for advanced equipment ought to have sought and been given the assistance of scientists, and been advised by their own technical liaison officers with the Admiralty. A letter written on 14 August 1942 by A.R. Pressey, the director Anti-Submarine, to his opposite number in the Admiralty outlines the dilemmas faced by the staff in making asdic policy.

The DA/S began by telling the British officer that the Canadian navy was falling behind just as it had with radar, and that the Equipment Division and the Naval Staff needed current information on asdic improvements 'so that we don't get caught in a jam.' He illustrated his point by outlining the liaison failures which had contributed to the slow pace of corvette improvements. For instance, there was a long delay in informing naval headquarters 'that Admiralty policy was to give corvettes a second binnacle and make drastic bridge alterations.' Even though the Admiralty policy to fit 123D was received promptly the drawing and specifications took time in arriving. Almost as soon as authorization was received for 123D, along came information on the hedgehog and 145. 'Here we are in this country,' he wrote, 'struggling with changing these ships into better fighting units and not having the foggiest idea of what the final answer is going to be.' Pressey went on to complain that production information on 127D had yet to arrive, and pleaded with his British counterpart to give Pew (at BATM) information as early a possible. Finally, he requested that the Admiralty supply the first sixteen 127DV kits, which would fulfil the RCN's requirements until Canadian production commenced.[11]

The British reply to the DA/S's letter was sympathetic, agreeing in principle 'on the question of giving you information of new policies, etc., but in practice, it is really difficult to know when to do this for the best.' Giving information too early, he warned, might cause the RCN to suffer 'through the teething, or perhaps more radical troubles which are inevitably met with all forms of alterations.' Information on the 145, for instance, had been sent out too soon, and caused unnecessary concern in Ottawa when the final design of the set was not yet ready. In conclusion the Admiralty anti-submarine director 'realized the fog caused [by the asdic situation] but I have yet to meet a case where a final answer can be given.'[12]

The Naval Staff had begun its search for the final answer with its first discussions on hedgehog on 30 April 1942. The meeting saw quick agreement to purchase fifty hedgehogs for new construction escorts. This rapid approval for fitting new construction frigates, Algerine minesweepers and RPV (Revised Patrol Vessels) corvettes with up-to-date equipment was typical of all discussions on equipment relating to vessels that would not be commissioned until mid-1943 at the earliest. The problem that haunted the Naval Staff was whether it was better to leave existing warships unaltered and in commission or to take a sizable number out of service for the lengthy refits required to mount the new equipment.

Early staff discussions indicate that the former course was initially preferred. On 26 May, approval was given to fit the 144 on frigates and the 145 on the RPV corvettes. However, existing corvettes were authorized only to upgrade their 123A set to a 123D. This involved the mounting of a second magnetic compass and indicator on the bridge to improve tactical control in a submarine hunt, but no steps were taken to acquire gyro-compasses or to begin the fitting of hedgehog.[13]

The Naval Staff had some very good reasons to defer re-equipping the corvettes, particularly given the poor state of the refit and repair facilities on Canada's east coast. While seemingly unrelated to technical developments, the issue of refit facilities is crucial because of a shortcoming in the original corvette design. The small bridge structure and forecastle were originally deemed sufficient for a ship that was intended to be a coastal patrol and escort vessel. To mount the 145 and hedgehog, however, required major alterations to the bridge for the former and a great expansion of the forecastle to fit the latter. The forecastle extension was also required to improve the ocean-going sea-keeping qualities and provide extra crew accommodation, desperately needed by 1942, as the vessels had long since transferred to mid-ocean escort work. These were major structural modifications. Hedgehog and the fitting of a gyro-compass needed for the 145 also entailed a major rewiring of the ship's power supply. Both pieces of equipment required a low-power supply that was not originally fitted in RCN corvettes. Installation of this equipment also required extensive time in a properly equipped shipyard.

While major investments had been made to upgrade and even create Great Lakes, St Lawrence River, and British Columbia shipyards, Mackenzie King's government limited capital expenditure in the Maritime provinces. Of the entire first construction program of Bangors and corvettes, only three of the latter were built in east coast shipyards. Halifax and Saint John, the only two facilities of note on the Atlantic coast, were quickly inundated with both naval and mercantile repair work. Smaller yards at places like Lunenburg and Pictou, which had suffered tremendously in the Depression, saw their meagrely trained work force drift away to jobs in central Canada or to the fighting services.[14] The yards on the St Lawrence and Great Lakes were subject to winter freeze-up, and they were strategically too far away, as were those in British Columbia, to take some of the burden off east coast yards. At any rate, they were soon involved with new construction work.

The issue of investment in shipyards was political, decided at the war Cabinet level, although controlled by C.D. Howe and his Department of Munitions and Supply. Howe's guide was political expediency: a government could only rule with a majority of support in Ontario and Quebec, and he followed his own personal blueprint for the post-war economy in which these provinces were to be the fulcrum. Canada's future was to be in developing the Great Lakes region, which included the completion of the St Lawrence River canal system and an even closer integration with the American industrial complex. Unfortunately, the flaw in his reasoning was that there was a war on; the Allies could have lost it because of the failure to create adequate repair and refit facilities close to the crucial fighting in the Atlantic.

Using his tremendous influence on and shared perceptions with King, Howe was able to prevent any major changes to his policy despite strong Maritime representation in cabinet which included the minister of defence, J.L. Ralston, and the naval minister, Angus L. Macdonald. The policy remained even after both the British and the Americans had asked for improvements to Maritime facilities. Canadian naval officers, who were painfully aware of the inadequate repair and refit capability by the beginning of 1942, amazingly were absent from any of the discussions. The civil-servant mentality as exemplified by Nelles prevailed despite the pressing need to alter a most ill-conceived government policy which was having a detrimental impact on the navy's ability to wage a successful anti-submarine war.

Information on British plans to improve the corvette's bridge and forecastle had reached Naval Staff in December 1940, well after it could have been implemented on the slip-ways and some three months after the Admiralty had approved the changes. In 1941, in light of inadequate repair facilities and with a short-sighted belief that an unimproved escort

was better than none at all, little was done to initiate corvette modernization. By March 1942 preliminary discussions on extending the forecastle and rebuilding the bridge had commenced, but it was not until
May that complete details reached naval headquarters.

In late June the director of Naval Construction tabled a memorandum
which stated that all of the structural alterations were required if hedgehog and the 145 were to be fitted, but that these changes were 'considered
beyond the capabilities of Canadian shipyards with their present commitments.'[15] He also expressed doubt as to the availability of hedgehog,
gyro-compasses, and the new asdics. Faced with these arguments the
Naval Staff typically could only agree to defer the matter until an Admiralty expert soon to be in Ottawa was consulted.[16]

The British expert's report was considered on 9 July and his strong
support for corvette modernization swayed the Naval Staff to agree to
proceed, but only after a 'step-by-step' program was developed by the
director Anti-Submarine and the director of Naval Construction. At the
next staff meeting, on 13 July, the two officers reported that the conversion program would take two years and cost approximately two mil-
lion dollars. Still not completely convinced of either the necessity or the
ability to undertake the upgrading, the Naval Staff authorized only a
trial alteration in order 'to ascertain time required.'

On 20 August, while the Naval Staff was grappling with the issue of
ten-centimetre policy, the issue of complete asdic modernization for the
corvettes was raised by the DA/S who asked that 123D sets be upgraded
to 145 standards. This was to take two years and be undertaken in two
steps: first, the supplying of gyro-compasses and bridge repeaters to
convert to a 127DV, and second, a series of gradual upgradings to 145.
Even though the DA/S cautioned that it would take nine months to begin
Canadian production, and the director of Operations stated that the
Admiralty had already converted forty RN corvettes, the program was
given only provisional approval.[17]

Two weeks later the director of Naval Construction asked that the
extent of asdic re-equipment be restricted and that the Admiralty Research Laboratory Plotter and Electric Logs not be fitted. The DA/S successfully opposed this proposed change in plans, pointing out that the
devices were 'most desirable, as they would be of considerable assistance
in U-boat hunting.'[18] Final approval for the asdic upgrading was given
only on 17 September.[19]

By the end of 1942, despite the Naval Staff's decision to modernize
asdic and fit hedgehog as well as radar, little had changed in operational

units. It was not until 5 January 1943, nearly six months after the decision to proceed with corvette modernization, that the first ship, HMCS *Edmunston*, was taken in hand at Halifax. This lack of alacrity was due to several factors, including the need during the summer and fall of 1942 to commit all available refit resources to the modernization of the corvettes destined to serve in the Torch invasion of North Africa. These ships required a greatly strengthened anti-aircraft armament. Another factor contributing to the delay was the British failure to deliver low power generators until early 1943.[20]

The consequence of the delays in effectively introducing modern asdic and hedgehog were to be grave indeed (see chapter 8). Certainly the Admiralty was no more impressed with Canadian efforts in this area than it was with those taken to acquire modern radar. The net result was that by the last quarter of 1942 Canadian ships were markedly inferior to British escorts in asdic and related weaponry.

In an area of such sophisticated technology it is surprising that scientists and other technical specialists had virtually no input into the debate which took place in the Naval Staff. Even though A.E.H. Pew was available for consultation, there is little to indicate that he attended any committee meetings although the director Anti-Submarine maintained close contact with him. Canadian scientists played little part in either the asdic-production program or the technical liaison. This was, in fact, the result of a rare attempt on part of the RCN and the RN to use effectively the talents of their respective technical personnel. While the asdic specialists at the British Admiralty Technical Mission provided expertise for asdic development similar to that of the Radio Branch on radar, the council's small group of scientists with knowledge of underwater acoustics concentrated their efforts on developing countermeasures against the acoustic mine, work undertaken specifically at the request of the Admiralty.

As we have seen previously, the NRC's role in the early stages of the asdic program was confined to producing quartz crystals and assembling oscillators. On 15 September 1942, these tasks having been perfected by the council staff, oscillator and crystal production was transferred from the overcrowded workshops of NRC to a new plant at Renfrew, Ontario, under the control of the Department of Mines and Resources. This was a natural progression since DMR's mining engineers and geologists had a great deal of experience with crystal manufacturing.[21]

After DMR took over oscillator production, the council involvement with asdic technology was minor and low key. It involved the development of some of the few original items of asdic equipment that were undertaken in Canada. The largest of several projects was the McGregor Recorder, a device developed from an idea of a young sub-lieutenant and mechanical engineer, D.E. McGregor. Unlike previous recorders, the device displayed a complete and immediately understandable picture of a submarine hunt. It was hoped that this would not only make tracking the submerged target easier, but that it would in turn reduce the time required to train asdic operators. Unfortunately, like all other original Canadian asdic developments, work was slowed by the inexperience of council staff and by the low priority given to the project. As a result, although the project commenced at NRC in May 1942, it was not until July 1944 that trials were completed. The war ended before production at Ford of Canada Limited could get under way and the McGregor Recorder had little impact on the war effort.[22]

Although an asdic research group had been established at NRC under the direction of R.W. Boyle in November 1940, little work was conducted in this area. Instead the Admiralty requested in January 1941 that the NRC concentrate its efforts on developing techniques to defeat the acoustical mine, yet another German secret weapon.[23]

The nucleus of this research group originated from the small staff of the Acoustics and Ultrasonics Section of the Division of Physics and Electrical Engineering. Up to 1940 this section consisted of two professionals, including the section-head Dr G.S. Field. Field had been one of the first of a group of young scientists recruited to NRC in early 1930. He spent his first ten years at the council working on a variety of projects ranging from theoretical experiments on acoustical behavior in cylindrical rods to practical testing of the sound properties of building materials. He had at least some experience with early ultra-sonic depth sounders, close technical cousins of asdic.[24]

Field soon took over control of the acoustic, formerly asdic, research group from Boyle, who proved himself ineffective both as an administrator and as a scientist. In January 1941 Field began with an extensive visit to the United States followed by a five-month trip to the United Kingdom.[25] There he learned everything there was to know about the acoustical mine and about countermeasures being developed against it. He was also provided with the latest information on asdic, degaussing, and magnetic minesweeping.

On both his trips Field was appalled by the state of Canada's technical-liaison apparatus, and by the fact that the still non-belligerent Americans were better informed on Admiralty developments than the council. In

Great Britain he found Admiralty scientists 'most anxious that we should receive all useful information but [also] under the impression that we are getting it.'[26] Upon his arrival back in Ottawa in June, Field became a leading proponent of establishing a permanent NRC office in London, and was instrumental in convincing C.J. Mackenzie to appoint L.E. Howlett to the post in August.

Also in June, Field assembled a small team of six physicists and electrical engineers to develop acoustic mine countermeasures. By the end of 1941 they had made impressive progress, having established an acoustical testing range in the Bedford Basin, near Halifax. It consisted 'of several hydrophones set out on the bottom between the buoys and connected to measuring apparatus on shore.'[27] After measuring ship acoustical patterns this team built various devices to simulate these noises, but much louder, in order to explode the mine at a safe distance.

In October the first Canadian acoustical minesweep was tested at Halifax. It was based on a British development and consisted of two parallel pipes fitted on a loose framework which, when towed, would bang together to produce the required sound.[28] Although it proved adequate in initial testing, devices of this type proved ineffective against the acoustical mine 'since the noise they produced was in the subsonic range and therefore too broad for mines.'[29]

In 1942 researchers switched their efforts to another sweeping device under development in the United Kingdom, the acoustical hammer box. It consisted of a pneumatic hammer or road drill 'fitted inside a steel conical box,' which when operated made sufficient noise to detonate an acoustical mine at a safe distance from the minesweeper. The box was mounted on a boom over the minesweeper's bow, 'being lifted out of the water when not in use, and lowered down below the sweeper's forefront when the sweep was being operated.'[30] This variety of sweep was designated by the British as the SA Mark II (acoustical) sweep. The first Canadian version was tested near Halifax in February 1942 on board HMCS *Standard Coaster*, and several were operational in Bangor minesweepers by the end of the year.[31]

The major original research project of Field's team was measuring and experimenting with ultrasonic underwater sound characteristics. The study was begun in late 1941 after the Admiralty requested that North American laboratories take over much primary sound research.[32] Fields team consulted with U.S. Navy laboratories and came up with an agreement that the Americans would concentrate on supersonic while the Canadians would emphasize ultrasonic sound research.[33]

To facilitate research in ultrasonics, large numbers of measurements were taken from a new combined degaussing and sound range constructed in early 1942 in the main channel into Halifax harbour, approximately one-and-a-half cables east of the Middle Ground Buoy off McNabbs Island. From here practically every ship that entered or left Halifax could have its sound characteristics recorded and the effectiveness of its degaussing verified.[34]

The main acoustical laboratories, however, remained at the NRC in Ottawa. The centralizing tendencies of Mackenzie's administration undoubtedly precluded any thought of shifting the facilities to Halifax, which was a far more logical location. Instead much work that probably would have been better accomplished in salt water was undertaken from an acoustical testing barge moored in the Ottawa River.[35]

Despite this handicap, Field led the Canadian team to unquestioned international status in acoustical research. Not only was its impact on operations profound due to a small force of acoustical minesweepers put in place by the end of 1942, but it also led to the most successful council project for the navy.

On the night of 20–21 September 1943 the destroyer HMCS St Croix, part of the new Escort Group 9 supporting the defenders of convoys ONS 18 and ON 202, became one of the first victims of the German GNAT acoustic torpedo. The new weapon homed in on the noises of an escort's propellers and was intended to allow U-boats to blow their way through the now formidable escort screen around a convoy. St Croix's survivors were rescued by HMS Polyanthus, which was in turn the second victim of a GNAT that night. The combined crews were picked up by HMS Itchen, which was itself sunk by yet another acoustic torpedo. Only three men (one from the St Croix) survived from the three crews.[36]

The introduction of the GNAT came as no surprise to Allied scientists since intelligence had correctly guessed its existence, and there were similar devices under development in the United States. Within weeks of the sinking of the St Croix, scientists at Halifax and Ottawa, using their extensive acoustical knowledge, developed an excellent countermeasure to the GNAT known as CAT (Canadian Anti-Torpedo) gear. CAT was intended to be towed behind an escort and generate a sound designed to decoy the homing torpedo away from its target. It was based on the earlier pipe acoustic sweeping devices, consisting simply of 'two lengths of pipe towed side by side, which banged together on account of the turbulence they engendered in the water.'[37] It was found to be an effective countermeasure and considered by RCN officers to be superior to the similar British Foxer device because the latter was more complicated and had a shorter endurance.[38] By early 1944 at least one CAT had been fitted to most Canadian warships.[39]

Unquestionably, the development of CAT was just the best part of this most successful naval scientific research program. Unfortunately, as we have and will continue to see, it was one of the few exceptions to the otherwise bleak tale of RCN-NRC co-operation.

8

Exile and Dissent

On 19 December 1942 the Canadian mid-ocean escort group C 1 set sail from Londonderry to accompany convoy ONS 154 across the Atlantic. The force was led by the River-class destroyer HMCS *St Laurent*, captained by Lieutenant-Commander Guy Windeyer. The rest of C 1 consisted of the Canadian corvettes *Battleford, Chilliwack, Kenogami, Naponee,* and *Shediac.* All had just been fitted with 271 radar during a recent layover in the United Kingdom where the *St Laurent* had also been mounted with an FH3 high-frequency direction finder. None of the escorts had had much opportunity to train with the new equipment, and *St Laurent* sailed without having her FH3 calibrated and without the operating officer. HF/DF coverage for this voyage was to be provided by the rescue vessel *Target* and the special-service ship HMS *Fidelity.*

On the night of 26 December, after entering the mid-Atlantic air coverage gap, U-boats gained contact and in a series of attacks sank three merchant vessels and crippled one. In retaliation *St Laurent* inflicted damage on one of the submarines; after the war it was shown that she had probably sent U356 to a watery grave. The next day the convoy managed to shake off its pursuers and only one vessel was damaged. The respite was brief. By the morning of 28 December the convoy was resighted and a dozen U-boats homed in during the day. That night five German submarines, in a devastating two hour attack, torpedoed nine members of the convoy at no loss to themselves. The battle ended the next morning as the U-boats finally lost their prey, but they had won a decisive victory that had apparently cost them but one badly damaged submarine in exchange for fourteen Allied merchantmen sunk or damaged and 486 lives.[1]

As Marc Milner has shown, the battle for ONS 154 was the last of a series of Canadian convoy defeats in the final quarter of 1942. These included the defence of convoys SC 107 and ONS 127 by group C 4; in those two actions alone twenty ships were sunk without loss to the enemy. In stark contrast the British group B 6, which also had two of its convoys, SC 104 and ONS 144, attacked during the same period, lost merely thirteen merchantmen while making the only two confirmed U-boat kills from early September to mid-November in the Mid-Ocean Escort Force. The RCN had suffered convoy defeats before without incurring serious British criticism, but the strategic situation was far different from that of a year earlier.

The American entry into the war in December 1941 had led to the arrival of U-boats off the coast of North America in early 1942. The Americans, with limited resources and also with a poor appreciation of anti-submarine warfare at senior levels, did not establish a series of interlocking convoys in the Western Hemisphere until August. The Germans took full advantage of American lapses and from January to September 1942 sank 755 merchantmen totalling 6,200,000 tons. By mid-summer the Kriegsmarine began to shift its attention back to the more lucrative mid-Atlantic convoy routes now that all shipping in North America was in properly escorted convoys. Allied intelligence reports indicated that the U-boats, reinforced by the completion of the first major wartime construction program, would launch a major assault that would, and, in fact, did prove to be the decisive campaign of the Battle of the Atlantic.[2]

The losses of the first eight months of 1942 caused a crisis in shipping, particularly among oil tankers. This, and a shortage of escorts caused by the need to support the Allied invasion of North Africa, resulted in great concern in London. So serious did the situation become that on 4 November Churchill established his Anti-U-boat Committee, which consisted of senior politicians, service personnel, technical specialists, and, in interesting contrast to Canadian practice, scientists. The competent, although quiet and reserved C-in-C Western Approaches, Sir Percy Noble, was replaced in mid-November by the more flamboyant ex-submariner Sir Max Horton. Horton could be ruthless in dealing with incompetence, and it is no surprise that he soon began to scrutinize Canadian escort group performance. Horton heard much criticism of the C groups' capabilities, from senior officers in his own command and from the Americans, in particular Vice-Admiral A.M. Brainard, the officer commanding forces in the North-West Atlantic.

There is no question that Horton had cause for concern. In all of the convoy defences in 1942 Canadian ships were hampered by their out-dated equipment. Even the defenders of ONS 154 in December had lacked modern gyro-compasses and asdics. In earlier engagements Canadian groups fought without centimetric radar and HF/DF, all standard kit in British escorts.

Without doubt operational commanders were aware of these deficiencies. Canadian escorts had attempted to compensate for their lack of modern electronics by the creation of new tactics such as operation 'Major Hoople.' Developed in the fall of 1942 by Lieutenant-Commander K.L. Dyer, captain of the destroyer *Skeena*, 'Major Hoople' was intended to illuminate U-boats on attack runs toward a convoy by the use of flares and starshells. This called for skilful, educated guess-work on the part of the escort-group commander, who would have to determine the correct time to call out the code word 'Major Hoople' based on intelligence reports, enemy radio activity, and 'the prevailing moon, sea and visibility conditions.'[3] Although used with some good results, it could dangerously expose the convoy should the situation be misread by the group commander; this was a truly peculiar Canadian solution to a peculiarly Canadian problem.

By September 1942 the Naval Staff had decided that the latest equipment had to be installed in RCN escorts, but as we have seen the policy had still not been transformed into concrete results by the end of the year. So by procrastinating over equipment policy from early 1942, NSHQ brought Canadian escorts to the point where they were thought to be incompetent by the Royal Navy.

There were reasons for the Canadian failures in late 1942 other than the dearth of modern equipment. These included a lack of training and adequate modern destroyers, failure to keep group cohesion, and poor tactical leadership. Milner has pointed out that, in part, it was simply a matter of bad luck that Canadian-escorted convoys were those most effectively intercepted in this period, and he correctly contrasts these disasters with similar British catastrophes in the winter of 1943.[4]

The RCN remained unaware of the depth of British concern over C group efficiency until the first week of December, when several disquieting tidbits of information reached Naval Service Headquarters. However, it was not until mid-month that NSHQ would receive a complete picture of British displeasure when Churchill cabled Mackenzie King outlining the First Lord of the Admiralty, A.V. Alexander's, proposal for redeployment of escorts. Concerned about a growing shortage of oil in the United Kingdom, Alexander had recommended the establishment of direct convoys from the oil fields of Aruba. Escorts for the new route were to be taken from the Gibraltar to United Kingdom convoys and would be replaced by four mid-ocean escort groups. He suggested that the Canadian groups be those reassigned since they could be retrained in Britain and be supplied with continuous air support on their way to Gibraltar. Churchill added, 'I appreciate the grand contribution of the Royal Canadian Navy to the Battle of the Atlantic but the expansion of the RCN has created a training problem which must take sometime to solve.'[5]

Nelles and other officers at NSHQ greeted the British proposal with anger and confusion. After the initial shock had worn off, however, calmer heads prevailed and naval headquarters began a careful assessment of the validity of British criticism and the causes of apparent Canadian inefficiency. NSHQ admitted after some reflection that the RCN had problems, particularly with insufficient training and outdated equipment.

Many staff officers, however, believed that the Admiralty had overemphasized training and that equipment was the key to the navy's woes. As Commander P.M. Bliss, the staff officer Anti-Submarine at Halifax, wrote, 'I cannot help feeling that when the C groups are brought up technically to B groups a very great efficiency will result without reference whatever to training and experience.'[6]

Bliss might have added that the British had themselves contributed greatly to the RCN's modernization problems. We have seen over and over again how failure in liaison, British insensitivity to Canadian requirements, and selfish supply allocation stymied the RCN's efforts to keep up-to-date. Only the Admiralty held the key to a quick solution of the equipment problem although the Naval Staff, politicians, NRC and REL had all contributed to the situation. Canadian production of centimetric radar and new asdic sets had yet to commence, and east coast shipyards were unable to handle the necessary refit work. If the Admiralty had treated the supply of Canadian vessels on equal footing to that of their own, the equipment crisis could have been greatly alleviated. Not surprisingly when Nelles was finally called to task on account of equipment problems in late 1943 he did place much of the blame on the Admiralty. However, as events unfolded in late 1942 no one questioned the Naval Staff's performance, only that of operational units.

The reasons why the British emphasized training over equipment remain unclear. It may have been that, as Nelles believed, the proposed transfer of the MOEF groups to United Kingdom bases was an attempt by the Admiralty not only to improve their performance but also to remove them from Canadian operational control. Also, it is possible that the British did not want to encourage the RCN to believe that it might expand its efforts to assist in escort modernization by improving equipment supply or providing yard space to modernize corvettes. The fact remains that Canadian escorts returned from their sojourn under British control newly fitted with centimetric radar, a commitment made in May 1942, but otherwise in much the same condition as when they left. Undoubtedly there were Royal Naval officers who emphasized training because without necessary skills all the equipment in the world would prove useless. It is hard to assess the actual state of training of Canadian sailors, but we must remember that by this time extensive experience had been gained in the North Atlantic that must have compensated, at least to a certain degree, for the non-professional origin of most of the crews.

The Admiralty's proposal was the basis for a three-day conference organized in Washington beginning 29 December, shortly after the disaster with ONS 154. The Admiralty was represented by Commodore Jack Mansfield, Admiral Horton's chief of staff. Mansfield's primary task was to convince the Americans of the necessity for the changes in escort allocation; convincing the Canadians was at best a secondary concern. The British viewed the Canadians as minor players who would fall into line if confronted by a united RN-USN proposal. The RCN was well represented at the conference by two Washington based officers, Rear Admiral V.G. Brodeur and Commander J.G. Mackinley, and by the director of the Plans Division, Captain H.G. DeWolf.

DeWolf's selection indicates that Nelles had reluctantly, although conditionally, accepted the British proposal even before the conference began, because the Plans director had counselled that the RCN not put up a fight but acquiesce and make the best of a bad situation. Nelles had agreed with DeWolf because he realized that the strategic situation was as serious as the British had indicated and that it did call for an immediate redistribution of escort groups. Reluctantly he also saw that a period in British waters would give the C groups a chance to use superior RN training facilities. However, sensing that the whole scheme might be a British plot to assume operational control over a majority of the RCN's warships, he made it clear to DeWolf that the length of the transfer from the mid-Atlantic must be strictly limited. 7

Delayed by a snowstorm, DeWolf missed the first day of the conference, an important absence since he was designated as the Canadian member on the escort subcommittee. That first day the American and British officers present agreed to redistribute escorts as Alexander had suggested. The second day, however, DeWolf, while indicating RCN acceptance, stipulated that the Canadian war Cabinet must have final say as to the allocation of HMC ships and that the C groups be transferred back to their mid-ocean escort force upon the completion of their retraining. Mansfield, sensing that the Canadian would compromise no further, agreed to a limited transfer sufficient for retraining of no more than a three to four months.[8]

Mansfield and DeWolf arrived in Ottawa on 2 January 1943 to gain approval for the agreement made in Washington. Diplomatically the British officer played down the faults of the RCN and emphasized the fact that the C groups were simply the first to benefit from a bigger scheme that would upgrade the skills of all the mid-ocean escort groups. After two weeks of reflection, and with the conditions laid down by DeWolf agreed to by Mansfield, Nelles accepted the transfer and on 6 January brought the matter to the war Cabinet.

Nelles brought with him to the war Cabinet two memos he had prepared on the subject for Angus Macdonald. The first, written before DeWolf had gone to Washington although not sent to the minister until after his return, explained at length the Admiralty's plan but skirted the main issue of RCN deficiency. Nelles told Macdonald that it was vital that forces be redistributed but cautioned that 'this is the ... most serious attempt on the part of the Admiralty to get operational control of our ships.' Training and equipment problems were mentioned only briefly on the third and last page of the memorandum. Concerning equipment Nelles admitted that the RCN was behind the RN, particularly in radar and something called the 'Air Asdic' – likely HF/DF. 'The most modern equipment,' he wrote, 'is simply not available, it is being installed as quickly as it does become available.' No attempt was made to explain why or how extensive these shortfalls were in equipment.[9]

A second memorandum outlined Mansfield's tactful argument that Canadian groups were simply to be the first to benefit from the training schemes and emphasized the necessity of providing escorts for the Gibraltar convoys. Nelles portrayed the agreement reached in Washington as a Canadian national victory over attempts to take operational control away from NSHQ. Instead, by getting Mansfield to agree to limit the transfer to no more than four months, 'we not only receive the benefit of the intensive training but we also establish the fact that we consider the North Atlantic to be our operational area.'[10]

In neither document was Nelles very forthright concerning the reasons behind the British request. By playing down charges of Canadian incompetence and mismanagement and by emphasizing his supposed victory over British attempts to exert imperial control over the RCN, he managed to mislead the war Cabinet into agreeing to the transfer to Gibraltar without any formal inquiry into the navy's performance. That he was able to get away with it indicates that the politicians were either not interested in the running of the war effort unless there were domestic political implications, or that Nelles had cunningly played on their nationalistic sentiment.

There is no proof, however, that Nelles intentionally deceived the war Cabinet. It may very well be that a man who could describe HF/DF as the 'Air Asdic' did not fully understand the growing obsolescence of the RCN's escort fleet and really did believe that Alexander's proposal was simply a scheme to subvert NSHQ's power. In fact, Nelles may have correctly guessed part of the motivation behind the British proposals. But if Nelles was not guilty of deceit then he was incompetent and ill-informed on the serious state of affairs within the navy; either way the results were the same. In exile the Canadian mid-ocean escorts missed the crucial period in the late winter and early spring of 1943 when the U-boats came close to victory only to be decisively defeated in their assault on the Atlantic convoys. It was the most critical period of the entire Battle of the Atlantic and the brunt of the fighting in the key mid-ocean routes was born by RN escorts, an embarrassing fact long-hidden and only recently revealed by Marc Milner.[11]

In the months immediately following the removal of the MOEF groups from the mid-ocean convoy routes, Nelles concentrated Naval Staff efforts on something other than equipment and training. Nelles believed that in part the RCN had been singled out because of unsympathetic foreign operational commanders, and emphasized the need to regain Canadian control of its escorts and of the North-West Atlantic operational area. The emphasis within the Naval Staff on gaining authority in the North-West Atlantic was not surprising; the RCN had been unhappy with command relationships in this area since September 1941, when it had been forced to relinquish control of the area to the United States Navy. Commodore Murray, the Flag officer, Newfoundland, had been given limited operational independence in May 1941, but this had been superseded when ABC (American-British Conversations) 1 and 22 came into effect. The two accords had been informal discussions without Canadian participation in which the British had successfully received agreement from the still-neutral Americans to assist in the Battle of the Atlantic. The Americans insisted that they be given strategic operational command in the western half of the Atlantic, the only exception being Canadian coastal waters. Understanding that massive American aid was promised to support the campaign against the U-boats, the Canadian chiefs of staff felt that they had no choice but to agree to have an American supercede Commodore Murray.[12]

When American Admiral A.L. Bristol raised his flag as the commander of Task Force 24 based at Argentia, Newfoundland, in September 1941, Canada had not only swallowed a great deal of pride but also relinquished control over waters where it rightly should have retained strategic preeminence. The RCN had only acquiesced to the ABC accords because they were accompanied by a promise of massive American naval aid from battleships to destroyers, aid desperately needed to defeat the U-boats. The USN's commitment to the Atlantic, however, lasted only to the attack on Pearl Harbor, and within a few months of December 1941 the American naval forces in the area had shrunk to a handful of Coast Guard cutters.

Still the Americans insisted that Task Force 24 remain, even though the Canadian contribution and strategic influence in the North-West Atlantic was now second to none. There were numerous conflicts between the USN and RCN concerning Task Force 24's attempts to interfere with NSHQ's authority over Canadian warships. However, it was Bristol's successor, Vice-Admiral A.M. Brainard's, involvement in the criticism leading to the exile to Gibraltar which acted as a catalyst and galvanized NSHQ to demand Canadian control over its primary operational area.

In the winter of 1942 the Naval Staff spent long hours preparing its case against American control of the North-West Atlantic. At the Atlantic Convoy Conference, which opened in Washington in early March 1943, the Canadian delegation won approval for RCN control of all escorts in an area north of 40 degrees north and west of 47 degrees west. After a month and a half of further wrangling with the Americans Admiral Murray was appointed C-in-C Canadian North-West Atlantic, replacing Admiral Brainard on 18 April 1943.

Although it was unacceptable that the RCN not be in charge of its own bailiwick, the struggle to replace Task Force 24 had diverted attention away from the equally vital task of re-equipping the escort fleet.[13] There were some minor steps forward including trying to increase the pace of centimetric radar development and stepping up efforts to secure Admiralty supplies of 271. Certainly the approval in February 1943 to upgrade all corvettes as quickly as possible was directly related to the events of December 1942. No doubt the same is true for the issuance on 27 February of Naval Order 2587, which allowed for all ships to fit approved additions and alterations whenever and wherever possible and 'such other A's and A's as have been approved for RN ships and are considered by Admiralty as necessary for RCN ships.' Exception was made, however, for new radio and radar equipment, which was still only to be fitted with prior permission of naval headquarters.[14]

Still no consideration was seriously given to finding an overall solution to the equipment problem. There is no evidence, for instance, that Naval Staff attempted to negotiate with the Admiralty for the re-equipment of the MOEF escorts. Instead NSHQ was content to allow the vessels to return to Newfoundland in the spring only marginally better equipped than they were in late 1942. Why was this allowed to happen? Either Nelles and his staff did not understand the severity of the problem or they did not wish publicly to admit its existence. Nelles should have made modernization of the escorts a condition for accepting the exile and should have asked his minister to find a political solution if the British were reluctant to agree. Whatever the answer, the results of the failure to deal with the equipment crisis in January would be disastrous to both Nelles and the navy.

Tentative steps were taken in early 1943 to re-examine NSHQ organization in order to improve management of the anti-submarine warfare (ASW) effort under the supervision of the newly appointed Director of Organization, but the lack of urgency associated with the study delayed any major changes until the beginning of June. It would appear that at least part of the motivation for organizational reforms when they did finally come were from the recommendations of American and British Naval Officers. The Allied Anti-Submarine Survey Board, which was formed as a result of the conference in Washington in March and was co-chaired by Admiral Mansfield and American Admiral J.L. Kauffman, came to Canada in May. The board was critical of several areas of Canadian organization, including the failure to make anti-submarine warfare the main operational concern of the Naval Staff. They also did not approve of the poor integration of RCAF ASW squadrons into the naval command structure. The board recommended the formation of the position of assistant chief of Naval Staff to co-ordinate ASW at naval headquarters.

The Mansfield-Kauffman board, however, was even more critical of the refit and modernization situation. It found east coast shipyards inadequate and saturated beyond the breaking point, and reported that the only solution was to accelerate 'the completion dates of escorts under refit and in hand for essential alterations and additions and this can only be achieved by allocating to escort repair work priority over merchant ships and all new construction.' In conclusion the board emphasized 'that escort vessels must be maintained in an efficient condition ... failing this ships cannot be formed into well trained groups nor can convoys be efficiently protected.'[15]

Soon after the Mansfield-Kauffman board issued its report the long awaited reorganization of NSHQ took place. The post of assistant chief of Naval Staff was established with the appointment of Commander W.B. Creery, who had formerly been Murray's chief of staff at Halifax. As recommended, Creery was placed in charge of co-ordinating the activities of the Naval Staff branch, including the directorates of Operations, Plans, Trade, Signals, Intelligence, the Naval Hydrographer, and the new Directorate of Warfare and Training. In essence this made the ACNS responsible for the 'conduct of anti-submarine operations,' an important step since this had previously been one of Nelles responsibilities that tended to get lost in the competition with his other duties.[16]

The creation of the Directorate of Warfare and Training, under the control of the deputy director Captain H. McMaster, was of great significance to improving Naval Staff handling of high-technology planning. In December 1943 McMaster was superseded by Captain K.F. Adams, who had been in command of group C 1. The DWT's original terms of reference were 'the establishment of fighting efficiency, research and development, the tactical use of HMC ships and weapons, analysis of reports of proceedings and actions; schemes of training; and advice concerning staff organization.'[17] In practice the DWT's office had less to do with training than with weapons-system policy and with keeping in touch with new research and development. It absorbed the operational functions of the director Anti-Submarine and the Technical Directorate, and eventually would control the new operational research unit at NSHQ and the Directorate of Technical Research.[18]

Two other new posts were created slightly later in the year to improve the equipment supply and maintenance situation. In July the directorate of Electrical Supply was established and placed in charge of 'all matters pertaining to the acquisition of W/T [radio], Radar and Asdic.' On 15 October Captain G.M. Hibbard was appointed Commodore Superintendent at Halifax with the 'responsibility of arranging and carrying through all refits, alterations and repairs throughout the east coast.'[19]

This was an important step, although taken over nine months after the showdown with the Admiralty over the inadequate performance of RCN escorts and five months after Admirals Mansfield and Kauffman had recommended it.

Despite these moves and the first gradual results from the decisions made on equipment policy in September 1942, by the spring of 1943 there was a growing dissatisfaction among operational commanders with the equipment situation and disenchantment at NSHQ with Nelles. The trouble seems to have been sparked by the gradual return of the C groups to MOEF from late March to early May 1943. Senior officers discovered that despite the Canadian escorts' sojourn in British waters they were still markedly ill-equipped in comparison to British vessels.

This was the essential point contained in the letter of Captain J.M. Rowland, the Captain (D), Newfoundland, sent on 1 May to H.E. Reid, the Flag officer, Newfoundland. Rowland pointed out that the current model of the 271 mounted on RCN escorts was being superseded by a superior model in the RN. He also mentioned deficiencies in asdic, since most corvettes still fitted 123A and carried no hedgehog, and complained that few destroyers had the latest FH4 HF/DF set. Rowland, a British officer, had been critical of NSHQ organization as early as September 1942 while still in command of an RN destroyer in Western Escort Force. Now he called for an immediate policy to enable his ships to fit the latest equipment at the earliest opportunity, an indication that he was ignorant of Naval Order 2587. Rowland, however, went beyond the order and insisted that the policy be extended to radar, and he was supported by Reid who had recently been assigned from NSHQ. It took Ottawa almost eight weeks to reply to Rowland's request, an unconscionable delay, and it only contained a summary of the naval order and a denial that things were as bad as he had indicated.[20]

Several other complaints by senior operational officers were received by NSHQ during the late spring and early summer of 1943. One of the most detailed assessments of the dilemma of Canadian mid-ocean escorts is contained in a report submitted by Acting Lieutenant-Commander Desmond W. Piers, captain of the destroyer HMCS *Restigouche*, to Reid on 1 June. Piers examined the navy in fourteen major categories from morale to refitting, including an analysis of the performance of HMC ships, shore establishments and even naval headquarters. His most telling comments were in the equipment area. 'It is blunt statement of fact,' he wrote, 'that RCN ships are outdated by 12 to 18 months, compared to RN ships doing the same job of convoy escort.' He insisted that this must be considered when comparing Canadian and British groups performance.

Piers found RN authorities in Londonderry 'most co-operative' in fitting the latest hardware during normal lay-over periods, and believed that Naval Order 2541 had expedited matters. He cautioned, however, that 'the initiation and success of efforts to get new equipment in HMC ships depend largely on individual commanding officers.' Interestingly, Piers did not blame Ottawa for the shortfalls but instead the British policy of not allocating equipment to the RCN 'until all RN ships are fitted, unless a particularly urgent request is made by a senior officer on our behalf.' He forcefully requested that NSHQ make 'every effort' to get Canadian ships treated on an equal basis with British vessels. He also cited the refit schedule, which forced ships to wait until their next major overhaul to mount hedgehog, 144 asdic, and HF/DF. Finally, Piers warned that the equipment problems had affected and would continue adversely to affect ship efficiency.

Piers's comments on Naval Service Headquarters are also most illuminating, even though many of the problems he pointed out were dealt with by the June reforms. Even Piers, a professional naval officer, was 'at a loss to explain fully how the RCN [was] organized for war.' He requested that a pamphlet or explanatory article be published to clarify the situation. He also suggested that commanding officers of MOEF ships should visit NSHQ on a regular basis to discuss the operational situation and problems. He then made a very interesting comment that must have reflected the doubts of many who had not recently been to Ottawa. Piers inquired if NSHQ treated, as it should, anti-submarine warfare as a top priority. He commented that in the Naval List, the only source on headquarter organization available, anti-submarine warfare was 'relegated to Section 7 of the Operations Division, on par with minesweeping and motor launches.' He also wondered why Ottawa could spare an officer in the United Kingdom to study the Fleet Air Arm when no permanent liaison officer was stationed at Derby House, Admiral Horton's headquarters.[21]

Criticism of the RCN from operational areas also covered things outside the equipment issue which were nevertheless important because they relate to the fighting efficiency of Canadian escorts and provide more detail concerning the depth of the dissent to headquarter policies. On 22 June 1943 R.E.S. Bidwell, the chief of staff at Halifax, submitted a memorandum to Admiral Murray which was passed on to Ottawa eight days later. Bidwell summarized a discussion he had held with the Captain (D)s at Halifax and St John's and with the Halifax staff officers in charge of operations, escorts and training. These six men, closer to operations then any other shore-based officers, believed that there were serious problems in training, refitting, and particularly in manning policies. They called for an end to the practice of drafting large numbers of a crew away from a refitting ship, and for 'leave and drafting be so arranged that as many as possible of the key officers and ratings who are going to run the ship in the future are on board for the refit.' They also insisted that nothing be allowed to interfere with a ship's working-up period after a refit or commissioning. Bidwell concluded by warning that, 'If we are to maintain our commitments and our efficiency at the same time, all the above points must receive due and constant consideration.'[22]

Dissent at naval headquarters is harder to trace but still appears to have been a growing phenomenon in the spring and summer of 1943. In his memoirs, H.N. Lay mentions a confrontation he had with Nelles that he believed occurred in March 1943. Nelles accused Lay of 'talking to the Minister behind my back about the lack of efficiency in training of the new Canadian escort vessels.' Lay was able to absolve himself of blame with the support of the vice-chief of Naval Staff, Rear-Admiral G.C. Jones. Jones, however, as Lay later discovered, was the culprit that Nelles sought. For the vcns had been discussing the replacement of Nelles as chief of Naval Staff with Angus Macdonald. Although there is evidence that Lay's chronology is incorrect, the events he described likely occurring at a somewhat later date, the fact that they occurred at all leaves no doubt that the picture of growing tension at nshq is an accurate one.[23]

9

The Ten-Centimetre Débâcle

On 11 November 1942 a dramatic confrontation took place in the office of Eric Phillips, president of Research Enterprises Limited, between F.C. Wallace, head of NRC's Radio Branch, and R.A. Hackbusch, manager of REL's Radio Division. Unfortunately the only account of this meeting is found in the War Diary of the head of the NRC, C.J. Mackenzie, and thus must be treated with some caution because, while Mackenzie presents a picture of REL incompetence, there were, in fact, serious problems at the council and within the navy and in the relationships between all of these institutions at a time when major pre-production work on RX/C was commencing. Mackenzie's account, however, illustrates the depth of the rift between REL and NRC. Wallace accused Hackbusch of allowing untested components into radar sets and then shipping the untried sets to operational units. He warned Phillips that the situation in the Radio Division was out of control and that he had better find out what was going on. Hackbusch, denying all allegations, brought in a Mr McArdle, the chief superintendent of the radio plant, with documentation to support his case. According to Mackenzie, under cross examination from Wallace, 'McArdle broke down and said that it was perfectly true that the sets were not tested; that none of them came up to specifications, intimated that he was doing this under Hackbusch's orders.'[1]

In his diary Mackenzie added that he thought that REL's operations represented 'the best example of industrial inefficiency which I have seen in the war.' He believed Hackbusch to be completely unreliable but found himself unable to force his dismissal since Hackbusch was protected by Phillips who in turn was supported by the all-powerful C.D. Howe.[2]

Mackenzie's belief that incompetence at REL's Radio Division severely hampered the Canadian radar program is confirmed by an examination of the lethargic pace of production of the RX/C and the RX/U antenna systems. However, it should be noted that the council and the navy contributed greatly to the manufacturer's predicament. The NRC failed to deliver a prototype that could be easily mass-produced and did not carry out sufficient testing to ensure that the sets would work in service. Further, the navy could not provide the expertise needed to guide the inexperienced REL staff. It delayed ordering the sets until early October 1942, and forced the company to deal with several major design changes.

These factors combined to crush any hope in the RCN that indigenous centimetric radar production would begin by the spring of 1943. By the beginning of 1943 the RX/U and RX/C programs were both well behind schedule and the source of most difficulties in the program had shifted away from council and navy to the Radio Division of Research Enterprises Limited. REL, unlike the other two institutions, was unusual in that it was entirely a wartime creation, with a staff that had been assembled from scratch since the fall of 1940. The company had commenced radar manufacturing in the summer of 1941, when both the SW1C and RCAF's ASV sets began rolling off the assembly line. There were what appeared to be normal start-up problems, such as the delay in delivering quantities of SW1CS until the spring of 1942, but it appeared that these had been rectified. In fact, however, radar production was still not running smoothly at REL as problems with the RX/C will illustrate.

One of the major results of the lowering of centimetric radar priority at the council between December 1941 and May 1942, when the navy unsuccessfully sought an American alternative to the Canadian design, was that the research laboratory failed to keep the manufacturer informed on RX/C developments. In February 1942 the navy asked the Radio Branch to build a second RX/C prototype for examination at REL but the council refused because it was reluctant to commit resources to a project that appeared at the time unlikely to go into production.[3]

It was not until 23 July, following the return of the first set from the trials on *Port Arthur*, that J.A. Warren, a REL production engineer, was given a detailed look at RX/C. He was not impressed because 'it shortly came to light ... that a great many modifications were absolutely essential' before tooling up for production could begin.[4] As both the head of the Radio Branch Naval Group, H.R. Smyth, and the project chief, K.C. Mann, admitted, NRC had decided 'that such matters as shock mountings, adequate cooling units, use of component parts to suit production specifications, rigid rack construction, special wiring methods etc., could and should be left to those with staff and experience to handle those things.'⁵ Warren felt, quite correctly, that with these limitations the NRC's model of the RX/C was far from a complete pre-production set.

Smyth and Mann were 'completely upset' by Warren's criticism, and in a lengthy memorandum defended the council's handling of the RX/C program. Wallace sent the report to Hackbusch along with a covering letter in which he supported his scientists and accused Warren not only of being an unfair critic but also of tampering with NRC designs 'very much to the disadvantage to all concerned.'⁶

Hackbusch and F.H.R. Pounsett, REL's chief engineer, wrote a conciliatory reply blaming the difficulty on 'the age old delineation between the viewpoints and different degrees of emphasis placed on various phases of the work as between the research man and the development engineer.'⁷ This conciliatory effort fell on deaf ears at NRC because the Radio Branch staff was incensed not only by Warren's comments but also by the growing problem of poor quality control at REL's Radio Division.

Problems between the two institutions had already greatly strained relations between NRC's and REL's staff. In late 1941 the matter of the separation of research, development and production responsibilities had been finally decided by Mackenzie, Howe and Phillips. NRC was to control research, REL production, and the two would share development work. On the whole they did create a good working relationship that saw the technical staffs of REL and NRC successful in the completion of the ASV and SW1C radar programs. Through the course of 1942, however, Wallace and Mackenzie came to believe that there were serious problems at REL which seemed to be centred on the management skills of Hackbusch.⁸

Unquestionably the ill-feelings generated by Warren's criticism of the council were just one of many factors which led to the 11 November confrontation between Wallace and Hackbusch described at the beginning of this chapter. The fact that no immediate solution seemed possible, since both sides refused to accept any responsibility, meant that work had to continue despite an unhealthy environment.

On 27 November 1942 there was a lengthy meeting at REL's Leaside plant between company, council and naval officials concerning RX/C development. The RCN told REL that it must redesign the entire rack assembly of the set so it would fit into a smaller-than-anticipated frigate radar cabin. The navy also informed the company and NRC that it had chosen a manually operated rotation system for the antenna instead of the council's proposed electric drive model. Another major modification requested by the navy was that the set be equipped so that a plan-position indicator system, the development of which had just started at the council, could be added with minimal difficulty. The cumulative effect of these proposed changes resulted in a major delay of the pre-production stage of the project.[9] There would be other design changes made during the course of the winter of 1942–3, all of which would further slow the pace of development.[10]

While REL tried to grapple with the RX/C it was also experiencing great difficulty with the delivery of the antenna for the RX/U. In late December 1942 the American SJ sets finally were delivered to the RCN, but the Canadian half of the hybrid radar was not completed until March 1943. REL had subcontracted the antenna system to Campbell's Limited, a small Toronto-based manufacturer which in peacetime produced golf clubs and had been building antennas for army radios since early on in the war. Late delivery meant that the first RX/U would not enter service until June 1943.[11]

As RX/U was belatedly coming available, RX/C production continued to lag disastrously behind schedule. On 3 January 1943 REL informed the Signals Production Branch of DMS that deliveries of the Canadian naval radar would commence with ten sets in March. The navy remained unconvinced and the new RDFO, Lieutenant-Commander T.J. Brown, investigated and 'found [that] in order to obtain 10 equipment by June at the earliest an AAA priority was required.'[12] Although this rating was quickly obtained in Canada, in February, for vital components required from the United States, it was becoming increasingly obvious that REL production would not commence until late 1943.[13]

The realization that REL could not provide sets in the summer caused great consternation at NSHQ because frigates were to be commissioned during that period and it had been planned to mount RX/C as their primary radar system. As a stopgap measure Brown approached Wallace and offered to provide fifty naval radio mechanics if the NRC would hand-build four, later increased to eight, RX/CS. Wallace reluctantly agreed to undertake this unusual task.[14]

The growing frustration with the slow rate of development at REL finally resulted in a direct challenge to REL's management by the services and the council in April. The issue that finally sparked this action was Hackbusch's refusal to provide parts for the RX/CS that were to be hand-built by the council. He argued that 'a supply of material to NRC for other than experimental or prototype use is contrary to the instructions which we have received from the Minister, the Honourable C.D. Howe.'[15] Two days later the naval liaison officer at REL, Lieutenant C.B. Campbell, reported to the deputy director of the Signal Division that RX/C production was delayed at least until July and that by the end of March the company had not used its AAA priority rating to secure vital components from the United States.[16] Matters were coming to a head. After the army, the air force, and the council indicated that they had similar problems with REL, the issue was deemed so serious that Mackenzie took the unusual step of settling the matter at the highest political level.[17]

On 28 April J.L. Ralston, the senior minister in the defence triumvirate, wrote to C.D. Howe, who was responsible for REL, concerning the services' difficulties with the radar manufacturer. In the letter Ralston summarized a detailed report on REL's problems written by Mackenzie on 12 April. Mackenzie complained that REL was giving higher priority to Allied orders than to Canadian service requirements. Mackenzie followed this with an in-depth itemized list of problems with radar projects experienced by the three services, and it is no coincidence that he led off with the RX/C. The situation, as Mackenzie pointed out, was now so out of control that some frigates 'will proceed to sea without RDF equipment.' To better manage REL, Ralston proposed that DMS report monthly to the chiefs of staff through the RDF Committee, showing the production position at REL, details of proposed new contracts, and a notation outlining the effect any new undertakings would have on radar production and deliveries.[18]

On 12 May Phillips and the REL staff responded angrily to Ralston and Mackenzie's accusations. After comparing the company favourably with manufacturers in the United States and the United Kingdom, Phillips launched into a vicious assault on the services and NRC's technical competence. He felt that the services 'quite unconsciously think of us as a special section of the Department [of National Defence], with the power to work miracles in production and to have at our command special facilities which enable us to produce complicated equipment without either prototypes or drawings and specifications.' He used as an example the RX/C 'on which Mr. Ralston complains that we are delaying delivery but about May 5th the service suggest that certain problems of installation can be settled by us if we visit a ship at Kingston in June.'[19] A detailed staff report which accompanied Phillips's letter listed over a dozen modifications to RX/C demanded by the navy and the council since October 1942 that were to blame for the lengthy delays.[20]

Typically, Howe's response was to look for a quick method to diffuse the issue by finding a peaceful impartial resolution. To accomplish this he appointed H.J. Carmichael, the chairman of the Production Board, to investigate. While Carmichael's report was ostensibly neutral it clearly supported Ralston's arguments, for he recommended that a new committee be created to supervise radar production along the lines that the minister of defence had suggested. This body was to be known as the Radar Co-ordination Committee and would have as its chairman the head of DMS's Signals Production Branch, A.H. Zimmerman. Other members would include Phillips for REL, Wallace for NRC, and one representative from each of the services. By intentionally excluding Hackbusch or a member of his staff from membership, Carmichael was indicating who he felt was to blame, and from this moment Hackbusch's days at REL were numbered.[21]

It is not certain if Hackbusch was a scapegoat, sacrificed instead of the well-connected Phillips, or a real villain. What is clear, however, is that Mackenzie had failed in his role as chairman of the RDF Committee and allowed the rift with REL to continue far longer than it should have. Whoever was to blame, from this moment onward REL's Radio Division was increasingly closely supervised and eventually controlled by the NRC, a situation which was formalized when Wallace replaced Hackbusch in September without giving up his position at the Radio Branch.[22]

While the dispute with REL still simmered the Naval Staff was being brought under increasing pressure from operational commands for a rapid solution to the centimetric radar problem. Although by the spring of 1943 the large majority of mid-ocean escorts mounted 271, many vessels of Western Local Escort Force did not. To make matters worse, the British had introduced one major improved version of the 271, the 271P, and were beginning the large-scale fitting of an even better model, the 271Q. Both these versions featured several important improvements including progressively more power, from 5 kilowatts in the original set to 90 kilowatts in the 271Q, which allowed for more accurate direction-finding with longer range. Thus while the RCN was still struggling to fit a first-generation centimetric set to every corvette, it was also being forced to try to upgrade existing radars with the added danger that both RX/U and RX/C might be obsolete before either entered service. Figures for different 271 types fitted are unavailable for this period, but by 1 September, when most RN escorts had 271Q, only fourteen had been mounted in the RCN, along with fifty-three 271Ps and three original production models.[23]

On 1 May Captain J.M. Rowland, the Captain (D), St John's, wrote a memorandum to H.E. Reid, now a commodore and the Flag officer, Newfoundland, calling for immediate approval of a definitive policy for fitting mid-ocean escorts with the latest and best equipment 'whatever the cost.' He wanted approval for the fitting of 271Q so that Canadian vessels could mount the set whenever and wherever they found it available.[24] Reid passed Rowland's memorandum to NSHQ on 13 May, giving it his unequivocal support.[25]

Reaction to the Newfoundland request was swift and hostile. Brown wrote a strong response stating that the situation was much better than pictured as 271P was not obsolete, just slightly less effective than the improved model. He argued that RN and Halifax dockyard staff had done a good job in fitting 271s at a rate which would see all corvettes fitted with the British set or with RX/U by the end of the summer. In a marginal note on Brown's letter, Worth added that Reid and Rowland were 'apt to fly off the typewriter before asking the staff RDF officers what the score is.'[26] Worth and Brown's confidence in their own assessment of the situation, however, was to be shattered before a reply could be sent to St John's, and it was not until July that NSHQ sent a toned-down response.

What humbled Worth and Brown was the first of the two débâcles that were to destroy the Canadian naval radar program: in June 1943 RX/U finally entered service, only to be withdrawn a few weeks later. On 10 June preliminary sea trials of one of the first of these sets to be fitted was undertaken on HMCS *Edmunston*, and the results were extremely unsatisfactory. The RDF Base Maintenance Officer at Halifax reported 'that the efficiency of RX/U is about 60% of Type 271 Mark III [P].' Even compared to SW2C the 'RX/U may be considered as a doubtful improvement.' In all other respects the set was found inferior to 271, because it was 'more difficult to operate' and because 'a much slower sweep has to be carried out in order to avoid missing small echoes.'[27] After reviewing the results J.D. Prentice, the Captain (D), Halifax, strongly recommended to NSHQ 'that RX/U sets at present installed in HMC ships be replaced by 271 sets, at the earliest opportunity.'[28]

NSHQ had little choice but to agree that RX/U was a failure, 'to be fitted in RCN ships only where type 271 is not available at the time of refit or completion.' NSHQ thought that eventually the set could be modified to an acceptable level but it never was, and no more than half-a-dozen or so ever saw service.[29]

The RX/U disaster seems to have been predetermined from the project's inception in March 1942. It was the choice of the SJ set, perhaps forced on the RCN by the Americans, that precluded success. The SJ was not suitable for submarine detection as a report, probably never seen by

Canadian officials, explained in July 1942. Written by an MIT Radiation Laboratory staff member, L.C. Marshall, it outlined the shortcomings of the set. Marshall wrote that, 'sj is designed exclusively for submarines as a general purpose detection set' and 'it will probably not find an application outside this field.' 'The gain,' he added, 'may not be sufficient to give adequate ranges on small targets such as a sub[marine] peri-scopes.'[30] The Canadian-designed antenna was supposed to correct this fault, but the problem rested at least in part with the radar set itself and, therefore, the program was destined to fail.

It also turned out that the antenna had a major structural fault. The design left 'insufficient areas of support between the rotator and the reflector.' The resulting 'very severe vibration caused considerable front to back motion of the reflector which has caused the lower surface of the reflector to tear at each end where supported.'[31] Although the RX/U was already withdrawn by the time the problem was discovered, this discovery had ramifications for the RX/C program. The antenna systems of the two sets were standardized in the summer of 1942 and it was not until the end of October 1943 that a solution was found to the vibration problem.[32]

The withdrawal of the RX/U delayed the completion of centimetric fitting in corvettes until late 1943 but the effect on operations was muted by the removal of 271s from west coast-based ships and their transfer for mounting at Halifax. Since the navy had been counting on using no more than twenty-two of the sets and on equipping the frigates and other second-generation escorts with RX/C, the effect of the failure was confined to a loss of confidence by operational commands in Canada's ability to supply its ships with modern radar.

Of greater concern to NSHQ was the continuing failure of REL to pro-duce RX/CS. By 15 November only four REL-manufactured sets had been delivered.[33] Eight other sets were finished except for their motor gen-erator which had not been delivered by the supplier, Great Lakes Electric Manufacturing Company of Chicago. REL was paying the price for its failure to use the AAA priority rating the navy secured for the RX/C project in February. Despite these problems the navy was able to find radar sets for frigates that were able to sail before the winter freeze-up at their Quebec shipyards. This included the mounting of the first RX/CS although more than half were NRC hand-built models completed in September.[34] By 1 February 1944 fifteen of the sets were mounted, ten on frigates, four on the new Algerine-class minesweepers, and one on a corvette. Shortages, however, had forced eight of the latest model 271s to be mounted on the frigates and one on an Algerine. It is likely that these sets were taken from supplies originally intended to replace earlier model 271s on other warships.[35]

Initial operational reports on RX/C received in December 1943 and January 1944 were cautiously optimistic if shortages of spare parts and certain teething problems could be cured.[36] In December the captain of HMCS *Wallaceburg*, Acting Lieutenant Commander E.E. Miles, reported on RX/C performance during the ship's voyage from Quebec to Halifax. He reported good echoes on land at 67,000 yards and on frigates at 17,000 to 18,000 yards. Side lobes, or false echoes caused by the supports of the protective dome around the antenna, were a problem but Miles believed that an experienced operator should have no difficulty. At any rate the fault could be corrected by the fitting of an all 'perpex' lantern which would be available in the summer. Accuracy was said to be as good as 271, with ranging ability somewhere between 271P and Q, and the set was said to be much simpler to operate than British equipment. The *Wallaceburg*'s set, however, broke down after three days of operation, something that was not unusual with any Second World War radar, and the ship could not yet judge its serviceability in comparison to other equipment.[37]

It did not take long, however, for disquieting accounts of RX/C performance to reach Ottawa. At the end of January 1944 NSHQ felt the matter serious enough to send a lengthy memorandum to Admiral Murray in Halifax defending the program's integrity. The memorandum blamed all difficulties with the set on a lack of training and spares as well as on normal teething troubles. Headquarters believed that part of the problem with accepting the RX/C was an unfortunate tendency to link it with the failed RX/U. NSHQ claimed quite inaccurately that the latter had only been an 'interim measure,' while the RX/C was 'a carefully engineered Canadian equipment, embodying the latest techniques, and believed capable of comparable performance to type 271Q.' Some of the reported faults were said to be limited to the NRC-built models which had been completed with a transformer known to be below specifications, while REL-produced sets were claimed to be much more reliable.[38]

Murray passed on NSHQ's evaluation of the situation to Prentice, the Captain (D), Halifax, but was not convinced of RX/C's suitability. On 1 February Murray sent to Ottawa a list of ten recurring faults and problems, the most serious of which was repeated overheating of the motor generators. Another complication was the rack design which prevented easy maintenance; as a result even minor trouble required 'excessive time to correct.' Murray added that 'this factor may eventually become sufficiently acute to lead to serious difficulties, particularly since there is a lack of sufficient information in the way of handbooks and data.'[39]

NSHQ counselled patience, informing Murray on 11 February that the shortcomings with the motor alternator were being remedied as quickly as possible. Headquarters ignored Murray's other more serious complaints partly because it was still preoccupied with continuing slow production at REL and with the introduction of a PPI display for the RX/C.[40] Ottawa continued its silence despite other damning reports received later on in the month. These included one by Prentice written on 21 February in which he concluded that 'until the remaining technical difficulties have been ironed out, type RXC cannot be considered a satisfactory set for operating ships.'[41]

NSHQ continued to support the integrity of the RX/C program until the end of April, when continuing complaints forced a complete reexamination of the situation. On 23 April the secretary of the Naval Board informed Wallace that sea trials of RX/C would be conducted to determine if the sets could be made satisfactory, and asked for NRC participation in the testing. The first of these tests were scheduled to take place in early May on board HMCS *Winnipeg* at the same time that the first PPI system was going through its trials.[42]

The trials on *Winnipeg* occurred on 4 to 15 May and confirmed many of the problems already reported, including frequent failure, confusing side lobes, and difficult maintenance. The NRC representative, however, defended the set and placed most of the blame on inexperienced and incompetent operators, radio artificers, and radar officers.[43] In fact, the NRC man was correct; there were serious problems within the radar branches of the service which would not be solved during the course of the war and greatly exacerbated the problems with RX/C.

Since the first operator training centre had been established at the Halifax-based Signals school in March 1941 the navy had tried to grapple with the almost unsolvable problem of properly training adequate numbers of specialists in this highly technical field. There had been steady improvement in training procedures and resources since facilities were first established, but these efforts had been hampered by a long delay in securing permanent quarters. From October 1941, when the Signals school minus the radar branch was transferred to St Hyacinthe, Quebec, to August 1943, when the two elements were finally reunited, operator training was conducted in a series of temporary facilities. Another major problem was that by the time the navy began recruiting radar personnel, many of the best candidates had already entered the other two services, and most of the officers loaned to the RN in 1940 and 1941 were never returned to Canadian control during the course of the war.

The RCN added to the hopelessness of the personnel situation because up until 1944 radar, an untraditional branch of the service, received the left-over entry seamen after gunnery, navigation, and asdic branches had made their selection. As a result of this and the pressing demand for operators, until 1944 many were sent to sea who were thought to be inadequately trained or simply incompetent.[44] As the Captain (D), Newfoundland reported in December 1943, radar operators were 'neither familiar with their equipment nor with the correct use of radar panel controls.' He also complained that these inexperienced operators lacked 'knowledge of correct methods and rate of [radar] sweeps, and general operating procedures as required by Escort work.' They also possessed 'little comprehension of radiation patterns and their effect on side and back echoes' and 'an understanding of convoy and escort organization and station keeping.'[45] The situation had changed little six months later when NSHQ warned radar operators not to 'turn knobs unless you know what the result you will get by so doing. Turning knobs indiscriminately with the hope that this will restore the set to operations will, in general, have one result: complete failure and possible damage to the RX/C.'[46]

The shortcomings of the radar operators were matched by a dearth of radio artificers. The navy did not begin the training of R.A.s in Canada until late 1942, when operators involved in maintenance work were assigned to courses in basic radio theory at the Universities of New Brunswick and Alberta, followed by practical training at St Hyacinthe, with the whole process taking approximately one year. At first this program too was hampered by poor selection and security requirements that prevented the navy from informing the university instructors about radar. Radio artificer training was centralized at St Hyacinthe in March 1944, far too late to improve the situation by the time RX/C entered service.[47] Artificers were in such short supply in the navy that in December 1942 it was forced to borrow twenty-seven from the RCAF. Despite desperate measures such as this artificers remained in short supply for the entire war. On 22 June 1944 Prentice informed Murray that RX/C operations could undoubtedly be improved by an artificer on each escort but 'that of 40 ships at present forming the Western Escort Force, 35 have no radio mechanic.' He added that 'from available information it appears highly improbable that the situation will improve for considerable time.'[48]

The supply of trained radar officers was as meagre as that of artificers or operators. In May 1943 G.A.Worth, the director of Signals, made an effort to have the RCNR radar officers on loan to the RN returned to the signals directorate but received no support from the rest of the Naval Staff on this issue. The British continued to benefit from these now well-trained and experienced men, while limiting technical assistance and supplies to the Canadians. Part of the reason for radar-staff shortages was that until facilities were established in Canada all training had to be done in the United Kingdom, where spaces for RCN personnel were limited. In fact in certain areas, including advanced officer and artificer training, the RCN was dependent on Admiralty facilities for the entire war.[49]

Although these personnel problems certainly played an important role in the final fate of the RX/C, they were by no means by themselves fatal. It must be remembered that the RCN, despite its problems, was able to keep the 271 in service to an acceptable degree. Canadian radar was always compared unfavourably to the British in terms of time between breakdowns and serviceability. A designer must keep in mind the realistic conditions of use and technical capability, something that the navy, the council, and Research Enterprises failed to ensure with the RX/C.

NRC's chief engineer for RX/C, F.R. Park, was forced to agree, after seeing the set in operation for six days on HMCS *Portage*, that the set had severe technical problems. These included the presence of bad side echoes, insufficient or unacceptable spares, lack of a 15,000 yard linear sweep, non-reliability of operation, and lack of technical and instructional information.[50] Some of these problems were corrected in May; a service manual was published and REL's production and supply problems were finally resolved. Serious technical problems remained, however, that could not expeditiously be solved.[51]

Even on ships with trained and experienced artificers and officers who were actually able to prevent the set from breaking down, RX/C proved to be a liability. An example is the 4 May report of Electrical Lieutenant R.A. Montgomery, the group radar officer of Escort Group w4 stationed on board HMCS *St Boniface*. Although Montgomery found the set remarkably free of electrical or mechanical faults, in his opinion the RX/C, 'as presently fitted, does not operationally meet the requirement of convoy escort work.' The largest problem was once again with side lobes or false echoes. He agreed with earlier reports that the side lobes could be distinguished when one target was present but that in a convoy 'there are so many ships, each giving numerous side echoes that a complete check is impractical.' This could have tragic results because 'any one of the smaller side echoes is a possible submarine periscope or conning tower.' Other problems noted by Montgomery as needing immediate attention were the cramped frigate radar cabin that made maintenance difficult, if not impossible, the absence of monitor points to allow preventive testing, a 15,000 yard wave-guide, and an electric drive rotation for the antenna.[52]

Montgomery may well have written the RX/C's epitaph, for on 29 May the issue was discussed by both the Naval Staff and Naval Board. At a meeting of the former Worth reported that of the three major faults, the side lobes, inadequate power supply, and poor layout and chassis design from a servicing point of view, the last was the most serious since it would take from eight to twelve months to correct. By this time the set would be obsolete and because of this he asked that the thirty RX/Cs then in service be withdrawn and the order for an additional 150 be cancelled if possible.[53]

The Naval Board agreed with Worth; it ordered that the sets be taken out of service as soon as possible, and that they be replaced by the most satisfactory RN or USN type. For this purpose an officer was assigned to the American navy 'to provide liaison and up-to-date reports on the developments of radar in the United States.'[54] On 5 June the operational commands were informed by NSHQ of the Board's decision. At the same time, since the set was to stay in service on ships for up to a year, they were directed to take whatever step was necessary, short of a major redesign, to make the RX/C as efficient as possible.[55] The RX/C, however, was never an adequate set and there were few in operational areas who were sad to see its demise.

The débâcle of the Canadian naval centimetric program left RCN escorts ill-equipped for the ASW role. Blame can be divided equally among the RCN, NRC, and REL; the Admiralty was also at fault for not taking the initiative to assist the Canadian effort. It was a catastrophe that had consequences far beyond naval operations, for it would destroy the delicate fabric of NRC-RCN relations, and the RCN's involvement in Canadian radar production.

The serious consequences on operational performance caused by the failure of the radar program can be almost equalled to the difficulty the RCN had in acquiring suitable numbers of modern high-frequency direction finding sets, the device that Nelles had so carelessly dubbed the 'Air Asdic.' When we last left Naval Staff planners in the fall of 1942 they had agreed that escort groups were to have no more than one of the soon-to-be obsolete FH3 sets. It was hoped that the improved FH4 would be available in large numbers and in January 1943 staff approved the fitting of the set in all River-class destroyers and new construction frigates.[56] By June this policy was extended to Algerine minesweepers and Town and Tribal-class destroyers.[57]

With this tremendous increase in the number of ships to be fitted with FH4 (the demand grew from less than ten to over eighty in six months), consideration was given to replacing British suppliers with Canadian production at REL or Spartan Ltd. of London, Ontario. In May Commander Worth, who retained responsibilities for HF/DF, advised against Canadian FH4 production because the device was unreliable and very difficult to operate. There were, as he pointed out, twenty-eight different control knobs and even experienced HF/DF officers had difficulty using it. Instead Worth recommended that Canadian production await information on yet another improved model, the FH5, then under development in the United Kingdom.[58]

By delaying Canadian production Worth acknowledged that the RCN must continue to count on unreliable British supplies. The Admiralty refused to guarantee FH4 deliveries or the completion date of the FH5, but it still had an ample stock of the earlier FH3. It is not clear what percentage of Canadian requirements was filled in 1943 and how many of these sets were FH4s but it is certain that British supplies did not meet the RCN's demand. In February 1944 the Admiralty informed NSHQ that it would deliver only twelve more FH4s but that twenty-four FH3s could be provided to meet any immediate shortfall.[59] Frustrated by the Admiralty's supply policy, the RCN abandoned British production in favour of the American DAQ HF/DF set.

In part the decision was also technical, because the DAQ was found superior in most respects to the FH4. It was, for instance, far simpler to operate, having only six controls as opposed to the twenty-eight on the British set. It was hoped that this would in turn reduce the time needed to train HF/DF operators. On 24 April the Naval Staff approved the ordering of fifty of the American sets with deliveries to start just one month later.[60] It was a successful switch and through the rest of the war the RCN continued to rely on American production of HF/DF, a sign of the weakening ties between the RN and RCN and of Canada's increasing technical reliance on the United States.

10

One Step Behind

On 27 October 1943 C.A. Banks, the Department of Munitions and Supply representative in London, cabled NSHQ to inform them that hedgehog production in the United Kingdom was about to be terminated and to be superseded by yet another improved ahead-throwing anti-submarine mortar, the squid. Six days later, the Senior Canadian naval Officer (London) repeated Banks's warning and advised Ottawa that if did not confirm additional orders of hedgehog by 8 November further supplies would not be forthcoming.[1] The two telegrams formed the basis of Naval Staff discussions on 9 November where it was agreed that the navy still had a requirement for hedgehog. An order was placed for 105 hedgehogs, possibly the last one to be placed for the device.[2]

This incident is typical of the continuing equipment crisis following the exile to Gibraltar; the RCN was just beginning to introduce hedgehog while production for the Royal Navy was being terminated. In fact, as this incident illustrates, the RCN's problems extended to all types of equipment, for the Canadian navy was habitually one step behind the Royal Navy in terms of asdic, anti-submarine weaponry, radar and high-frequency direction finding equipment. Even in acoustical research, the Canadian effort fell behind its Allies and the RCN's performance suffered accordingly. Thus despite the exile to Gibraltar the equipment crisis remained through to the cessation of hostilities. Characteristically, most of the problems defied any quick solution.

Perhaps the best example of the continuance of the equipment crisis was the slow pace of corvette modernization. As we have seen, the events of late 1942 and early 1943 finally convinced the Naval Staff by February 1943 that, without waiting for the completion of the trial conversion on HMCS *Edmunston*, they would proceed with a total corvette modernization program. Even the most optimistic of reports, however, indicated that Maritime yards could take on only thirty corvette rebuildings in 1943, less than half of those required. The Admiralty was approached and agreed to take six RCN vessels, 'one at a time,' and arrangements were made for RN-owned, Canadian-manned corvettes to be refitted in the United States. Despite these efforts, by June 1943 only *Edmunston* and *Calgary* (the latter the first to be refitted in the United Kingdom) were complete and just seventeen others were under way.[3]

Work was slowed by the inexperienced and poorly equipped Canadian yards which took twice as long on average as the British did, and by the Admiralty's failure to live up to the even its minimal commitment of six vessels. In total, only three vessels were rebuilt in British yards. It was not until October, when the Americans agreed to refit an additional dozen corvettes, that the reconstruction program could be said to be well under way, and it was not until the summer of 1944 that the majority of the project was completed.[4]

Developments in asdic technology did not slow down to the lethargic pace of RCN planning and implementation. In February 1943 the Admiralty informed the Naval Staff that the asdic in RN Bangors, type 128, was being superseded by 128A. Type 128A was electrically rather than mechanically manipulated, and was kept on target automatically by the gyro-compasss as the ship turned. The Naval Staff quickly approved the change for Canadian Bangors, because 128A production in Canada had been under way since 1942, filling Admiralty orders to equip RN destroyers. That the RCN had to await a British policy statement before improving the ASW capabilities of its second most numerous class of escorts is a clear statement of the inability of naval headquarters to take independent action.[5]

In May 1943 the navy began considering yet another asdic development, the Q attachment added to the 144 or 145 to allow contact to be maintained at close range with deep submarines. Asdic projected a fixed beam at an angle of only 10 degrees from the horizontal, enabling deep-diving submarines to escape detection by going beneath the cone of the asdic beam. Although hedgehog had solved part of the problem, not all tactical situations were suitable for its deployment. The Q device was an extra oscillator mounted to produce a vertical, wedge-shaped beam at up to 45 degrees but 'only about 3 degrees wide on the horizontal plane.'[6] This minimized the dead zone and helped prevent U-boats from manoeuvering away from a depth-charge attack.

The DA/S received details on the Q attachment on 13 April 1943, only after British production was scheduled to commence. He reported to the Naval Staff on 5 May but did not receive sufficient information for a decision on Canadian production until 21 June, at which time 281 sets were ordered, to be mounted on corvettes, frigates, and Algerines. Only in July were the surviving River-class destroyers added to the list.[7]

Just four months after considering the Q device, the Naval Staff examined another even more radical anti-submarine technical development. This was the first completely integrated asdic weapons system which consisted of the 147B depth-determining asdic and the squid ahead-throwing anti-submarine mortar. Together they formed the most effective anti-submarine system of the Second World War.

Squid threw three or six large projectiles in a triangular pattern ahead of the ship. They were detonated by a depth fuse similar to that found on depth charges and were carefully designed to form a pattern that provided the greatest chance of a kill. Squid's partner, the 147B asdic, was the one completely new asdic set of the war. Designed to work in conjunction with 144/145Q asdic, the precise and narrow-beamed 147 followed a target and guided weaponry only after the target was located by the main set. When deployed the 147 looked like a sword attached to the hull of an escort, and it could track a target within twenty feet of its actual location. This was due to its fan-shaped beam, which could be trained up to 65 degrees on the horizontal plane and 45 degrees on the vertical. New style recorders automatically gave range and direction for steering, while the set could automatically set squid fuses and fire them. After the war it was estimated that a well-trained squid and 147 team could achieve a 50 per cent kill rate, nearly nine times that of depth charges and substantially more than that of hedgehog.[8]

The system was first tested in March 1943 and began to enter British service the following September when two new classes of escorts, the Castle-class corvettes and the Loch-class frigates, both specifically designed to carry it, began to be commissioned. It is not clear when the RCN was first informed of 147 and squid, but discussions did not commence in the Naval Staff until 6 September 1943. At that time the deputy director of Warfare and Training informed the Naval Staff that the BATM had placed an order for 500 Canadian-built 147s, and that it was necessary for the RCN to place its orders 'with the least possible delay in order to have equal status with BATM when it comes to priorities of supply, etc.' Approval was swiftly given to order 150 of the sets with the intention of eventually fitting all RCN escorts, except the aging Town-class destroyers, which had or were to mount hedgehog.[9]

While the Naval Staff had no difficulty in agreeing to adopt the highly accurate 147 set, there was great reluctance to introduce its weapons-system partner. During the course of the war only twelve Castle-class corvettes and three Loch-class frigates, all transferred from the Royal Navy in 1944, mounted squid. Many reasons for this reluctance to introduce squid were mentioned in Naval Staff meetings from late 1943 to the end of the war, but an unstated one must first be considered. The British, with a much more capable ship-building industry, were able quickly to supersede their escort program with two classes of vessels specifically designed to mount squid. River-class frigates, which were only just being commissioned into the RCN in the summer of 1943, required extensive alterations to fit the device and no such modification was attempted by the Admiralty during the course of the war. Canadian shipyards took far longer to tool up for the River-class frigate and could not accommodate the new designs. Without Admiralty guidance on conversion, it would have been against every trend established during the course of the war to take such radical independent action.[10]

On 9 November 1943, the first time squid policy was discussed by the Naval Staff, the D/DWT set a trend that would continue to the end of the war by arguing against introduction of the squid. Making a virtue out of past mistakes, he stated that the RCN should not adopt a weapons system that had not yet been proven operationally. He warned of the considerable effort that would be required to train squid operators just when hedgehog training was becoming effective. The Naval Staff agreed and deferred ordering squid in preference to additional hedgehogs.[11]

Discussions on squid continued in 1944 because of an apparent conflict between front-line units and staff planners. In late 1943 the RCN had been drawn into a new offensive against U-boats which had begun operating around the coast of Great Britain following their defeat in the mid-Atlantic in the spring. Several of the new RCN frigate-support groups were sent to the United Kingdom because the Royal Navy was having difficulty keeping some of its older escorts in service. This brought Canadian escorts into close contact with the most modern British vessels which had 144Q, 147, and squid.[12]

The support groups operating in British waters demanded squid. However, on 7 February the new DWT, Captain Ken Adams, advised against mounting the new ahead-throwing mortar, cautioning that squid mounting would involve the sacrifice of gunnery armament on River-class destroyers and frigates. Hedgehog could be mounted without any such loss of fire-power and 'will become much more valuable as experience is gained in its operations, and the necessity for squid will deteriorate.' Clearly Adams had not comprehended, or simply chose to ignore, Admiralty operational research reports that correctly predicted the superiority of the new weapons system.[13]

Later on in the year and in 1945 a new twist was added to the gunnery argument when the RCN began considering its role in the Pacific war. Gunnery was said to be far more important than a marginally more effective anti-submarine weapon.[14] In a completely new approach, staff officers opposed to squid also cited early Canadian operational research reports that indicated that the device could not possibly be introduced in time to have any effect on the course of the war. Of course by the summer of 1944 this prediction was undoubtedly correct, but it had already been nine months since the issue was first raised at the Naval Staff level.[15]

'The failure,' writes Milner in his recent study of frigate support groups, 'to appreciate the potential of the squid combination early on undoubtedly cost the RCN a number of U-boat kills in the last months of the war.'[16] The RCN was very lucky that the war ended when it did and that the Germans were unable to get a large number of their high underwater speed U-boats into service. Had the Germans been successful in their efforts, Canadian escorts would have found themselves once again trying to fight a dangerous enemy with obsolete equipment.

Most RCN escorts were, therefore, forced to do without squid because of a Naval Staff decision made in far-off Ottawa. However, even when the staff did approve the fitting of modern equipment, such as the Q device and types 147 and 144, ships were still forced to do without for a considerable amount of time. In particular, bureaucratic incompetence grealty affected asdics as the D/DWT discovered after a six-week delay from Naval Staff's approval to ordering the 147 and to informing the Department of Munitions and Supply. Measures were taken by Naval Headquarters in November 1943 to rectify the problem and to quicken the flow of paper-work through the department, including the creation of a Secretary of the Naval Board's Priority file. The deputy minister was also requested to investigate ways to expedite naval requests through other government departments.[17]

Other than problems within naval headquarters, the number one factor in delaying the introduction of new equipment into the RCN was the poor co-operation from the Royal Navy. As with radar, supplies from the United Kingdom were at best uncertain, even though Canadian demands were limited to a small number of sets required before indigenous production commenced. Type 144/145 production in Canada, for instance, only began in January 1944 and British supplies in the interim were insufficient even for newly constructed vessels. At least two frigates and three Algerines were forced initially to mount the 128D instead of 144. By 23 September 1943, a full year after the policy decision to fit the sets, only sixteen type 144s and no 145s had arrived in Canada. This meant that none of the corvettes had 145, and by 1 October only nineteen were equipped with 127D. In total British suppliers delivered only forty 144s and no 145s.[18]

British supplies of the Q device and of the 147 were even less forthcoming. In November 1943 the Naval Staff was informed that only six of each device would be provided for training purposes. The RCN would have to wait until Canadian production began in mid to late 1944.[19] Under heavy Canadian pressure the Admiralty did finally relent and agree to accept a Canadian order for seventy-three 147Bs with deliveries to commence in March 1944. By mid-August, however, when Canadian production had commenced, none of the British sets had been delivered and a month later the Admiralty requested that the RCN reduce its order to just forty-five sets. Ever agreeable, the Naval Staff complied with the Admiralty's wishes and removed corvettes from the list of ships destined to receive the 147.[20]

There were some very good reasons for the Admiralty's behaviour. To begin with, it was experiencing a number of difficulties in getting its own production of the new devices underway. There were, for instance, tremendous difficulties with the Q device's oscillator, and by mid-August 1943 only fifteen had been mounted on RN escorts.[21] In addition the Royal Navy could not be expected to be sympathetic to the mounting of 147 on vessels that were not to fit its weapons-system partner, the squid. The British certainly understood that even without squid the fitting of 147 improved anti-submarine capabilities, particularly in coastal waters where conventional asdic was more subject to reflection and distortion, but they would not release supplies while still struggling to equip escorts that were to mount the improved ahead-throwing A/S mortar.

At the same time, however, there was something more insidious about British policy in meeting Canadian asdic requirements. On 21 April 1944 Lieutenant-Commander G.M. Neale informed the DWT that RCN practices for allocating Canadian-built asdic on a pro-rata basis between the RCN, RN, and other customers was not being reciprocated. 'It is clearly evident,' he wrote, 'that the Admiralty satisfy their own demands before considering the demands of others.' In emergencies Canadian 'delivery has been adjusted to meet the requirements of the moment', but the Royal Navy, and for that matter, the American navy, insisted on maintaining a 'me first' policy. Despite this Neale recommended that the Canadian policy be continued.[22]

Poor technical liaison was, once again, another factor that hampered decision-making and delayed the implementation of production. Since NRC-RCN cooperation in asdic was minimal the navy must bear the full Canadian blame. Until the spring of 1943 the one-man technical staff in London could not hope to keep Ottawa properly informed on the latest asdic developments. Although as early as January 1943 the commander of the Canadian naval mission in London had requested a larger technical staff, it was not until September that the first anti-submarine liaison officer, Lieutenant E.G. Law, arrived. By the beginning of 1944 a general increase in technical officers in London allowed for their placement in a separate section under Commander A.R. Pressey, which enabled close co-operation with Admiralty research establishments.[23]

There were still, however, major faults in information exchange. In late 1943 Law visited Ottawa and discovered that information he had forwarded to NSHQ had not been received by the right staff officer.[24] Although this was corrected in early 1944, Lieutenant-Commander Neale noted that serious flaws in liaison procedures continued as late as May. 'Time and time again,' he wrote, 'the manufacturing of essential equipment of the highest priority has been impeded due to the lack of drawings and technical data.' Some of the fault lay with the Admiralty, which still did not produce production drawings until manufacturing had commenced in Great Britain. Neale, however, believed that the RCN's technical staff in London needed to speed-up the transmission of letters and technical reports in order to intensify liaison with research establishments and Admiralty policy makers, and to avoid being diverted to staff duties.[25]

It would seem that during the course of the summer of 1944 some of Neale's recommendations were acted upon; for the first time NSHQ began to receive information on British developments before they were on the production lines. On 20 November 1944 the Naval Staff actually approved the fitting and manufacturing of an improved 147 set, the 147F, and of a replacement for the Q attachment, called the T device, before British production had begun, and prior to Admiralty policy being established.[26] But it was too little too late; neither device saw wartime service and throughout the rest of the campaign against the U-boats RCN escorts would remain one step behind their British counterparts.

Another area where Canadian efforts faltered was in the new science of oceanography. Throughout the war there were a series of U-boat infiltrations into Canadian coastal waters. These submarines had operated with relative impunity in the Gulf of St Lawrence, the approaches to Halifax, and the waters surrounding Newfoundland. In 1942 alone twenty-two ships had been sunk in the Gulf of St Lawrence, a figure not only of military importance but also, in waters so close to home, of great political significance.[27]

The RCN was placed under considerable political pressure to stop U-boats off the coast, but most naval efforts proved futile. In part the problem was a technical one, since the waters on Canada's east coast are notorious for being difficult for the proper operation of asdic.[28] A number of factors govern the propagation of asdic-generated sound waves in sea water. 'Of these,' said an early technical report on the subject, 'the refraction of the sound beam by temperature, salinity and pressure gradients, and the reflection of the sound beam by surface and bottom' were of particular significance.[29]

Until 1943 very little was known of the underwater characteristics of ocean water and how conditions affected asdic performance. The 1942 campaign in the Gulf of St Lawrence, however, made A.R. Pressey, the director Anti-Submarine, begin negotiations in September 1942 to establish a joint organization with NRC to collect scientific data on the acoustical conditions in Canadian waters.[30] Although details are scarce, it appears that by the beginning of 1943 G.S. Field's excellent Acoustics Section at NRC had taken responsibility for conducting a basic survey of the acoustical conditions on the east coast. To perform this task NRC took delivery of six bathythermographs from the United States Navy. These devices, recently developed by the American Woods Hole Oceanographic Institute, measured water temperatures at a given depth quickly and accurately.[31]

In 1943 the first general bathythermographic (BT) survey was conducted from warships, and became the basis of all subsequent work in this field. The survey was under the direction of Lieutenant Colonel H.B. Hatchey, who in peacetime had been a leading oceanographer. The researchers were amazed by what they found, because it soon became apparent that for most of the year Canadian coastal waters were distinctly layered into zones of different temperatures. This meant that a U-boat could escape from an escort by diving into a lower layer which had quite different sound characteristics than those at the surface. With no reliable way of judging underwater conditions, an escort would likely either be unable to find the U-boat or would misinterpret the data it received.[32]

Building from this preliminary survey, in May 1944 Hatchey established the Atlantic Oceanographic Research Group (AORG) at St Andrews, New Brunswick, a joint navy-council effort under the control of G.S. Field in Ottawa.[33] In August Hatchey's team submitted its first detailed report on asdic conditions in the approaches to Halifax harbour.

This study added to the details provided by the 1943 survey. Researchers reported that water conditions around Halifax changed noticeably with the seasons. For example, in summer a negative temperature gradient existed, i.e., water temperature decreased with depth. As a result asdic beams were 'refracted sharply downward resulting in very short ranging.' In winter the situation was reversed; there was a positive temperature gradient, where temperature increased with depth. This caused upward refraction of the asdic beam, giving good distance but poor depth-ranging. Only briefly, in the spring and fall, was the sea isothermal, or mixed water of uniform temperature, which provided generally good asdic conditions.[34]

This report was followed in November by a detailed survey of asdic conditions in the late summer in the river and Gulf of St Lawrence, which examined the confusing situation when river water mixed with the waters of the Atlantic and the Arctic oceans. The report concluded that only by knowing the ranging conditions could a ship conduct a successful hunt.[35] A third report issued in the same month considered the problem of different bottom sediments and their effect on shallow water asdic conditions.[36]

The establishment of the AORG and the submission of its first reports was a positive technical accomplishment, but once again these results were not transformed effectively into operations. Even though the United States Navy had been 'issuing charts of asdic conditions for the North Atlantic, including the Canadian zone, with details of temperature gradients and likely assured ranges' as early as 1942, the first experimental operational use of BT in the RCN occurred only in the fall of 1944.[37] These early attempts against the renewed autumn 1944 U-boat assault into Canadian waters ended in failure and subsequent attempts to expand and improve BT use met with equally poor results.[38]

In part the fault lay in ineffective communications, since AORG reports were sent to NSHQ via Field at NRC and not directly to Halifax as they might have been. Admiral Murray apparently did not receive the first three reports of the St Andrews group until March 1945, eight months after the first one was submitted to Field.[39] Other problems included the belief that the successful American experience was confined to deep open water, and was therefore not applicable to coastal conditions. As Captain D.L. Raymond, the DWT, stated in January 1945, BT 'has not been used extensively for determining the distance apart of searching vessels, since it is new gear, and there is not as yet enough data on its performance to prove its value.'[40]

The failure to use BT effectively had operational impact, for it was a major factor in the failure of the RCN to sink even one U-boat west of 50 degrees and north of the Caribbean. American successes in these same waters, on the other hand, were undoubtedly due in part to the fact that they utilized the new technology earlier and to a much greater extent than the RCN. Once again the RCN's failure was caused partly by poor communication between the laboratory and the front line, even though in this case the laboratory in St Andrew's was much closer to the sea than the Ottawa River.

11

Confrontation and Dismissal

In July of 1943 Lieutenant Commander William Strange, the assistant director of Naval Information, travelled to the United Kingdom on the destroyer HMS *Duncan*. On board he met the ship's captain, Commander Peter Gretton, one of the most renowned escort-group commanders of the Battle of the Atlantic. Gretton startled Strange by telling him that RCN warships 'were almost without exception, inadequately equipped to fight submarines.' In his staff position Strange had not been privy to the inner circle at NSHQ who were at least aware of some aspect of the ongoing equipment crisis. In England, according to Strange's own testimony, he heard several prominent RN officers confirm Gretton's claims without any prompting on his part.[1]

Strange returned to Canada in early August aboard the command ship of group C 1, the destroyer HMCS *Assiniboine*, captained by Commander K.F. Adams. Adams verified the British accusations and Strange convinced him that they should co-author a report on the situation in his group. Together they composed a devastating indictment of the RCN's inability to supply ships with modern equipment.[2]

The report, submitted to Captain (D), St John's on 9 August, included as its centre-piece a direct comparison between the five Canadian and three British vessels that composed C 1. Despite the fact that they were among the vessels sent to the United Kingdom to be retrained and re-equipped in January 1943, of the Canadian ships only the destroyer *Assiniboine* was reasonably up-to-date, being equipped with the latest 271Q radar and hedgehog although it still mounted the 124 asdic and the older FH3 HF/DF set. The situation of the second Canadian destroyer, the *St Laurent*, was worse, for she had yet to mount hedgehog and HF/DF and had only 271P radar and 124 asdic. The three HMC corvettes, the

Agassiz, Sackville, and *Galt* were the worst of all. Not yet refitted, they had only the obsolete 123A asdic and 271P radar, and none had hedgehog or a gyro-compass.

The three RN vessels, the destroyer *Forester,* the frigate *Itchen,* and the corvette *Celandine,* were far better equipped. All had 271Q, hedgehog, and the latest version of the 144 or 145 asdic. *Celandine* was also one of the first ships fitted with a Q device.

Adams felt that the disparity in equipment had potentially grave consequences for the RCN. 'I have found myself,' he wrote, 'again and again forced to the conclusion that the RN ships would – in the interests of safety of the convoy and destruction of the enemy – have to form the striking units.' He believed that this situation might have already damaged morale, for 'men faced with such a realization may be expected to lose pride in their ships.'[3]

On his return to Ottawa Strange took the somewhat unorthodox step of submitting a copy of his and Adams's report and a summary of his own findings directly to Angus Macdonald's executive assistant, Mr John J. Connolly.[4] By not allowing Adams's report to pass through channels and by not submitting his evaluations of operational matters to the Naval Staff, Strange appears to have violated procedure, although in his defence he did report directly to Macdonald's office.[5] Whatever the case, it is doubtful that Strange appreciated what he had set in motion.

Strange's information reached Macdonald at a crucial time in the history of the Allied cause and the political fortunes of Mackenzie King's Liberal government. The naval minister was in Quebec for the great conference between Churchill and Roosevelt that was to set Allied strategy for the year ahead, including the invasion of France. Although the Canadians were not privy to the innermost sessions, the conference had the effect of focusing attention on the war effort.

The Liberal government had also just suffered two traumatic political disasters. The first was the provincial Liberals' crushing defeat in Ontario on 9 August, which left the party in third place behind even the socialist CCF. The second, just five days later, was the federal party's defeat in four by-elections. Undoubtedly Macdonald remembered Prime Minister King's talk to the caucus on 9 June, when he had stated that the Liberals' strongest suit in the next election would be their 'splendid record' in the war effort. 'There was only one thing,' cautioned King, 'that could undo it, which was a failure at some point on the Government's part to have anticipated the needs of the soldiers that had to be met.'[6]

Macdonald sensed the political danger should the information in Adams's and Strange's report ever be made public. The fact that a naval officer was willing to come directly to the minister's office rather than going through channels must have worried him, since it might only be a matter of time before someone leaked information to the press or to the opposition parties. On 21 August Macdonald wrote to Nelles ordering him to provide a detailed report which was to include 'the completeness of our anti-submarine equipment as compared to similar equipment on U.K. escort vessels on the North Atlantic run ... [with] particular attention given to the comparison as regards to Asdic equipment, RDF, Gyro Compasses and Hedgehogs.'[7]

Nelles's reply of 1 September was anything but satisfactory. There was no direct comparison of equipment in RCN and RN escorts. Instead his reply consisted mainly of a general summary of fitting policy in the two navies and a chart listing certain types of equipment in the RCN ships only. He included with his report several staff memoranda on the subject which were equally circumspect in dealing with Macdonald's request.[8]

The staff memorandum written by the new ACNS, W.B. Creery, must have given Macdonald some food for thought. Creery said that 'it was not possible to draw a comparison between the A/S fitted equipment in H.M. Escort Vessels and H.M.C. Escort Vessels, since details are not available at N.S.H.Q. of the actual gear that is fitted in the former.' He admitted that in general British escorts are better equipped than their Canadian counterparts and cited poor technical liaison with Admiralty and British allocations of supply as the main culprits. In conclusion, he mentioned steps then being taken to expand the technical staff in London, 'whose duty it will be to keep pace with development and to ensure that information necessary for the manufacture of equipment in Canada is forwarded at as early a date as possible, or that arrangements are made for production in U.K.'[9]

What the minister wanted, however, was a detailed and indepth comparison of advanced technology equipment fitting. Macdonald found more information in this regard in Adams's report than in all of the memoranda sent to him by Nelles. As a result Macdonald lost confidence in his chief military adviser. He decided to conduct a secret and politically controlled investigation and asked Nelles, without briefing him as to his purpose, to arrange passage to England for his assistant, John Connolly. Connolly was ordered to investigate the charges contained in the information received in August and was provided with letters of introduction by Commander Strange to the RN officers who had talked to him in July.[10]

While Connolly was in the United Kingdom, for nearly six weeks Macdonald gave no indication to Nelles that he was dissatisfied with either the CNS's answer to his questions or the navy's equipment situation. Instead Macdonald kept his own counsel until his assistant returned with information that he could use to undermine the credibility of the Naval Staff. Connolly, upon his return to Ottawa in early November, provided the evidence Macdonald was looking for.

On 10 November Connolly unleashed his first broadside by sending Nelles an anonymous letter written by an RN officer evaluating the RCN's equipment policy with particular emphasis on the modernization of existing warships. It was a damning indictment of naval headquarter's handling of equipment but showed a great ignorance of Canadian organization, procedure, and problems. After mislabelling the chief of Naval Equipment and Supply as the director of Supplies and Equipment, the writer stated that 'the modernization of Canadian corvettes is an extremely simple matter.' He added, 'It is only required for Director of Supplies and Equipment to say that a ship is to have its foc'sle extended and to be fitted with Sperry [gyro-compasses], Hedgehog, and modern A/S set.' He went on to attack the disarray in the corvette modernization schedule but failed to mention that a major cause was the Admiralty's refusal to honour its own inadequate commitments.[11]

Five days later, on 15 November, Connolly made a full report of his own findings to the Naval Staff. Connolly's visit to the United Kingdom had included lengthy interviews with RN officers in Londonderry, Liverpool, and the Admiralty, including a two-hour session with Admiral Horton. He had come away with the 'impression that [senior officers] in the RN ... are concerned about the small percentage of RCN ships which have been modernized.' Connolly argued that this caused a lack of fighting efficiency, and echoing Adams's report, that it hurt morale. Part of the reason put forward by British officers and echoed by Connolly was that the new construction program had incorrectly been given priority over the refits of existing ships.

Poor technical liaison was cited as another factor. While the RN officers approved of recent steps taken to expand the technical liaison staff in London, they called for a far larger effort. They also cited continued frustration with the slow pace of modernization, and in a measure likely aimed at causing problems for NSHQ, offered to help by modernizing two additional corvettes. This was a magnanimous gesture providing one forgets that the Admiralty had only undertaken three of the six corvette refits promised in March. Connolly did not appear to know this and was duped into believing that the Admiralty was always willing to lend a hand if only NSHQ asked when, in fact, naval headquarters had requested assistance from the British who had promised little and delivered even less. Finally Connolly reported to the Naval Staff that he had taken the opportunity to ask for a 'higher priority with Admiralty sources of supply for Radar, Asdic, Hedgehog, and Antisubmarine.'[12]

Reaction from the Naval Staff to Connolly's report and to the anonymous letter he had brought back was swift in coming. Connolly's information, as the chief of Naval Engineering and Construction, G.L. Stephens, said when it was presented, was nothing new and contained little that staff officers viewed as damning evidence. The anonymous letter, however, coming in such a provocative manner from an outside source and filled with such inaccuracies caused a great deal of consternation. Commander G.L. Griffiths, the new head of the Operations Directorate, was infuriated, calling 'anonymous commentary to be one of the basest that man can employ.'[13] G.L. Stephens felt that the letter showed 'a complete misunderstanding of the situation.'[14] Only the VCNS, Admiral Jones, thought the letter contained anything of value, preferring to 'interpret it as constructive criticism.'[15]

Griffiths, Stevens, and Jones all pointed out that the problem was at least in part caused by the Admiralty, and cited its failure to live up to commitments made in corvette modernization. A fourth staff officer, Acting Captain E. Johnstone, the chief of Naval Equipment and Supply, emphasized the long delays in getting production drawings of British designs for vital equipment to be manufactured in Canada. These drawings were usually only available to the RCN after the prototype had been built and tested at sea. This would have been acceptable if the Admiralty had kept commitments to supply Canadian requirements as an interim measure. 'Unfortunately,' he wrote, 'the Admiralty do not always live up to their bargains in this respect, and in consequence further delay in fitting HMC ships occurs.'[16]

Another theme stressed by these officers in their memoranda to Nelles was the significant strides made to improve NSHQ's handling of the equipment problem. As Commander Griffiths explained, in his six months at NSHQ the staff had been reorganized, a Commodore Superintendent had been appointed to co-ordinate ship repairs, technical-liaison personnel had been increased in both Washington and London, and arrangements had been made to modernize corvettes in the United States.[17]

What Griffith did not say, and perhaps did not know, however, was how little all these administrative improvements had affected operations.

As we have seen, in 1943 they had little impact in radar, HF/DF and asdic fitting, which were still far behind the Royal Navy. Macdonald wanted operational comparisons with the RN, not a litany of excuses or of management reorganization. The bottom line was results at sea not in Ottawa. The fact that the Naval Staff did not understand this would become increasingly apparent.

Macdonald, however, did not immediately receive copies of these memoranda and decided that the lack of response required further action on his part. He requested that Nelles provide him with all available reports pertaining to equipment. According to Connolly, he ended up scrutinizing the files himself after the minister's request got lost in the NSHQ bureaucracy.[18] Connolly found at least two additional critical reports that Macdonald had not been informed of by his CNS. These were Captain Rowland's report on equipment of 1 May 1943 and Captain R.E.S. Bidwell's memorandum on manning policy dated 22 June 1943.

Frustrated by Nelles's failure to respond and incensed by Connolly's discovery, Macdonald sent a blistering memorandum to Nelles on 20 November. He used Rowland's and Bidwell's reports, the still confidential memorandum written by Strange, and Connolly's summary of his trip to the United Kingdom to give his personal assessment of the Naval Staff's performance. He blasted Nelles for his apparent failure to keep his minister informed and was outraged that he had learned of the inadequacies of the RCN from outside sources. Macdonald was unimpressed by the naval headquarter's handling of the issues contained in the four documents, citing a 'lackadaisical attitude' and unsuitable 'energy and capacity.' He also accused senior naval officers of incorrectly emphasizing quantity over quality, which resulted in not one of the last 150 submarines sunk being attributed to Canadian forces.

Macdonald also complained bitterly about Nelles's failure to reply in detail to his inquiry in August concerning the equipment situation, in particular to the direct comparative study between RN and RCN escorts that he had specifically requested and had not received. It was unacceptable that NSHQ was incapable of conducting such a study. Although he offered no explanation of why he had waited three months to inform Nelles of his dissatisfaction, it was obvious that Macdonald waited for evidence to accumulate before he acted, to ensure that he did not base his case on the information of a handful of possibly disaffected officers. He did not ask Nelles directly for the evidence because, after the memorandum of 1 September, he did not trust him. The independent inquiries he made took considerable time to verify Adams's and Strange's accusations. It is also possible that after Connolly's information reached him, the naval minister still hoped that his CNS would offer a satisfactory explanation. It was, after all, Nelles's primary duty to advise and inform his minister. Macdonald correctly believed that he should not have to seek out the chief of Naval Staff and was angry that he had been forced to compose this memorandum.

Macdonald rejected, out of hand, the prevailing view at Naval Staff that shortfalls in equipment were inevitable 'due to the fact that new weapons are first developed in the U.K.' He stated correctly that the issue of British supply should have been settled at a political level, something made impossible by the fact that he was not properly advised. Macdonald, however took the point to a ludicrous extreme by stating that if Churchill offered no acceptable solution then 'I would have recommended that our ships be withdrawn from the North Atlantic Run.'[19]

Despite the serious charges contained in Macdonald's memorandum Nelles did not reply immediately, but instead began methodically preparing a detailed account of the Naval Staff's handling of the equipment crisis. Kept in the dark by Macdonald about his growing anger concerning equipment, Nelles clearly had neither sufficient knowledge of the daily situation nor the necessary temperament to reply quickly to a letter with such serious and wide-reaching implications.

After waiting five days, Macdonald on 25 November decided to unload another salvo from his growing stockpile of evidence by sending Nelles a copy of Adams's report of 9 August. In his covering letter the naval minister showed his growing anger, demanding to know why the report was 'not drawn to my attention, without me calling for the files personally.' He added that he considered Adams's account of great significance because it answered the question, 'Why over a period of nine months has the Canadian Navy had such comparatively little success in dealing with submarines?' As a result of all he had learned, Macdonald concluded 'that the RCN part in the first nine months of 1943 has been of relatively minor character.' All this occurred, he believed, because 'our ships had not had the equipment.' Blame must, he asserted, be placed on NSHQ, which had again displayed a lack of energy and a tremendous amount of bureaucratic red tape.[20]

The CNS apparently was shaken by this action, for in a brief letter written on 26 November he confessed to Macdonald that he had never before seen Adams's report even though it had been received at naval headquarters on 2 September, positive proof that Nelles was himself not fully informed on the equipment problem. While Nelles still did not respond in detail, at least he finally sent the memoranda written by Jones, Griffiths, Stephens, and Johnstone earlier in the month.

The next day, after learning that Macdonald was to be out of Ottawa for a week from the 28th, Nelles finally sent a hastily composed, somewhat timid and tentative reply to the minister's accusations. Nelles began by expressing bafflement over why his minister 'did not know the state of affairs practically from the time ... [he] took office.' 'Time and time again,' he added, 'at Naval Council, and afterwards at Naval Board, I have heard the Chief of Naval Engineering and Construction informing you that we could not get on with the work "because we have no plans" – no plans of forthcoming ships, no plans of Asdic modifications, no plans from the Admiralty of any kind until they are dragged out of them some six months or longer after they are in use in U.K.'

Nelles then proceeded to give Macdonald an elementary history lesson, tracing the RCN's troubles right back to its founding in 1910. He concluded the lesson by stating that 'so long as we rely on Admiralty for the initial thought, the experiments, and in many cases, production ... I think it is a physical impracticability to be completely abreast of the times.' Nelles absolved the navy of any blame in situations involving Canadian production, since the service was only in charge of setting requirements and originating demands while the Department of Munitions and Supply was responsible for manufacturing. He provided no examples of Canadian industrial difficulties, such as with the RX/C, perhaps because he knew that the navy was not completely without fault. The memo then concluded with a long summary of efforts to improve NSHQ's organization such as the creation of the positions of assistant chief of Naval Staff and director of Warfare and Training and with a detailed analysis of the methods of procuring equipment used by NSHQ.[21]

After a week's reflection, and bolstered by the support of other Naval Staff officers, Nelles wrote a far bolder memorandum in time for Macdonald's return.[22] He criticized Macdonald because 'at no time from the 1st of September to the 20th November (2 months and 20 days), did you intimate that the table given to you on the 1st of September did not contain *all the information you wanted.*' He denied that there was any 'neglect' on the part of naval headquarters and stated 'emphatically that *nothing was or ever has been intentionally withheld from you.*' He also stated that a complete comparative study of equipment in the RN and RCN was now being undertaken, but that it was a difficult task that required 'a Mahan or a Richmond.'

Nelles then summarized the main factors he believed had contributed to the equipment problems:

(a) Delays in obtaining plans and details of inventions and modifications from the Admiralty;
(b) Delays in the provision of U.K.-produced equipment contributed to at least in part by losses of equipment in the North Atlantic;
(c) Delays in Canadian production due partly to (a) above and partly to the sheer inability to produce to time in Canada (viz REL);
(d) Delays through having to assemble, in some cases, equipment from U.K., from U.S.A., and from Canada for each job modernization;
(e) Delays due to insufficient number of repair plants at which refits and modernization including installation, etc., could be made;
(f) Delays in actual installation due to lack of experienced shop repair workers;
(g) Delays due to lack of material.

Nelles concluded by dealing with each of the points raised in Macdonald's memo of 20 November. Interestingly, although he had assessed British supply priorities as being a major difficulty, he told Macdonald that he did not feel that the RCN should or could have received more equipment from the Admiralty. He believed that it was perfectly logical to give RN escorts top priority since 'that would have been the quickest method of getting equipment into action against the enemy.' As for political intervention with the British, Nelles admitted that he had not considered it. However, he added, 'At the time we considered the situation so serious that we did not think the U.K. could or would be willing to allow our ships priority.'[23]

Macdonald issued a blistering reply to both of Nelles memoranda on 10 December. He denied having been properly informed by his CNS on the shortfalls in equipment. 'I could not,' he wrote, '[being] responsible to our Parliament and people, accept in our equipment a permanent and generally prevailing inferiority to the equipment in British ships, doing the same work as ours, in the same places and under the same conditions.' He repeated his order for a detailed comparative study of equipment and told Nelles that his response that such a paper would require a Mahan or Richmond *'runs pretty close to impertinence.'* It was to the naval minister simply unacceptable that such a study was not readily available.

Macdonald placed the blame for the entire situation squarely on Nelles shoulders. 'It was,' he stated, 'the duty of the CNS to bring before me in the most forcible and graphic and explicit way possible the true position of the Canadian Navy.' More could have been done had Macdonald been properly advised. Reorganization, so lengthily examined by Nelles, was not enough, for any system 'must be in the hands of men who see the problems of the Canadian Navy as a whole and who are prepared to put first things first.'

As for naval headquarters, Macdonald believed it to be out of touch with the sea. 'We have become,' he wrote, 'in some respects, merely a headquarters, and we have got the idea that by passing files back and forth and minuting them hither and yon, we have discharged our task and taken our responsibility.' The staff, he insisted, must be responsible for the changing situation in the Battle of the Atlantic. He concluded by stating that 'no amount of argument or defence can reconcile me to an acceptance of this result with *any degree of equanimity or approval.*'[24]

From this moment on Nelles was on his way out as CNS, if for no more reason than that the relations between him and Macdonald had by now completely broken down. In early January 1944 Nelles was transferred from the post he had held since 1934 and replaced by Rear-Admiral Jones. This gives some credence to the account of Jones's complicity with Macdonald as given by Lay in his memoirs.

Nelles's fate was less than honourable. He was sent to London to serve in a new post especially created for him of Senior Canadian Flag officer (Overseas). Here Nelles was conveniently out of the way of the Ottawa press corps and given ambiguous responsibilities that duplicated the Canadian liaison structure already in place. He tried to make himself useful by advising Ottawa on the RCN's role in the invasion, and on its possible future role in the Pacific, but it soon became clear that his reports were being disregarded. In January 1945, still young at fifty-two years of age, Nelles retired from the service. Macdonald delivered his *coup de grace* by refusing to promote Nelles to the rank of Admiral until after his retirement, thereby giving him a pension only at his previous rank.[25]

Nelles must have felt stabbed in the back by Macdonald and betrayed by his former colleagues at NSHQ. No doubt Nelles was the victim of Macdonald's wrath, but was this wrath justified? How can one assess the blame? First we must consider whether the equipment crisis continued into late 1943. While both Macdonald and Nelles agreed that there was a continuing problem with the introduction of modern equipment into the RCN, Nelles argued that the situation was improving. To a certain extent he was right since, as we have seen, in 1943 all corvettes and destroyers were fitted with centimetric radar and had begun to be fitted with hedgehog and improved asdic. Yet despite Nelles's assertion that even bigger improvements lay just around the corner, the long-overdue comparative report on RN and RCN equipment tells a different story.

The only surviving copy of the report is undated but appears to have been written in the spring of 1944. The report showed that RCN escorts generally had equivalent radar to RN ships but found a continuing disparity in asdic and hedgehog. Over 37 per cent of the Canadian ships still mounted 123 asdic, as opposed to less than 18 per cent of British. This also meant that over a third of RCN corvettes still did not have gyrocompasses. While 58 per cent of the Canadian corvettes had 127 asdic (compared to 40 per cent of the British), a minuscule 3 per cent had the fully modern 145 (compared to 37 per cent of the British). Nearly nine out of ten of the British vessels had hedgehog but less then six out of ten in the Canadian navy were so fitted.[26]

Interestingly, the report also compared Canadian ships to other Allied warships including French, Norwegian and Polish ships, all of which served under direct RN command. It found that the British treated these Allied vessels on an equal footing with RN vessels, something that tends to lend credence to Macdonald's belief that political intervention with the Admiralty was necessary. For the Royal Navy was somehow able to supply Allied warships provided that their governments were willing to place their vessels under complete Admiralty control. This would imply that the supply problem was at least in part politically motivated and thus required a political solution.

The report rather cheerfully stated, however, that Canadian River-class frigates, only then entering commission in large numbers, were equivalent to their RN counterparts. While this might perhaps have been true at the time of the report, it must be remembered that the River-class was already being superseded in RN service by the third generation squid-equipped Loch-class frigates and Castle-class corvettes. None of these squid-equipped vessels were to be built in Canada, although fifteen were acquired from the Admiralty in 1944. In this regard at least, the gap in equipment was actually growing and would remain for the rest of the war.[27]

The next question we must consider is why Macdonald did not take on Nelles earlier in 1943, when the equipment situation had, at least in part, led to the British insistence on transferring the C groups out of the mid-ocean escorts at the height of the Battle of the Atlantic? Here Nelles clearly did mislead his minister, and for this alone deserved dismissal whether or not his deception was intentional, since the results were the same. This is not to say that Macdonald should be completely exonerated for his treatment of Nelles. It would seem that the naval minister was not interested in the workings of his department as long as problems did not run the risk of becoming political ones. The minutes of the Naval Board, filled with trivialities and with few indications that there were discussions of substance, show Macdonald's disinterest. It was only Strange's unusual step of going directly to the minister's office following the political defeats of August 1943 that caused Macdonald to take action. Macdonald dealt with the equipment situation too late really to affect the RCN's performance in the war, and for the wrong reasons, and used methods, such as Connolly's secretive trip, that were highly questionable.

If Nelles's dismissal was justified then so was Macdonald's, something that unquestionably would have happened had the story been leaked to the press or to the opposition. Macdonald denied the principle of ministerial responsibility and did everything he could, including whisking Nelles away to London, to hide what had happened.

The conclusion that both men must share the blame equally for the equipment crisis is further reinforced when it is considered that they had really only scratched the surface of the equipment problem. For example, Nelles had made but passing reference to problems with Canadian radar development and supply. No mention was made of the failure of the RX/U, something that Nelles was unquestionably aware of, and there is no indication that he had informed Macdonald. Nor did either man deal with the difficulties associated with the navy's relationship with the National Research Council and Research Enterprises, or with the political reasons behind the poor refit and maintenance facilities on the east coast.

It seems clear that neither man really understood the big picture. They did not, for instance, consider the failure to provide scientific advisers at Naval Staff, even though it was a long-standing British practice and the RCN established its own operational research unit in late 1943. It could also be that neither wished to tackle the issue in such a way as to bring in outside agencies such as DMS and NRC; even at its worst both men kept their dispute a family affair.

Still, the bitter fight between Macdonald and Nelles did have a salutary effect on the navy in that it did foster a desire for reform far greater than did the withdrawal of the mid-ocean escorts a year before. Many of the reforms which resulted from the quarrel, including the major expansion of the technical liaison staffs, the creation of the secretary of the Naval Board's Priority file, and the assignment of the Commodore Superintendent to coordinate ship refitting and repair, have already been discussed. On 16 November Canadian officers and British Admiralty Technical Mission members held a long meeting with a senior Admiralty scientist. Arrangements were worked out to speed transmission to Canada of data on new devices even in the pre-production and research phases of development.[28]

In February 1944 the Fighting Equipment Co-ordinating Authority was established under the Director of Warfare and Training 'responsible for maintaining accurate records of the fighting equipment fitted in H.M.C. Ships.' It was also responsible for allocating supply of new equipment 'in accordance with priorities established by Naval Staff based upon a full study of the supply situation and refitting program.' For the first time accurate planning was a possibility, and the Authority religiously maintained up-to-date information on the equipment situation in every RCN warship.[29]

The conflict also had a positive psychological effect on most senior RCN officers. By being given a chance to consider in some detail the problems in quality rather than quantity, staff and operational personnel appear to have emerged with a better idea of what was required to get the navy into shape. There were, however, some exceptions to this, the most notable of whom was the secretive director of the Signals Division, George Worth.

12

The Case of the Missing Scientists

On 14 July 1945 H.G. DeWolf, now a commodore and recently placed in charge of scientific research for the RCN, held a private meeting with C.J. Mackenzie at the National Research Council. It was a frank discussion of the serious problems that had developed during the war between the council and the navy. Mackenzie told the naval officer that he believed the difficulties centred on the 'personalities of minor officials.' The NRC President found DeWolf unusually capable and forthright, and felt that it was 'the first time that any senior officer in the RCN had ever discussed details of research and development with anybody at the Research Council.'[1]

Although Mackenzie's diary entry may well have exaggerated and oversimplified a complex experience, he was right that central to the RCN's problems was the failure to make his scientists an integral party of naval planning. We have already seen how the high hopes generated by the signing of the December 1940 agreement between NRC and the RCN were soon proven to be unfounded. The rift between the two institutions continued to grow to such a degree that, at a crucial period when scientific advice could have greatly helped the navy in its handling of radar, asdic and high-frequency direction finding, no such assistance was asked for or given.

It is ironic that this drift away from the scientists at NRC occurred when in the Royal Navy and United States Navy scientists were moving closer to the inner sanctums of naval policy-making and strategic and tactical planning. Indeed in Great Britain, P.M.S. Blackett, who had championed the new science of operational research, was influencing even the most fundamental strategic decisions concerning the Battle of the Atlantic.

Operational research was in essence the application of scientific methods of observation and analysis, particularly statistics and other mathematical means, to assess the effectiveness of operations and to offer advice on their improvement. The origins of OR can be traced to the First World War, but it was not well established in the military until well into the Second World War. Blackett introduced the Royal Navy to OR in December 1941, after perfecting its techniques with stints in the army's Anti-Aircraft Command and the RAF's Coastal Command.[2]

In his earlier work Blackett had learned that several things were required to make OR effective, including access to all relevant operational data – 'all signals, tracks, charts, combat reports, meteorological information, etc.'[3] He also insisted that OR be conducted at or near operational headquarters and that his scientists have the right to give advice to everyone, including the most senior officers. It was also considered essential that the scientist become an integral member of the staff while remaining outside the normal chain of command. As the scientist needed to be free to choose his own research topics he had to remain a civilian.

At Coastal Command operational researchers had become familiar with the anti-U-boat campaign and had already made significant contributions. Just one example was Blackett's calculation that aircraft were sighting only one-quarter of the theoretically expected number of U-boats. Blackett discovered that the poor sighting record was in part due to the fact that anti-submarine aircraft, like night bombers, were painted black. He reasoned that dark aircraft would be easily spotted during the day and suggested that they be repainted white. When this was done the ratio of submarine sightings to sorties flown increased by nearly one-third.

With Blackett's and others' skill and knowledge OR quickly gained acceptance at Derby House. Blackett was a regular member of Churchill's U-boat Committee and in late 1942 used his position and statistical analysis to support Admiralty demands that more long-range bombers be shifted from Bomber to Coastal Command. These arguments were a major factor in swaying Churchill to the Admiralty's position. As a result, in the spring of 1943 there were enough very long-range aircraft to close effectively the mid-Atlantic air gap and, thus, deny these vital waters to U-boats using wolf pack tactics.[4]

In the United States in the spring of 1943 Vannevar Bush demanded that Admiral Ernest J. King, the chief of Naval Operations, give scientists a role in the USN's 'planning of overall submarine strategy.'[5] Bush called for the USN to shift to a strategy based on offensive anti-submarine patrols from that of defensive convoy protection. King, however, who was tough as nails and obstinately single-minded, did not believe that the scientist had any place in planning and refused to consider Bush's request or any change in ASW policy.

Bush turned to Admiral Julius Furer, a leading technical officer who was co-ordinator of Naval Research and Development, to intercede on his behalf. Furer, an Annapolis classmate of King, was able to persuade him to meet with Bush. Bush, for his part, sent King a letter 'shrewdly careful in word and tone, to illuminate how the U-boat crisis had raised the general question of the proper relationship in wartime between the armed services and the nation's scientists.'[6] Bush told King that neither the scientist nor the sailor alone could plan the strategy of the technically complex and rapidly changing Battle of the Atlantic.

On 19 April 1943 Bush and King met and agreed to assign three scientists to the staff of Admiral Francis Lowe, King's assistant chief of staff in charge of anti-submarine warfare, to conduct operational research. The scientists were to have access to all relevant information and to be free to make recommendations directly to King himself.

So successful was this OR group that by the end of 1943 similar teams were working in all areas of naval warfare. In the fall of 1944 King set up the Scientific Council in the USN's Naval Staff group. The council had direct access to discuss problems or give advice to all senior USN officers including the now-converted Ernie King.[7]

As Mackenzie wrote in his diary in July 1945, the RCN had much greater difficulty than even the USN in integrating the scientist into the senior planning and decision-making bodies at Naval Staff Headquarters. We have already traced the failure of the December 1940 agreement between the council and the navy and the conflicting priorities that prevented Mackenzie from becoming an effective director of Scientific Research. Nelles and his staff, for their part, did not have the vision to understand the assistance that a scientist could have given them in making technical decisions. Mackenzie and everyone else at NRC seemed content with their status as long as they had control of most of the funding for scientific and technological research and development.

By the summer of 1943, after the exile to Gibraltar and the continuing difficulties with the procurement of modern equipment, particularly with the slow pace of the radar program, there was finally a realization at NSHQ that changes were needed. In the general reform of headquarter organization in the spring and summer of 1943 it was decided to abandon the collaborative agreement with the council and set up a naval scientific administration along the lines proposed by J.R. Millard in February 1942.

Millard, who in July 1943 was still the navy's senior liaison officer with NRC, was assigned to establish a new Directorate of Technical Research. In his memorandum of 22 July 1943 to the director of Training and the assistant chief of the Naval Staff Millard outlined the flaws in the NRC-RCN agreement. He wrote, quite incorrectly, that the arrangement with the council had never been more than a 'temporary expedient' and that as such had never been satisfactory to either party. 'The DSR [director of Scientific Research] as President of the National Research Council,' Millard commented, 'was unable to protect the interests of the RCN since the NRC is a Government institution, created for public service ... [and] carried out duties of a similar nature on behalf of the Army and RCAF.'

Millard then pointed out more accurately that Mackenzie, as the director of Scientific Research had never been more than a 'figurehead.' 'Since he was not a member of the Naval Staff group, he did not enjoy the confidence of that group, and in consequence thereof, could not be intimately familiar with the problems arising in the service.' Millard also speculated that poor technical liaison with the Admiralty was at least in part caused by it being 'cognizant of the above situation, and as a result has been rather loath to take the NRC into its confidence in the matter of providing up-to-date information and reports.' In this case Millard was stretching the point since there is no evidence that the British treated council representatives any differently from those in uniform.

Millard envisioned the DTR's office as the centre-piece of a newly independent naval, scientific, and technical research and advisory system. Millard wrote that with the creation of the new directorate, 'for the first time, a sound means for ensuring satisfactory conduct and co-ordination of research, experiments and development [was] carried out on behalf of the RCN.' The DTR was placed under the control of the director of Warfare and Training, but Millard hoped that this would only be for 'the performance of staff duties.' Otherwise it was 'considered essential that the DTR be given freedom of action in his operations as the research representative of the RCN.'

Millard then took an interesting turn, for he argued that the DTR's office be given similar freedom to scientists in the RN and USN to advise the Naval Staff but that its personnel remain in uniform. He reasoned that although an officer might feel constrained to tackle someone of higher rank, civilians would 'be much more difficult to dislodge if unsatisfactory.' This shows a misunderstanding, perhaps for strictly personal reasons, of Blackett's desire to keep the scientist out of the direct chain of command. Only by being a civilian could a scientist feel free to criticize and advise anyone, anywhere, and anytime.

Millard finally concluded his lengthy memorandum by listing seven criteria for the future conduct of the DTR including, in addition to those already mentioned, the establishment of a policy to allow for the transfer to the new directorate of scientific and technical personnel suitable for research duties, the provision of peacetime scientific personnel by enlisting RCN Volunteer Reserve officers in the RCN, and the expansion of the Halifax experimental station into a 'full scale research laboratory for the future.'[8]

What Millard envisioned, therefore, was an all-powerful scientific directorate that would control naval laboratories, outside research contracts, and be able to give technical and scientific advice to anyone up to and including the chief of Naval Staff. This concept was a direct challenge to C.J. Mackenzie's scientific empire and he was unlikely to accept the formation of the DTR with equanimity. In fact, Mackenzie would soon put obstacles in Millard's path that would shatter the naval officer's dream.

Mackenzie's first action upon learning of the formation of the DTR was to insist that his appointment as director of [Naval] Scientific Research and D.C. Rose's as deputy director be withdrawn because they were now redundant. He refused to cooperate in the navy's efforts to become scientifically self-sufficient and would not allow any Ottawa-based council staff to join the RCN's new organization. Even Rose, who since February 1941 had been in charge of liaison with the navy, ended up in October 1943 as the scientific adviser to the army chief of General Staff.[9] Mackenzie also denied direct naval access to the council's liaison office in London. As a result the RCN felt compelled to set up its own parallel structure, and to expand its technical staff in the United Kingdom in August.[10]

The NRC President, however, desired to have his own representative in the DTR's office. On 26 July he requested that Mr A.D. Turnbull of the Division of Physics and Electrical Engineering be assigned to the DTR as the council's liaison officer. NSHQ did not reply to Mackenzie's request until September, the same day that Nelles sent his fatal memorandum to Macdonald. The navy sent a carefully worded acceptance of Mackenzie's offer to abolish the post of director of Scientific Research and a rejection of his liaison proposal. NSHQ suggested 'that the establishment of a liaison office to handle the paper work and routine details connected with Naval matters be deferred for discussion at a later date.'[11] Mackenzie, who had clearly wanted something more than a paper-pushing liaison office, quietly let the matter drop.

Part of Millard's concept for an all-encompassing naval research establishment had already begun to take shape in August 1942 when staff members at the Halifax research station were offered the opportunity to enter the navy. The younger staff members felt tremendous pressure in the great naval port to wear a uniform in order to validate their participation in the war effort. The council had little objection to this since it had already allowed the establishment to become nothing more than a glorified testing station. By the summer of 1943, when the DTR took over responsibility for naval personnel at the station, the large majority were already in uniform.[12] In November Mackenzie, noting that only four boys and one girl remained on the council's payroll, requested that the station 'be taken over by the Navy and that the Research Council be relieved from all administrative contacts.' Mackenzie, however, did state that the NRC would carry on 'scientific and technical associations, which are satisfactory.' The council would also continue to send experts to Halifax for 'specific jobs, and to co-operate in every way possible.'[13] By 1 January 1944 the Halifax station had been completely taken over by the navy.[14]

Despite the formation of the DTR and the transfer of the Halifax station, the NRC remained the pre-eminent centre for Canadian naval scientific research and development for the rest of the war. The Halifax station was unable, after years of neglect by the council, to develop into a major research centre. Although there was a steady increase in the number and sophistication of projects undertaken, it proved impossible at this late date in the war to find staff capable of major original research work. Instead the station mainly confined its work to applied engineering projects related to improving and testing existing equipment, weapons, and degaussing techniques.

The DTR's office also did not live up to Millard's expectations. It was crippled from the beginning by having its director and staff in naval uniform, and it never received the direct access to the Naval Staff and Board that was so vital for effective input into planning and policy decisions. Instead Millard was forced to report to the staff through his superior at DWT. Other directorates, particularly Signals with radar and HF/DF, and the DWT with asdic, denied Millard the opportunity to advise on technical matters under their control.

All that remained for the DTR was the loosely defined responsibility of 'co-ordinating research, development and test work in the RCN ... [to provide] means for the pooling of facilities, technical data and personnel for the mutual benefit of all Directorates in the Department.' This mainly consisted of the creation of standard requisition forms issued by the DTR for the services of NRC, other government and private laboratories.[15]

As a result, Millard's staff remained small and consisted of junior officers. In April 1944, other than Millard who was an acting commander, the entire staff contained but two electrical lieutenants, two lieutenants, and three sub-lieutenants.[16] Millard tried unsuccessfully to improve the status of his office until his replacement by R.O. King in mid-1944.

King also tried with little success to upgrade the directorate's position. In late September 1944 King proposed that the DTR be retitled the Directorate of Scientific Research and Development. The new DWT, Commander D.L. Raymond, immediately approved this, but when a few weeks later King asked for permission to appoint a deputy director in charge of research and another responsible for development the suggestion was rejected. Raymond refused to approve a deputy director Research because there was insufficient research work being undertaken to justify a separate position.[17]

As early as December 1943 Millard complained of his lack of access to the Naval Staff and the restrictions on his freedom of action. To Millard's chagrin what he desired for the DTR was in fact being granted to yet another new scientific division at naval headquarters – the Directorate of Operational Research.[18]

The origins of the DOR can also be found in the tumultuous summer of 1943, and can be traced to the development of operational research in both Great Britain and the United States, along with the successful introduction of OR into the RCAF in the spring of 1942. NSHQ received both American and British OR reports and were undoubtedly aware of their utility. There were problems peculiar to the RCN and the Naval Staff which needed a Canadian organization, but the navy had to find scientists of sufficient calibre to head OR groups both at Ottawa and Halifax. In July the navy turned to the two men who were, when the special relationship with the NRC ended, the best scientific talent available: Dalhousie University physicists G.H. Henderson and J.H.L. Johnstone, still jointly in charge of the Halifax research establishment.

Johnstone was reassigned to Ottawa to form an OR directorate at NSHQ. Before he went, he and Henderson began a methodical examination of the system in both the United States and Great Britain to see just how

OR might best be utilized by the RCN.[19] Johnstone began by visiting U.S. naval operational researchers in July.[20] From 4 August to 4 September both Johnstone and Henderson were in Great Britain to assess in detail the methods and operations of Admiralty OR groups.

They returned to Canada with a plan that closely followed Blackett's prescribed methods. They insisted that Canadian OR groups have a definite advisory role and a staff of the highest scientific calibre. They also required that the heads of OR research groups 'have direct access to the Chief of Staff and Assistant Chief of Staff,' which allowed them to attend all staff meetings and to be on the distribution lists for all operational signals. In order to preserve intellectual freedom the OR staff was to serve in a civilian capacity although given nominal reserve rank to be used only when travelling overseas.

Initially, Johnstone and Henderson proposed that two OR groups be established, one commanded by Johnstone in Ottawa at NSHQ and the other under Henderson assigned to the staff of the C-in-C Canadian North-West Atlantic, Halifax. Johnstone's team was to consist of three advisory OR officers, two WRENS and a stenographer. Henderson, who was also to remain in charge of the Halifax research establishment, was to have a staff of two AORS and two WRENS. They proposed that in the near future smaller OR groups be created at St John's and on the Pacific coast.[21]

By the end of September the Naval Staff had accepted the proposal in its entirety, a quick decision perhaps indicative of changing attitudes to the role of the scientist but just as likely a typically whole-hearted acceptance of a long-established Admiralty method. Johnstone then set out on the difficult task of recruiting suitable OR officers. Like Millard, when he attempted to staff the Halifax station, Johnstone found slim pickings, and by 10 March 1944 only two researchers had joined Johnstone's group: University of Toronto physicist H.L. Walsh and Dr Andrew Mckellar of the Dominion Observatory in Victoria. Henderson was joined by B.N. Moyls, a young post-graduate student of mathematics, who had previously worked at the Halifax research station.[22]

By the end of 1944 only two other OR researchers had been recruited to the Ottawa group, one the head mathematician of a life insurance company, the other a graduate student in physics at the University of Toronto. Henderson's staff was augmented further in May by the transfer of yet another research station staff member, Dr O.M. Petrie, who also had formerly worked for the Dominion Observatory.[23]

Without an adequate operational history of the RCN for the last half of war it is impossible to assess accurately the influence of OR researchers. Certainly the large number of reports on a wide scope of topics shows that the small staffs were very active. By VE-Day the two groups had submitted thirty formal reports and made numerous informal presentations. Although many of these reports were on visits to Allied OR research groups, most offered advice on how to improve tactics, strategy and equipment.[24] Johnstone told P.M.S. Blackett in a letter written in December 1944 that he found naval officers receptive to his ideas and that they made definite use of them.[25] Undoubtedly Johnstone was a major factor in the improvement of Naval Staff decision-making on technological matters in 1944 and 1945 but had little effect on the war effort since few if any decisions made at this late date had a significant impact.

Johnstone was still establishing the OR Directorate in the fall of 1943 and there is no indication that he played any role in the dispute between Nelles and Macdonald. It is a shame that Johnstone, who had been, after all, involved in naval science and was familiar with operational requirements since February 1940, was not in Ottawa earlier as it is entirely possible that he would have brought in a viewpoint quite different from that of the staff officers and the politicians. One can only speculate on the benefits had Johnstone been transferred to NSHQ in January 1941 as proposed (see Chapter 3) and had been as free to advise the Naval Staff then as he was in late 1943. Certainly it would have meant that at least one person at NSHQ would fully have understood the scientific advantages of the new technology.

At the same time that Johnstone was getting his OR group established the final tragic sequence in the relations between the research council and the RCN was beginning. The spark that started the final battle was the failure of the RX/C in the spring of 1944 and the defensive reaction of the staff officer in charge of the project, Commander G.A. Worth.

Worth was perhaps the true black sheep of the Naval Staff. He was an empire builder second only to C.J. Mackenzie, the man who would soon become his arch-enemy. He isolated his department from the other naval technical divisions; for instance, information on radar cannot be found in general staff publications, such as the quarterly 'Summary of Naval War Effort,' which list all other technical developments. The DTR was denied any input into the naval radar program, as was any other staff officer, and he intentionally hid the truth on at least one very important occasion.

On 22 November 1943 Worth submitted his memorandum to Nelles on the equipment situation. Undoubtedly aware that the memorandum would be passed to Macdonald, it appears that Worth phrased it more to deceive the minister than to inform Nelles. This is supported by John Connolly's statement following the war that he believed Worth and Nelles were conspiring to deceive Macdonald.[26] In his report Worth spent most of his time in a carefully limited point-by-point refutation of the charges in R.E.S Bidwell's six-month-old memorandum. By doing so he avoided having to mention the failure of the RX/U or the slow pace of RX/C development, two issues not raised in Bidwell's memorandum since it was written before the former event had even occurred.

In his brief general comments Worth claimed that his directorate had close contact with the Admiralty, but a few lines later he confided, 'It is difficult to lay blame on the Admiralty for these delays [in radar and HF/DF allocation] since *we have no knowledge* of their production, factory damage or general loss of equipment through ships sinking.' Worth's only comment on RX/C, which he would regret just a few months later, claimed that the Canadian radar had 'proved' itself equivalent to 271Q, a fact not verified by any report on the set's performance.[27]

Although Worth survived the dismissal of Nelles he found himself in a precarious position indeed when, in the spring of 1944, evidence became overwhelming that RX/C was having serious operational problems. He was not the sort of man to accept blame, no matter how well deserved, and set about finding a suitable scapegoat for the project's forthcoming demise. Worth turned his attention to the most likely candidate and set out on a one-man crusade against Mackenzie and the council's continuing control of military science.

On 8 April 1944, shortly after the first reports of the problems with RX/C, Worth proposed, at a meeting of the interservice Joint Communications Subcommittee, that Mackenzie's Radar Committee be made a technical subcommittee of the JCC.[28] Worth outlined the reasons behind his actions in a memo to the new CNS, Admiral G.C. Jones, complaining that 'the Radar Committee had advised the Chiefs of Staffs on operational as well as technical problems ... which accounts for the discouraging delays in the production by NRC and REL of essential equipment for the services.' Mackenzie was held directly responsible because he 'alone has geared the progress of radar to NRC tempo when exactly the reverse of wartime requirements.'[29]

Mackenzie was successful in thwarting Worth, by convincing the chiefs of staff that his committee was still the best way to manage the radar program. He warned the service heads of potential interservice rivalries, something that had plagued radar development before his committee's formation in May 1941.[30] Privately Mackenzie expressed the belief that Worth and those supporting him knew 'nothing about RDF and the history of the thing.'[31]

Worth continued to attack Mackenzie, trying four more times between May 1944 and March 1945 to supplant the Radar Committee. He recruited some support from the air force and army signal heads, but they did not agree with the venomous nature of Worth's assaults against the council. From June 1944 Worth forbade naval officers to attend meetings of Mackenzie's committee and withdrew the navy from the Canadian radar program.[32]

Worth's assault on the Radar Committee effectively destroyed the last vestiges of senior level NRC-RCN co-operation. Mackenzie perhaps meant Worth when, to DeWolf, in July 1945, he alluded to the 'personalities of minor officials' that had crippled any effective input by the council into the navy's technical plans and policy. But if he was referring only to Worth it was a very narrow view of wartime council-navy relations, for Worth's actions were just the last nail in the coffin; the grave of the NRC-RCN agreement had been dug by both the navy and council long before Worth's machinations.

Perhaps more important than Worth's role in shattering council-navy relations was his complete abandonment of the radar program which, it must be remembered, was the largest Canadian military-industrial-scientific project of the war. Worth was responsible for finding a replacement for the RX/C and never considered a possible Canadian substitute. Instead he limited his examination to two American sets, the SG and SU, and the British type 277.

The SG, a well-tried and tested destroyer-mounted search set, and the 277, the long-awaited replacement for the type 271Q, both operated at ten-centimetre wavelength. The SU set, on the other hand, was a new design employing the recently developed three-centimetre wavelength which gave greater resolution at lower power than ten-centimetre sets. The SU, specifically intended for ASW work on the American equivalent of the frigate, the destroyer escort, had just entered production in May.

Both American sets were found more reliable than the British set, and although all were said to be equally available, the RCN was increasingly suspicious of British supply commitments. With the British set discounted for this reason, the SU was then chosen because it weighed less than half of the SG while offering at least equivalent performance. On

21 August 1944 Naval Staff approved the ordering of sixty of the American radar to replace RX/CS already mounted on frigates and Algerines.[33]

Worth and his staff, while making an excellent choice in the SU, did not consider the council-designed and -developed (and REL-produced) three-centimetre naval set – the 268 – which was probably the best Canadian radar of the entire war. The origins of this project can be traced to October 1941 when the Admiralty Signals Establishment decided to give priority to improving existing models over any radical new design. ASE scientists, aware of the technical feasibility and advantages of sets operating with a three-centimetre wavelength, made inquiries as to Canadian capabilities to undertake work in this area. By the end of the year council scientists had begun preliminary investigations into three-centimetre technology.[34]

In May 1942 Commander P.H.E. Welsy-Everard, a senior RN technical officer, and Mr C.E. Horton, the superintendent scientist at ASE, arrived in Ottawa to negotiate for the design and construction of a three-centimetre motor torpedo boat set. Typically, without any hesitation, the RCN, NRC, and REL readily accepted the project even though it was these men who advised the Naval Staff that British centimetric supplies would not be readily forthcoming for Canadian escorts. Work on the 268 commenced in the summer of 1942 after the council handed over the pre-production model of the RX/C to Research Enterprises.[35]

The route taken by the 268 through the design, development, and production phases of the project was as straight and smooth as the RX/C's was crooked and flawed. It is true that the staffs at REL and NRC had learned much from the RX/C and RX/U disasters, as well as from projects with the other two services, but the real reason behind the radically better ending to the 268 story was that 'radar scientists from ASE made visits to Canada while the work was underway to maintain efficient liaison, and ensure that the apparatus conformed to the latest naval requirements for radar equipment.'[36] These men were the first Admiralty radar specialists assigned to assist with a council radar development because never before had the RN been interested in Canadian production. What the British provided was the crucial link between the laboratory and the factory and operational conditions. These men had the knowledge to tell NRC scientists that something which might work in an Ottawa testing station would not function similarly on a small vessel being tossed about in the English Channel.

NRC completed design and development work in mid-1943, and by the end of 1944 the set was in production at REL. It soon proved to be very popular with the RN; 2,000 were on order by VE-Day and by the spring of 1945 the set was being produced at a rate of 250–300 per month. The 268 gained a reputation for reliability and continued to be used for many years after the war.[37]

The RCN's interest in the 268 was limited since the antenna for the small boat set did not provide sufficient accuracy or range for escort operations. Only eighty sets were initially ordered for MTBS and other small patrol craft although some consideration was given to mounting it on Bangors, which still relied on SW2C.

While the technical objections to mounting the 268 on escorts was valid, the RN did modify a small number of the sets with a larger antenna to overcome this problem. The set, known as the 972, was intended for use on frigates to enable them to detect the new schnorchel device beginning to make its appearance on U-boats in late 1943. The schnorchel was a narrow breathing tube that enabled submarines to travel for prolonged periods and use their diesel engines while underwater. Even the latest ten-centimetre sets proved only marginally effective at locating the small schnorchel while three-centimetre radar proved much more successful. The 972 proved itself in tests but did not enter service because the RN were receiving a sufficient number of SU-equipped, American-built destroyer escorts (known in the RN as Captain-class frigates).[38]

Although members of the Signals Directorate did hold some discussions with the council in the spring of 1944 over the broader applications for the basic 268 design, there is no evidence that the RCN considered an improved version of the set, like the 972, as a replacement for the RX/C. Either Worth had enough of Canadian radar failures, or in his efforts to blame the council for the RX/C débâcle he refused to give the radar program any validity by approving of any set tainted by C.J. Mackenzie. Whatever the reason, the RCN ended up abandoning the Canadian radar program just when it was producing sets of world-class calibre.[39]

Certainly it was the greatest of all ironies in the history of advanced technology and science in the RCN that the British, who had contributed so greatly to equipment problems, would end up as the main beneficiary of the Canadian radar program. As Mackenzie told C.D. Howe in March 1945, 'The 268 set is one which was completely developed by the National Research Council for the Royal Navy [and] represents the *best example* of perfect co-operation between the services, our research institution, and Research Enterprises Limited – as an industrial production unit.'[40]

Epilogue

Well before the cessation of hostilities the planning for the post-war naval-scientific-industrial system had commenced. The RCN had begun thinking about its peacetime composition as early as 1940 when the concept of a well-balanced peacetime fleet of cruisers, fleet destroyers, ASW vessels, and minesweepers was accepted. Later aircraft carriers and a fleet air arm were added to this list.[1] Not surprisingly there was nowhere near the same effort to examine the future naval-scientific requirements, though as J.R. Millard's memoranda in February 1942 and July 1943 indicate they were not completely ignored. In October 1945 Millard's concept of a service-controlled research team located at the Naval Research Establishment at Halifax formed the basis of the first detailed plan for post-war research submitted by Admiral Jones to the chief of the General Staff. Jones stated that the navy intended to keep thirty-five scientists and engineers on the Halifax station staff but that this number would eventually be increased to over one hundred as personnel became available. To finance the laboratory a fixed figure of 2.5 per cent of the annual naval appropriation, a minimum of $500,000, would go to research within the navy, while an additional $650,000 would be spent on joint service projects and work undertaken by outside agencies.[2]

Naval plans both for a large, well-balanced fleet and for a moderately sized and funded research program, however, were quickly scuttled. The King government, in a move reminiscent of the ill-conceived policies between wars, slashed military appropriations far more than the still politically naive Naval Staff had anticipated. Within a year of the end of the war the Halifax Naval Research Station was cut from forty to a skeletal staff of five professionals. Two of them, Professors Johnstone and Henderson, were only part-time superintendents, dividing their work day with teaching duties at Dalhousie University.[3] It should be noted that this cut in naval research mirrored similar reductions in the fleet: by September 1947, only eight warships, albeit mainly large vessels, remained in full commission.[4]

Much of the accumulated wartime scientific and technical expertise was lost as a result of these cut-backs and the return of most personnel to civilian life, but enough remained for work in a select number of specific research areas to continue. In 1947, for instance, the RCN linked together the excellent wartime bathythermographic and acoustical research with its acquired expertise in asdic production to begin work on the variable depth sonar [asdic] – sets lowered through ocean temperature gradients on a special cable. To this day Canada retains a well-deserved reputation for excellence in this field.[5]

The navy also supported the formation in 1947 of the Defence Research Board, a central co-ordinating and resource allocation body for Canadian military research. The close integration of the post-war Directorate of [Naval] Scientific Research and Development with the Naval Research Division of the DRB was held up as a model to the other services. G.S. Field, the head of the successful wartime acoustic program, became one of the few scientists to leave the council and join the Defence Department. Field held a joint appointment as deputy-director of the Defence Research Board and as the first scientific adviser to the chief of Naval Staff.[6] These actions show that the navy had now fully accepted the scientist as an integral part of the defence establishment. While this happened too late to have greatly influenced wartime operations, it is at least an indication of just how far the service had come since 1939.

As for the NRC, the bastion of wartime military science, it too had post-war plans. C.J. Mackenzie's primary goal was to build a much larger, more powerful and prestigious research council. In 1954, upon his retirement from public life, Mackenzie wrote:

Physically, in 1954 the NRC is very different from the institution that went to war fifteen years ago. Today there are eleven times more employees than in 1939 and the budget, due in part to inflation and modern sophisticated equipment, is only eleven times greater.

Things were very different after World War II. In the six years of war Canadian science and technology, led by the initiative of the NRC, had come of age. By the war's end, its standing was high amongst scientists in our Allied countries and, of most importance, was recognized at home. This in turn brought out an unanimous and enthusiastic support from both government and general public.

As Prime Minister Mackenzie King announced on 13 October 1944, in his unrestrained manner, 'Research will be extended and more liberally supported in the post-war period.'[7]

Of almost equal importance to Mackenzie was the replacement of military projects with civilian research. To the NRC president military science was only the means to an end to be dispensed with as soon as possible. Mackenzie admitted in a 1956 interview that, as early as 1943, he had become reluctant to 'undertake new long-term projects which would have little chance of being brought to a successful conclusion before the end of the war.'[8] In a submission made to the Treasury Board prior to VE-Day on peacetime council policy, Mackenzie asked that 'highest priority [be given] to the setting up of a military research organization to take over responsibility for defence research policies.'[9] Mackenzie strenuously resisted several attempts by the army and air force – there is no evidence of naval participation – for the NRC to continue to manage at least part of the military's research under a new council division. Instead Mackenzie actively encouraged the formation of the Defence Research Board.[10]

Post-war industrial strategy was mapped out by C.D. Howe's ministry, renamed in mid-1944 the Department of Reconstruction and Supply. The central theme of Howe's plan was a quick reversion to peacetime practices, and this is reflected in the rapid demobilization of industry that began before the end of 1944.[11] Asdic production was terminated as soon as practicable after the ending of the European war. By the close of 1946 Research Enterprises was broken up and sold to a variety of private concerns including Corning Glass Limited and Rogers Majestic Limited. A small radar assembly plant was retained by the government under the auspices of Canadian Arsenals Limited, a new crown corporation established to provide 'a small peacetime munition industry for research purposes and for supplying the Armed Forces.'[12] Small-scale radar manufacturing continued at this plant until the early 1960s, when production was terminated in favour of private industry.[13]

Perhaps the greatest naval-industrial change in the post-war years was the RCN's growing acceptance of equipment based on North American industrial standards. The adoption of the American SU radar and DAQ HF/DF equipment instead of Admiralty devices was much more than a transfer of technological masters, for it was a sign of the growing independence of a service that in 1939 wished to be nothing more than a squadron in the imperial battle fleet. Although British standards prevailed in planning the St Laurent class of frigates, the first Canadian-designed peacetime warship building program North American techniques were soon accepted for most aspects of ship construction and equipment supply.[14] This resulted in the navy becoming reliant on Canadian industry to supply most of its requirements; since the war virtually all new warships have been planned, built, and at least partially equipped by indigenous manufacturers.

Certainly in the immediate post-war period the country was far better prepared for modern technological and scientific warfare than in September 1939. The building up of this military-scientific-industrial complex, however, had been a painfully slow process which had matured too late to alleviate totally the equipment problems in RCN warships by the end of the war. The difficulties with equipment had commenced with the decision in 1940 to fit the first corvettes with the already obsolete 123A asdic, and continued through to the summer of 1945 when some frigates and Algerines still mounted the ineffective RX/C radar and only a handful of British-built ships had the squid anti-submarine mortar. The effects of this equipment crisis were profound both on operations and in the way Allied navies and Canadian politicians judged the RCN's performance. Obsolete equipment in RCN warships was a major consideration when the British insisted that the Canadian Mid-Ocean Escorts take their sojourn in less troubled waters during the peak of the Battle of the Atlantic. It comes as no surprise that this same issue was the central theme in Macdonald's assault on Admiral Nelles and the navy in the closing months of 1943. Such an important subject, however, has not been thoroughly explored before and many of the answers as to why this situation occurred can only now be provided.

The root of the equipment crisis was the small pre-war base of military, scientific, and industrial expertise from which the navy had to build. Added to this were the nationalistic policies of the King government which prevented the navy from integrating with the Royal Navy, as pre-war planners had anticipated, and in the RCN's unexpected participation in the Battle of the Atlantic. These factors meant that the RCN found itself involved in one of the most technically sophisticated military campaigns of the war while at the same time being forced to divorce itself from the Admiralty expertise that it had always relied upon in the past. This confusion was added to by the rapid completion of a large number of small ASW vessels, all of which needed the latest advanced electronic-detection systems and anti-submarine weaponry.

To bring order from the chaos that reigned within Naval Service

Headquarters would have required a leader with tremendous energy, drive, technical knowledge, and management skill. Unfortunately Admiral Nelles, who gave everything he had to the service, was not the man for the job. It is easier to believe that he did not fully understand the extent of the ramifications of the equipment crisis than that he intentionally misinformed Angus Macdonald, his political superior. We wait in vain for Nelles to take a stand with the British, the war Cabinet, REL, NRC, or other naval officers but he seemed content with plodding, sometimes ill-considered, steps to improve the equipment situation. When he was finally forced out by Macdonald in January 1944 the navy was still a generation behind in fitting most new technologies, and was about to face the complete collapse of the centimetric radar program, the largest naval-scientific-industrial project of the war.

Macdonald for his part was no better a leader. Interested more in politics than in ensuring the efficient operation of his department, he made little effort to learn the details of naval administration. He either did not know or did not care about the serious problems with equipment, even though the exile of the MOEF groups must have sent him a crystal-clear signal that all was not well within the navy. When he finally did act in late 1943 he was motivated by outside political considerations and he delayed the reckoning with his chief of Naval Staff until it was too late to have any serious impact on getting up-to-date equipment into service.

No other politicians took a genuine interest in the navy's war and all were content, like Macdonald, to leave the management of operations completely in the hands of sailors. C.D. Howe did run a highly efficient department but his extreme loyalty to friends, in particular Eric Phillips at Research Enterprises and Mackenzie, precluded quick solutions to nagging industrial problems. Howe's dedication to the war effort ended when it conflicted with political requirements. Certainly the failure to invest in east coast shipyards is a classic example of political expediency taking precedence over military necessity.

With such leadership it is easy to see why the Naval Staff, board, and council were, through most of the war, indecisive in establishing equipment policy. The Naval Staff procrastinated so much that often a decision was delayed until pressure was brought to bear from operational commands or until Admiralty directives or expert opinion became available. Of course there were factors other than Nelles's and Macdonald's leadership. Although there were competent senior officers, such as Reid, Pressey, and Argus, there were many others with more dubious qualifications, like Worth and Nelles. No one on staff or in any other senior position within the service, however, had the technical knowledge and foresight to steer the navy along the proper path, or to develop such things as effective communications with front-line units or an accurate system to keep track of the actual equipment situation. Conflicting interests within the professional officer corps concerning the primacy of the ASW role were a major problem. It took over six months, for instance, to agree to replace the gunnery control gear on the River-class destroyers with the centimetric radar vital for convoy defence, because some officers feared that this would end the utility of these vessels in the fleet support role.

The British added to the RCN's difficulties because of their insistence that Canadian vessels be given a lower supply priority than RN or other Allied escorts. We can sympathize with the Admiralty to a certain extent because there undoubtedly were equipment and other material shortages, but we suspect that this policy was also motivated by an unfair reaction to the nationalistic policies of the King government and, by late 1942, to the RCN itself. British supply policy must be seen in sharp contrast to consistent RCN generosity which allowed the Admiralty to be treated as an equal in the allocation of Canadian manufactured goods.

Technical liaison with the British was also a problem; fault lay on both sides of the Atlantic. Mackenzie's delay in establishing a permanent office in London and the RCN's failure to provide adequate numbers of technical officers to its overseas mission hampered equipment planning, development, and production out of all proportion to the effort required to make the system function. It is true that the confusing and competitive research organization in Britain obstructed easy information exchange. There was also a continual British misunderstanding of the Canadian need for the prompt delivery of detailed specifications and drawings of new equipment.

When Anglo-Canadian co-operation occurred the results were impressive, as asdic production and the 268 radar program illustrate. We can only wonder what would have happened if both sides had taken early and prompt action to evaluate each other's strengths and weaknesses and to form an effectively co-ordinated effort.

Throughout this discussion one issue keeps recurring as a major factor in the equipment crisis – the complete failure to integrate scientists with sailors. American and British historians have long understood that scientists played a key role in the successful campaign to defeat the U-boat assault on the ocean trade routes. Writers on the history of the NRC such as Eggleston and Middleton have incorrectly stated that this was also the case in Canada. In truth the RCN and NRC failed to work together effectively in several key areas, including radar development and senior level planning and management, although in other fields, such as asdic and acoustical research, co-operation had proved satisfactory.

The difficulties stemmed from two fundamentally irreconcilable problems. One was the different institutional goals of the navy and the council. Mackenzie saw as his first priority the fulfilment of the council's pre-war dream of becoming an internationally recognized research centre. He did not see the future of the NRC as resting with military research and did not give satisfactory attention to working out the organizational details that would have led to the more effective utilization of scientific resources by the RCN. Mackenzie and other NRC staff, such as Wallace and John Henderson, did not understand what was required of them to produce equipment fit for production at Research Enterprises that would stand up to the rigours of operational service at sea. As a result, among other mistakes, the council took the ill-advised step of pursuing an independent centimetric radar program rather than adapting reliable British technology to Canadian industrial standards, a skill in which the council had acquired recognized expertise.

The navy also did not provide the leadership necessary to pursue these goals. It did not place scientists in the senior levels of Naval Staff Headquarters and when problems arose it took the easy way out and blamed the NRC. The navy was suspicious of council intentions because it could not control it. As a result the navy attempted to develop its own scientific and technical organization which could not become fully effective during the war.

While the United Kingdom and the United States were no strangers to petty jealousies and institutional conflict, they avoided many such problems because scientific research was more closely integrated into their navies. What both these countries had which Canada lacked was a pre-war base of military science from which to build. No Canadian scientist or sailor had the inspirational genius of a Bush, Goodeve, Blackett, or Tizard. Throughout the war both the NRC and the RCN were hampered by this absence of men and women who understood the special requirements of both the warship and the laboratory. Without this crucial link, weapons systems failed in service, and neither the council nor the navy could develop effective co-operation. Since Canada was forced to supply much of its own naval requirements for modern equipment, the results of this failure was an accentuation of the equipment crisis which helped make the RCN's escorts less effective than their Allied counterparts.

Notes

INTRODUCTION

1 Vannevar Bush in Irvin Stewart, *Organizing Sciencific Research for War*, ii
2 Winston Churchill as quoted in Terry Hughes and John Costello, *The Battle of the Atlantic*, 11
3 It is not practical here to examine the extensive American and British literature on science in the Second World War. For details on the American historiography see the bibliographic essay in Daniel Kevles, *The Physicists*; and Carrol W. Purcell, Jr, 'Science and Technology in the Twentieth Century,' in R. Higham, ed., *A Guide to Sources of United States Military History* (Hamden: Archon Books 1975), 269–91, and the Supplement (1981), 69–71. At the moment no adequate guide of British sources is available but it is understood that Higham's forthcoming update of *A Guide to Sources in British Military History* will contain a chapter on science and high technology.

CHAPTER ONE From Nothing but Possibilities

1 G.N. Tucker, *The Naval Service of Canada*, 1: 122–211; D. Brodeur, 'L.P. Brodeur and the Origins of the Royal Canadian Navy,' in J.A. Boutilier, ed, *The RCN in Retrospect*, 13–32
2 Tucker, *Naval Service*, 1: 212–383
3 James Eayrs, *In Defence of Canada*,1: 165–72; Tucker, *Naval Service*, 1: 304–20
4 Comm. A.R. Pressey, 'Memorandum on the Prewar Situation,' 12 June 1940, Directorate of History (DHist), National Defence Headquarters, Ottawa, 8/1520/1000–973, vol. 2; Tucker, *Naval Service*, 1: 333–5; Eayrs, *In Defence of Canada*, 1: 270–2

5 Eayrs, *In Defence of Canada*, 1: 260
6 Ibid., 272–83
7 Tucker, *Naval Service* 1: 356–7, 362–9
8 Richard H. Leir, ' "Big Ship Time": The Formative Years of RCN Officers Serving in RN Capitol Ships,' in *RCN in Retrospect*, 74–9
9 Tucker, *Naval Service*, 2: 7
10 H.N. Lay, *Memoirs of a Mariner*, 87; Tucker, *Naval Service*, 1: 365–7; 2: 418–19
11 Tucker, *Naval Service*, 2: 418
12 Ibid., 272–83
13 Interview with D.C. Rose, National Research Council of Canada (NRC) Oral History Series, NRC
14 T. Hughes and J. Costello, *The Battle of the Atlantic*, 28. For information on RN asdic research between the wars see Willem Hackmann, *Seek and Strike*, 97–228.
15 Pressey, 'Memorandum on the Prewar Situation,' 12 June 1940, DHist 8/1520/1000-973, vol. 2
16 Leir, ' "Big Ship Time," ' 74–9; Lay, *Memoirs of a Mariner*, 8–11
17 Marc Milner, *North Atlantic Run*, 8–11
18 Brand to Rear Adm. J.H. Godfrey, Admiralty Director of Naval Intelligence, 25 July 1939, Public Archives, Canada (PAC), RG 24, 8086, NS 1272-24 vol. 1
19 For a history of the Canadian physics community see Yves Gingras, 'Les physiciens canadiens: genealogie d'un groupe social, 1850–1950.'
20 Wilfrid Eggleston, *National Research in Canada*, 1–3
21 Ibid., 24
22 Ibid., 27–54; Mel Thistle, *The Inner Ring*, 45–328
23 Thistle, *Ring*, 305–7
24 W.E.K. Middleton, *Physics at the National Research Council of Canada, 1929–1952*, 83
25 'NRC Annual Report,' 1930–1, 89
26 W.E.K. Middleton, *Radar Development in Canada: The Radio Branch of the National Research Council of Canada, 1939–1946*, 1
27 H.M. Tory to Hon. James Malcolm, 4 April 1929, in Thistle, *Ring*, 324
28 Thistle, *Ring*, 346
29 Middleton, *Physics*, 45, 48–50
30 Eggleston, *NRC*, 90–1
31 For details of McNaughton's career up to 1939 see John Swettenham, *McNaughton*, vol. 1.
32 Eggleston, *NRC*, 155–6; Middleton, *Physics*, 64–6
33 Middleton, *Radar*, 59–60
34 Swettenham, *McNaughton*, 209–24

35 Eggleston, *NRC*, 145; Middleton, *Radar*, 2
36 Middleton, *Physics*, 52–6
37 'War History of the Associate Committee of the National Research Council,'
   100
38 NRC Annual Report, 1938
39 Ibid.
40 Wilfrid Eggleston, *Scientists at War*, 29
41 For a detailed study of early British radar development see R.W. Clark,
   Tizard.
42 F.V. Heakes, 'Liaison Notes,' 44, Heakes Papers, DHist, 77/51
43 For an example of British security paranoia concerning radar see Heakes,
   'Liaison Notes,' 121–5.
44 Henderson to McNaughton, 6 April 1939, 19 April 1939, NRC File S45-2-
   16, vol. 1; Henderson and Heakes, 'Electrical Methods of Fire Control in
   Great Britain,' April 1939, NRC, PRA Report 6; Henderson, 'Electrical
   Methods of Fire Control in Great Britain,' Part 2, June 1939, NRC, PRA
   Report 7
45 Henderson to McNaughton, 6 April 1939, 19 April 1939, NRC File S45-2-
   16
46 McNaughton to Henderson, 19 July 1939, NRC File S45-2-16
47 'Co-operation of NRC in RDF Programme of the Defence Department,' NRC
   File, S45-2-16, vol. 1
48 John Henderson, 'Progress Report for the Period June 1939 to 1 January
   1942,' 1–2
49 Michael Bliss, 'A Canadian Businessman and War,' in *War and Society in
   North America*, 20–36; Michael Bliss, 'War Business as Usual,' in *Mobilization
   for Total War*, 23–42
50 H.G.J. Aitkens, *American Capital and Canadian Resources*
51 J.N. Kennedy, *History of the Department of Munitions and Supply*, 1: 76–7
52 H. Duncan Hall, *North American Supply*, 3–10, 28–33; Kennedy, *A History*,
   1: 196; C.P. Stacey, *Arms, Men and Government*, 101–6
53 'History of the British Admiralty Technical Mission,' 110
54 Stacey, *Arms, Men and Government*, 69, 104
55 As quoted in Stacey, *Arms, Men and Government*, 101
56 Kennedy, *A History*, 1: 4–5

CHAPTER TWO Science Found

1 For a detailed account of a war at sea during this period see S.W. Roskill,
   The War at Sea, 1939–1945, vol. 1
2 These were the chief of Naval Staff (CNS), the deputy chief of Naval Staff

(DCNS), the director of Naval Intelligence (DNI), the director of Naval Engineering (DNE), the director of Plans Division (DPD), the director of Operations Division (DOD), and the director of Naval Stores (DNS).

3 'Miscellaneous Papers on the History of the Royal Canadian Navy, 1939–1945,' DHist 84/115, section v, 1–2, Section vi, 1–3

4 C.P. Stacey, *Arms, Men and Government*, 309

5 Ibid., 309; Marc Milner, *North Atlantic Run*, 16–26

6 Houghton to McNaughton, 5 Oct. 1939, Henderson Papers, PAC

7 Interview with William Bennett, 23 April 1987. For a biographical sketch of Mackenzie see Mel Thistle, ed., *The Mackenzie-McNaughton Wartime Letters*, xiv–xviii.

8 The chief of the Bureau of Ordnance (USN) to the chief of Naval Operations (USN), n.d. but 1940–2; see also the secretary of the Admiralty, 'Counter-measures to the Magnetic Mine,' 27 May 1940, Degaussing History Part 1, 1940–1, General, DHist; see also Peter Elliott. *Allied Minesweeping in World War Two*, 31–4; Roskill, *The War at Sea*, 1: 98–102

9 CBO to CNO, n.d.; see also 'Countermeasures to the Magnetic Mine,' 27 May 1940, Degaussing History Part 1, 1940–1, General, DHist

10 Middleton, *Physics at the National Research Council of Canada, 1939–1946*, 92; COAC to Naval Secretary, 1 Dec. 1940, Degaussing History, Part 1, 1940–1 General, DHist

11 Mackenzie to McNaughton, 1 March 1940, in Thistle, *Mackenzie-McNaughton*, 21

12 Mackenzie to McNaughton, 11 March 1940, in Thistle, *Mackenzie-McNaughton*, 25

13 Eggleston, *National Research in Canada*, 154

14 Elliott, *Minesweeping*, 33; COAC to NSHQ, 28 March 1940; Ballard to Captain J.F. Bell, 6 June 1940; NSHQ to COAC, 1 June 1940; PAC, RG 24, 3955, NS C1038-16-1, vol. 1

15 Ernest Forbes, 'Consolidating Disparity: The Maritimes and the Indus-trialization of Canada during the Second World War'

16 Naval Staff Minutes 12, 16 April 1940, DHist

17 Naval Staff Minutes 19, 3 June 1940, DHist

18 Naval Staff Minutes 22, 25 June 1940, DHist

19 H. Duncan Hall, *North American Supply*, 14–18; R. Bothwell and W. Kilbourne, *C.D. Howe*, 124

20 Naval Staff Minutes 19, 13 June 1940

21 Mackenzie to McNaughton, 17 June 1940, in Thistle, *Mackenzie-McNaughton*, 40

22 Summary of Naval War Effort, 1 Oct to 31 Dec 1940, DHist

23 Willem Hackmann, *Seek and Strike*, 107–8, 118–19, 169–70, 260
24 'History of the British Admiralty Technical Mission,' 1–2
25 Pew to DSD Bath and Capt. A/S, 21 July 1940, Public Records Office (PRO), CAB 115, vol. 166
26 Summary of Naval War Effort, 1 Oct. to 31 Dec. 1940, DHist
27 Memo from CNS to A.B. Coulter, DNS, 6 Dec. 1940, PAC, RG 24, 4035, NS 1070-3-101
28 Ibid.
29 D.G. Whittle, Chief Treasury Officer Army and Navy Service, 'Accounting Regulations and Instruments No. 219,' 30 Jan. 1941, PAC, RG 24, 4035, NS 1074-3-1, vol. 1; 'Memorandum on the Equipment Division for the Acting Deputy Minister of Naval Service,' 25 October 1940, PAC, RG 24, 4035, NS 1070-3-1, vol. 1
30 Summary of Naval War Effort, 1 Oct. to 31 Dec. 1940, DHist
31 J.N. Kennedy, *A History of the Department of Munitions and Supply*, vol. 1, 4–6
32 R.P. Brown to acting deputy minister, 9 Jan. 1941, PAC, RG 24, 4035, NS 1074-3-1, vol. 1
33 Ibid.; 'Memorandum on the Equipment Division for the Acting Deputy Minister,' 25 Oct. 1940, PAC, RG 24, 4035, NS 1070-3-1, vol. 1
34 'History BATM,' 101; Coulter to CNS, 6 Dec. 1940, PAC, RG 24, 4035, NS 1074-3-1, vol. 1
35 Naval Staff Minutes 47, 19 March 1941, DHist
36 Angus to acting director Naval Stores, PAC, RG 24, 4035, NS 1074-3-1, vol. 1
37 'RDF Work in Canada,' 5 June 1940, NRC File S45-7-16, vol. 2
38 G.H. Henderson, 'Report to the President of NRC at Ottawa on RDF,' 26 July 1940, NRC S45-2-16, vol. 2
39 A.V. Hill, 'Report,' 18 June 1940, National Archives, Waltham (NAW), Radiation Laboratory Records, Box 49
40 'War History of the Radio Branch,' 89
41 John Henderson, 'Progress Report for the Period June 1939 to 1 Jan. 1942,' 17; 'Minutes of the Meeting of the Radio Research Committee (Section III),' 5 June 1940, NRC S45-2-16, vol. 2
42 Wallace to Mackenzie, 'Memorandum Re: The RDF Installations at Halifax as of 29 July,' 29 July 1940, NRC File B45-2-32, vol. 2
43 G.H. Henderson, 'Report to the President of NRC,' 26 July 1940
44 Marc Milner, *North Atlantic Run*, 22
45 E.F. Burton, *Canadian Naval Radar Officers*
46 'War History of the Radio Branch,' 5
47 R.W. Clark, *Tizard*, 248–71; 'War History,' 6, 89

48 Minutes of the Electrical Methods of Fire Control Subcommittee, 9 Jan. 1941, PAC, RG 24, 8086, NS 1272-24, vol. 1

49 McKinley to Howe, 1 Jan. 1941, Howe to Beaverbrook, 2 Jan. 1941, both in NRC S45-2-16, vol. 4; Beaverbrook to Howe, 2 Jan. 1941, NRC S45-2-16, vol. 5

50 Chief of General Staff to chief of Naval Staff and chief of Air Staff, 12 July 1940, PAC, RG 24, 8086, NS 1272-24, vol. 1

51 W.T. Rowley, 'Memorandum to DPD,' 16 July 1940, PAC, RG 24, 8080, NS 1272-24, vol. 1

52 'Minutes of the Meeting of the Interservice Committee on Research Enterprises Limited,' 21, Henderson Papers; Professor E.L. Bowles, 'Report on Canadian Government Defence Agencies NRC and REL,' 6–8 Aug. 1941, PAC, Howe Papers, vol. 43, file 59-85-7(2)

53 Mackenzie Diary, 31 Oct. 1940, PAC

54 Maclachlan to Harrison Smith (President, Imperial Oil), 22 Nov. 1940, Mackenzie to Maclachlan, 25 Nov. 1940; Lt Col W.S. Fenton to Maclachlan, 6 Dec. 1940, Smith to Maclachlan, 18 Dec. 1940, all in PAC, RG 24, 5590, NS 10-39-6

55 Mackenzie Diary, 26 Nov. 1940, PAC

56 Ibid., 26 Dec. 1940, PAC

57 Ibid., 30 Dec. 1940, PAC

58 Maclachlan to Mackenzie, 31 Dec. 1940, RG 24, 5590, NS 10-39-6

59 Mackenzie Diary, 26 Dec. 1940, PAC

60 Ibid., 22 Jan. 1941, PAC; Mackenzie to Maclachlan, 23 Jan. 1941, Maclachlan to Nelles, 24 Jan. 1941, DCNS to Maclachlan, 29 Jan. 1941, Mackenzie to Boyle, Henderson, etc., 15 Feb. 1941, all in PAC, RG 24, 5590, NS 10-39-6

61 Maclachlan to Mackenzie, 19 Feb. 1941, PAC, RG 24, 5590, NS 10-39-6

62 Cossette to COAC and COPC, 17 Jan. 1941, PAC, RG 24, 5590, NS 10-39-6

CHAPTER THREE The Discovery of Radar

1 For a more detailed discussion of the problems of NEF in 1941 see Marc Milner, *North Atlantic Run*, 65–70.

2 Minutes of the Electrical Methods of Fire Control Subcommittee, 9 Jan. 1941, PAC, RG 24, 8086, NS 1272-24, vol. 1

3 Norman Friedman, *Naval Radar*, 196

4 Ibid.

5 Naval Staff Minutes 42, 14 Jan. 1941, DHist

6 Henderson to Boyle 18 Jan. 1941, NRC B45-2-33, vol. 1

7 Ibid.
8 Henderson to Boyle, 18 Jan. 1941, NRC B45-2-33, vol. 1
9 Marginal note of DPD to DPD on Houghton to DOD, DCNS, CNS, 28 Jan. 1941, PAC, RG 24, 8086, NS 1272-24, vol. 1
10 Marginal note signed Reid, DCNS 29 Jan. 1941, on Houghton to DOD, DCNS, CNS, 28 Jan. 1941, PAC, RG 24, 8086, NS 1272-24, vol. 1. Emphasis added
11 Pressey to DPD, 5 Feb. 1941, PAC, RG 24, 8086, NS 1272-24, vol. 1
12 Admiralty to NSHQ, 18 Feb. 1941, PAC, RG 24, 8086, NS 1272-24, vol. 1
13 Pressey to DPD, 5 Feb. 1941, Pressey to DCNS 22 Feb. 1941, Cossette to Rose, 26 Feb. 1941, all in PAC, RG 24, 8086, NS 1272-24, vol. 1
14 Reid to Pressey, 21 Feb. 1941, PAC, RG 24, 8086, NS 1272-24, vol. 1
15 See Chapter 6
16 Naval Staff Minutes 46, 11 March 1941, DHist
17 Ibid.
18 Pressey, DA/S to DCNS, 13 March 1941, PAC, RG 24, 3981, NS 1052-1-1, vol. 1
19 Ibid.
20 Pressey to Shenstone, 17 March 1941, PAC, RG 24, 4041, NS 1074-6-1
21 Conversation with Dr Marc Milner 10 Nov. 1985; marginal note on letter, R.T. Lawson to G.H. Henderson, 13 Aug. 1940, Degaussing History Pt 1, 1940–41, General, DHist
22 Mackenzie Diary, 21 July 1941, PAC. See also interview with F.R. Park, 10 July 1984.
23 Mackenzie Diary, 20 May 1942, PAC; Conversation with Dr Marc Milner, 10 Nov. 1985
24 Mackenzie Diary, 10 March 1941, PAC
25 Interview with F.R. Park, 10 July 1984
26 McKinley to Henderson, 18 March 1941, NRC S45-2-16, vol. 5
27 Henderson to Boyle, 22 March 1941, NRC B45-2-33, vol. 1; Naval Staff Minutes 47, 19 March 1941, DHist
28 Henderson to Boyle 22 March 1941, NRC S45-2-16, vol. 5
29 'Awarding of Contract for 100 Sets to REL,' meeting of the Privy Council, 17 April 1941, DHist 81/520, 1000-198, vol. 1
30 Naval Secretary to President NRC, 24 April 1941, DHist, 81/520, 1000-198, vol. 1
31 A-scope form was the presentation of information on a simple cathode-ray tube display which gave indication of distance and not direction. Direction was provided by determining which way the antenna was pointed when the signal given by the target was the strongest. The more familiar

Planned Position Indicator display shows the transmitting ship as being in the centre of a 360 degree picture which constantly changes as the antenna sweeps on its search pattern.

32 NRC to A.H.R. Smyth, 6 June 1941, NRC B45-2-30, vol. 2

33 War History of the Radio Branch, 21; Summary of Naval War Effort, 1 April to 30 June 1941, DHist, NS 1000-5-8

34 As quoted in E.K. Middleton, *Radar Development in Canada*, 48–9

35 Ibid.

36 Naval Staff Minutes 50, 20 May 1941, DHist

37 Summary of Naval War Effort, 1 April 1941 to 30 June 1941, DHist, NS 1000-5-8

38 Summary of Naval War Effort, 1 July 1941 to 30 Sept. 1941, DHist, NS 1000-5-8

39 Summary of Naval War Effort, 1 Oct. 1941, to 31 Dec. 1941, DHist, NS 1000-5-8; Cossette for Argyle to Henderson, 4 Oct. 1941, PAC, RG 24, 3981, NS 1052-1-1

40 Summary of Naval War Effort, 1 July 1941 to 30 Sept. 1941, DHist, NS 1000-5-8

41 Summary of Naval War Effort, 1 April 1941 to 30 June 1941, DHist, NS 1000-5-8

42 'Defects in Co-axial Transmission Line Type sw–1C,' Captain (D), New-foundland to Naval Secretary, 29 Jan. 1942, DHist, NSHQ file 7401-430-7

43 Summary of Naval War Effort, 1 Oct. 1941 to 31 Dec. 1941, DHist, NS 1000-5-8

44 Third Meeting of the RDF Committee, 21 July 1941, Henderson Papers; Mackenzie to Houghton, 23 July 1941, PAC, RG 24, 8086, NS 1072-24, vol. 1; Argyle to Wallace, 1 Nov. 1941, PAC, RG 24, 8086, NS 1072-2, vol. 2

45 First Meeting of the RDF Committee, 4 June 1941, Henderson Papers

46 Summary of Naval War Effort, 1 Oct. 1941 to 31 Dec. 1941, DHist, NS 1000-5-8

47 Unpublished monograph by David Zimmerman, 'Equipment in the RCN, 1939–43,' summer 1983

48 Captain (D), Newfoundland to secretary Naval Board, 23 Jan. 1942, NSHQ file NSC 7401-430-7

49 Captain (D), Newfoundland to the Naval secretary, 23 Jan. 1942, NSHQ file NSC 7401-430-7

50 Smyth to secretary Navy Board, 14 July 1942. NSHQ file NSC 7401-430-7; 'RDF Type sw1/2C Failure of Type 878A Valve,' 17 July 1942, NSHQ file NSC 7401-430-7

51 Argyle for Cossette to Radio Branch, PAC, RG 77, 173, file 45-2-52, vol. 1

52 Argyle to Hackbusch, 16 Feb. 1942, PAC, RG 77, 177, file 45-2-52, vol. 1

53 Milner, *North Atlantic Run*, 136–40
54 Ibid., 79–80
55 C-in-C Western Approaches to NSHQ, 25 Sept. 1943, PAC, RG 24, 11,579, NSD 019-1-3; Murray to C-in-C Western Approaches and secretary Navy Board, 30 Sept. 1943, PAC, RG 24, 11,580, NSD 019-1-6; FONF to NSHQ, Sept. 1943, PAC, RG 24, 11,580, NSD 019-1-6; secretary Naval Board to C-in-C Western Approaches, PAC, RG 24, 11,580, NSD 019–1–6
56 Prentice, Captain (D), Halifax to C-in-C Area Combined Headquarters, 29 Oct. 1943, PAC, RG 24, 11,580, NSD 019-1-6

CHAPTER FOUR Nuts and Bolts – Organization

1 Cossette to the Chairman, Electrical Methods of Fire Control Subcommittee, 12 June 1941, PAC, RG 24, 3981, NS 1052-1-1, vol. 1; Gilbert Tucker, *The Naval Service of Canada*, 2: 418
2 Tucker, *Naval Service*, 2: 430
3 Ibid., 420
4 Ibid., 419
5 'Miscellaneous Papers on the History of the Royal Canadian Navy, 1939–1945,' Part VI, 'The Naval Staff,' 4, Part VII, 'The Naval Board,' 4, Naval Historical Section, Naval HQ, Ottawa, Aug. 1960, unpublished monograph, DHIST 84/115
6 'Miscellaneous Papers,' Part VII, 'The Naval Board 1942–45,' 4, DHist 84/115
7 As quoted in 'Miscellaneous Papers,' Part VI, 'The Naval Staff,' 4. Emphasis added
8 Tucker, *Naval Service*, 2: 422
9 'Miscellaneous Papers,' Part VII, 'Navy Board,' 6
10 'Miscellaneous Papers,' 'Naval Staff,' 5; Various Naval Board and Staff Minutes, DHist
11 Hibbard to VCNS, 8 April 1941, PAC, RG 24, 3982, NS 1052-1-5
12 Conversation with Dr Marc Milner, 10 Nov. 1985
13 Tucker, *Naval Service*, 2: 421; Pressey to deputy secretary of Supply, 18 June 1943, PAC, RG 24, 4035, NSS 1070-3-1, vol. 1
14 Particulars of Canadian War Vessels, Half-Yearly Returns, Feb. 1942, DHist
15 NSHQ to all HMCS Ships, 4 Nov. 1942, PAC, RG 24, 3995, NS 1057-1-26
16 C.Supt to C-in-C CNA, NSHQ, FONF, 12 Feb. 1944, PAC RG 24, 11,747, HQ C5392
17 Jones (COAC) to Naval secretary, PAC, RG 24, 3982, NS 1052-1-5, vol. 1. Emphasis added
18 'Subject: RDF Policy,' 16 Dec. 1941, PAC, RG 24, 3982, NS 1052-1-5, vol. 1

19 H.N. Lay, *Memoirs of a Mariner*, 39
20 K.E.B. Jay and J.D. Scott, 'History of the Development and Production of Radio and Radar,' Part 11, 154, unpublished monograph, PRO, CAB 102/ 64; 'Memorandum on Admiralty Research and Development Organization,' undated but likely 1942, Churchill College, Goodeve Papers 3/1
21 Alfred T. Drury, 'War History of the Naval Research Laboratory,' 23, unpublished monograph, 6 Aug. 1948, Library U.S. Naval History Division
22 Milner, *North Atlantic Run*, 43–4; C-in-C Western Approaches to NSHQ, 25 Sept. 1943, PAC, RG 24, 11,579, NSD 019-1-3
23 Minutes of a Meeting of the Committee of the Privy Council, 22 March 1943, National Archives, Washington (NA), RG 227, Box 32, file A2700
24 Mackenzie Diary, 7 March 1941, PAC. Emphasis added
25 Irvin Stewart, *Organizing Scientific Research for War*, 35–52
26 Mackenzie to Maclachlan, PAC, RG 24, 5590, NS 10-39-6
27 'National Research Council of Canada acting as the Scientific, Research and Experimental Department for the Royal Canadian Navy,' undated but found with Mackenzie to Maclachlan, 8 April 1941, ibid.
28 Margaret Gowing, *Britain and Atomic Energy, 1939–1945*, 190
29 Cossette to Mackenzie, 25 April 1940, Degaussing History, Part 1, 1940–1, General, DHist
30 Mackenzie Diary, 4 Aug. 1942, PAC
31 Rose to Hibbard, 13 Nov. 1942, PAC, RG 24, 4039, NS 1074-3-1, vol. 1
32 See J.B. Conant, *My Several Lives*, and R.V. Jones, *Most Secret War*
33 Crerar to Mackenzie, 3 Aug. 1940, NRC file S45-2-16, vol. 2; Minutes of the Meeting of the Interservice Committee of Electrical Fire Control, 16 Nov. 1940, NRC, file S45-2-16, vol. 3. For a more detailed account of the management of the Canadian radar program see David Zimmerman, 'Organizing Science for War: The Management of Canadian Radar Development,' *Scientia Canadiensis* 10, no. 2 (Autumn-Winter 1986), 93–108.
34 Power to Howe, 16 May 1941, PAC, Howe Papers, vol. 30, file 5-9-85(2)
35 'REL Staff Memorandum on Electrical Fire Control,' 23 April 1941, PAC, Howe Papers, vol. 43, file 5-9-85-7(2). Emphasis added
36 Phillips to Taylor, 24 April 1941, PAC, Howe Papers, vol. 43, file 5-9-85-7(2)
37 Howe to Ralston, 29 April 1941, PAC, Howe Papers, vol. 43, file 5-9-85-7(2)
38 Hibbard, 'Memorandum to DCNS,' 4 May 1941, PAC, Howe Papers, vol. 43, file 5-9-85(2)
39 Macdonald to Howe, 6 May 1941, PAC, Howe Papers, vol. 43, file 5-9-85(2)
40 RDF or Radio Direction Finding Committee, name changed to Radar Committee with general change of nomenclature in June 1943

41 Minutes of the 108th Meeting of the Chiefs of Staff Committee, 6 May 1941, DHist
42 Ibid.
43 Various Meetings RDF Committee, Henderson Papers and in PAC, RG 24 vol. 8086, NS 1272-24, vol. 1
44 W.E.K. Middleton, *Radar Development in Canada*, 21–2, 28
45 'War History of the Radio Branch,' 30–3; First Meeting of the RDF Committee, 4 June 1941, Henderson Papers; Heads of Group Meeting, 30 Aug. 1941, NRC Physics and Electrical Division Director's Office
46 Mackenzie Diary, 15,18,20 Aug. 1941, PAC; First Meeting of the Heads of Groups, 16 Aug. 1941, NRC Physics and Electrical Engineering Division Director's Office
47 Middleton, *Radar*, 30–2
48 Mackenzie Diary, Dec. 1941 to Jan. 1942, PAC, Mackenzie to G.C. McBurney, 13 Jan. 1942, PAC, RG 24, 5281, F.HQ 34-3-8; Middleton, *Radar*, 30–3; Minutes of the First Meeting of the Co-ordination and Management Committee, 10 Jan. 1942, NRC office files
49 Various Meetings of the Heads of Groups and the Co-ordinating and Management Committee, NRC office files
50 E.F. Burton, 'Memorandum Re: Interview with Dr Henderson of the Radio Laboratory,' NRC, 3–4 Oct. 1940, Henderson Papers
51 See various letters between Mackenzie, Phillips and Howe in PAC, Howe Papers, vol. 43, file 5-9-85-7 (1 and 2)
52 Middleton, *Radar*, 44; Phillips to Howe 31 March 1944, PAC, Howe Papers, vol. 43, file 5-9-85(2)
53 Conversation with Roger Sarty, 26 Sept. 1986
54 Millard to CNES, 18 Feb. 1942, PAC, RG 24, 5590, NS 10-36-6

CHAPTER FIVE Liaison

1 'Miscellaneous Papers on the History of the Royal Canadian Navy,' Part III, 'RCN-RN Relations,' 1–15
2 A.V. Hill, 'Science in the War: Co-operation with Canada and the United States,' found in NA, RG 227, vol. 37; D.J.C. Phillipson, *International Scientific Liaison and the National Research Council of Canada, 1916–74*, 26–30
3 G.H. Henderson, 'Report to the President of NRC at Ottawa on RDF,' 26 July 1940, NRC S45-2-16, vol. 2
4 Phillipson, *International Scientific Liaison*, 14
5 Fowler to Mackenzie, 22 October 1940, NRC S45-2-16, vol. 3
6 J.S. Barnes to CNS Canada, 12 May 1941, PAC, RG 24, 5590, NS 10-39-6

7 See 'Miscellaneous Weapon Development Department: History of Department and Projects,' unpublished monograph, PRO, ADM 116/230

8 These were the Telecommunications Research Establishment (TRE) run by the RAF and the Ministry of Aircraft Production; the Radio Department of the RAF; Admiralty Signal Establishment; Radar Research and Development Establishment; and the Signal Research and Development Establishment both of the army.

9 Vannevar Bush, *Pieces of the Action*, 41–2

10 Smith to Boyle, 2 July 1941, NRC B45-2-30 vol. 2

11 Boyle to Smith, 21 June 1941, NRC B45-2-30 vol. 2

12 Fowler to Mackenzie, 25 June 1941, NRC B45-2-30, vol. 2; McNaughton to Mackenzie, 2 July 1941, in Mel Thistle, ed., *The Mackenzie-McNaughton Wartime Letters*, 83

13 Smith to Boyle, 13 June 1941, NRC B45-2-30 vol. 2

14 Smith to Boyle, 4 July 1941, NRC B45-2-30 vol. 2

15 Boyle to Smith, 21 June 1941, NRC B45-2-30 vol. 2, Mackenzie to McNaughton, 19 June 1941; *Mackenzie-MacNaughton Letters*, 78–82

16 Mackenzie to McNaughton, 2 Aug. 1941, *Mackenzie-McNaughton Letters*, 83–7

17 'Miscellaneous Papers,' Part III, 16–22

18 'The British Central Scientific Office,' uncredited account of its activities up to 1942, NA, RG 227, Box 37, file BCSO

19 'Memorandum on Interchange of Scientific Information between NDRC and Great Britain and Canada,' 25 Oct. 1940, R.P. Patterson to James Forrestal, 20 Nov. 1940, NA, RG 227, Box 227. file Cooperation UK; also see the OSRD/NDRC-NRC correspondence files in NA, RG 227

20 Mackenzie Diary, 23 Jan. 1941, PAC

21 'Memorandum on the Procedure for Co-operation between the British Central Scientific Office and Representatives of Dominion Scientific Effort for War Purposes,' 30 June 1941, NA, RG 227. Box 29

CHAPTER SIX Shortwave Confusion

1 K.E.B. Jay and J.D. Scott, 'History of the Development and Production of Radio and Radar,' Part II, 360, PRO, CAB 102 / 641

2 Ibid., 350–65; Commander HMS *Orchis*, 'Results Obtained with Type 271,' 3 June 1941, PRO, ADM 1/11063

3 John Henderson, 'Progress Report for the Period June 1939 to 1 January 1942,' 26

4 Howlett to Henderson, 27 Oct. 1941, NRC S45-2-16 vol. 7; Minutes of a General Meeting of the Heads of Group, 25 Oct. 1941, NRC S45-2-16, vol. 6

5 Minutes of a Meeting Held at the Field Station, 25 Aug. 1941, Henderson Papers

6 RX/C was originally code named the SS2C but, to avoid confusion, it will be called throughout by its more common operational designation.

7 John Henderson, 'Progress Report,' 26

8 'War History of the Radio Branch,' 45; W.E.K. Middleton, *Radar Development in Canada*, 76

9 Cossette for Argyle to Henderson, 4 Oct. 1941, PAC, RG 24, 3981, NS 1052-1-1; Henderson to Cossette, 9 Oct. 1941, Henderson Papers; Minutes of a Meeting Held, 24 Oct. 1941, Henderson Papers

10 Minutes of a Meeting of the Heads of Group, 3 Jan. 1942, PAC, RG 24, 173, file 45-2-52, vol. 1; Howlett to Mackenzie, 6 Nov. 1941, NRC B45-2-30, vol. 3

11 Cossette to Henderson, 12 Nov. 1941, PAC, RG 77, 173, file 45-2-52, vol. 1

12 Minutes for the Special Meeting of the Committee on RDF, 4 Dec. 1941, Henderson Papers

13 Worth to DWT, 19 July 1943, PAC, RG 24, 3982, NS 1052-1-1, vol. 2

14 Cossette to the Chairman, Radio Branch, 31 Jan. 1942, Smyth to Wallace, 31 Jan. 1942, Mackenzie to Argyle, 31 Jan. 1942, Smyth to Wallace, 12 Feb. 1942, Wallace to Phillips, 12 February 1942, all in PAC, RG 77, 173, NRC 45-2-52, vol. 1

15 Argyle to Smyth, 24 Feb. 1942, Henderson Papers

16 Argyle to Wallace, 13 March 1942; Argyle to Wallace, 13 March 1942, Henderson Papers

17 Naval Staff Minutes 143, 26 May 1942, DHist

18 'Detailed Reply to the Items Raised in the Honourable Mr. Ralston's Letter of April 28th, 1943,' 12 May 1943, Howe Papers, vol. 43, file 5-9-85-7 (1), PAC

19 Conversation with Dr Marc Milner, 10 Nov. 1985; Mackenzie Diary, 10 March 1941, PAC

20 Naval Staff Minutes 70, 2 March 1942, DHist

21 Naval Staff Minutes 72, 9 March 1942

22 NSHQ to SCNO London, 16 March 192, PAC, RG 24, 11,580, NSD 19-1-12; see also Naval Staff Minutes 77, 26 March 1942

23 Naval Staff Minutes 90, 14 May 1942

24 Naval Staff Minutes 95, 1 June 1942; Memorandum to CNES, 23 May 1942, Memorandum to CNES, 1 June 1942, PAC, RG 24, 3982, NS 1052-1-1

25 Worth to CNS, 17 Sept. 1942, PAC, RG 24, 6986, NS 8374-4
26 Marc Milner, *North Atlantic Run*, 112–13; A. Watts, *The U-Boat Hunters* 148–9
27 Naval Staff Minutes 94, 28 May 1942
28 Secretary Naval Board to Smyth, 13 July 1942, PAC, RG 77, 173, file 45-2-52; see also Henderson, 'Progress Report,' 27: Naval Staff Minutes 120, 21 Sept. 1942; 'Report of Tests on SS-2C Equipment – Halifax, May 29th–June 8th, 1942,' PAC, RG 77, 173, file 45-2-52
29 Milner *North Atlantic Run*, 130–50
30 Naval Staff Minutes 123, 1 Oct. 1942
31 Naval Staff Minutes 120, 21 Sept. 1942
32 Naval Staff Minutes 199, 17 Sept. 1942
33 Memorandum to the CNES, 17 Sept. 1942, 20 Sept. 1942, PAC, RG 24, 3982, NS 102-1-1, FD 690 Staff
34 Naval Staff Minutes 117, 31 Aug. 1942
35 Worth to CNEC, 29 Oct. 1942, PAC, RG 24, 6796, NS 8375-4
36 Worth to CNS, 24 Dec. 1942, PAC, RG 24, 6986, NS 8375-4
37 Memo on Radar Fitting, 6 Dec. 1942, PRO, ADM 1/12104

CHAPTER SEVEN Sound Problems

1 'History of the British Admiralty Technical Mission,' 100
2 Naval Board Minutes 8, 5 March 1942; Minutes of a Meeting, 20 May 1942, PAC, RG 24, 4035, NS 1070-3-1, vol. 1
3 Asdic sets generally were designed in two different models. One was housed in an asdic dome fixed permanently to the bottom of a vessel near the bow, while the second type was housed in a retractable dome that could be protected inside a chamber built into the hull of a vessel. Normally this last type was fitted onto vessels whose operations could damage an unretracted housing. Destroyers, which could damage their sets while operating at high speeds, and minesweepers, which could foul asdic domes with their sweeping gear, were typically fitted with a retractable dome. To protect asdic sets from ice damage the RCN decided in mid-1942 to fit all new vessels with retractable domes.
4 Milner, *North Atlantic Run* 37; 'Modernization of Armament and Equipment,' 2–5; Naval Staff Minutes 27, 30 July 1940; NS Minutes 28, 5 Aug. 1940; NS Minutes 29, 12 Aug. 1940, DHist
5 Summary of Naval War Effort, 1 July 1941 to 30 Sept. 1942, DHist
6 G. Tucker, *The Naval Service of Canada*, 2: 287–8; Summary of Naval War Effort, 1 Oct. 1941 to 31 March 1941, DHist

7 W. Hackmann, *Seek and Strike*, 306–8; 'Modernization of Armament and Equipment,' 10

8 Ibid.; Miscellaneous Weapon Development Department, Admiralty, History of Department and Projects Developed 1940–1945, PRO, ADM 116/454

9 Hackmann, *Seek and Strike*, 272

10 Ibid., 271–4; 'Modernization of Armament and Equipment,' 11–12

11 DA/S to DA/SW (Admiralty), 14 Aug. 1942, as quoted in 'Modernization of Armament and Equipment,' 32–3

12 DA/SW to DA/S, 26 Aug. 1942, ibid.

13 NS Minutes 86, 26 May 1942; NS Minutes 93, 26 May 1947, DHist; 'Modernization of Armament and Equipment,' 11–12

14 The account on the Maritime ship repair industry and the economic policies of the King government is taken from Ernest Forbes, 'Consolidating Disparity: The Maritimes and the Industrialization of Canada during the Second World War;' 1986; see also 'Modernization of Armament and Equipment,' 4, 12–13; G.L. Stephens to Nelles, 26 Aug. 1943, PANS, Macdonald Papers, F276/37.

15 'Modernization of Armament and Equipment.' 12; Stephens to Nelles, 26 Nov. 1942, PANS, MacDonald Papers, F276/37

16 Naval Staff Minutes 101, 29 June 1942

17 Naval Staff Minutes 114, 20 Aug. 1942

18 Naval Staff Minutes 117, 3 Sept. 1942

19 Naval Staff Minutes 119, 17 Aug. 1942

20 Stephens to Nelles, 26 Nov. 1943, PANS

21 'Statement Showing the Final Cost of Oscillator Assembly,' 30 March 1943; Deputy Minister DMS to W.B. Timon, Director, Mines and Geology Branch, 5 Sept. 1942, both in PAC, RG 24, 4035, NSS 1070-3-4, vol. 1

22 W.E.K. Middleton, *Physics at the National Research Council of Canada, 1929–1952*, 89; Hibbard to Mackenzie, 7 Dec. 1942, 'Projects Under Study by NRC,' 18 Dec. 1942; Electrical Lt. Commander N.M. Anderson to DWT, 28 July 1944; all in PAC, RG 24, 4039, NS 1074-3

23 Wright (Director of Scientific Research, Admiralty) to Mackenzie, 29 Jan. 1941, PAC, RG 24, 4038, NS 1074-2-2, vol. 1

24 Middleton, *Physics*, 87, 198–200

25 Field, 'Secret War Mission to the U.S. to Obtain Information on the Acoustic Mine and U.S. Navy Echo-Ranging Equipment,' NRC Report no. PS101

26 'Report on Visit to United Kingdom by Geo. S. Field,' July 1941, NRC Report no. PS105

27 Middleton, *Physics*, 88

28 NRC Report Phx 24, 8 Oct. 1941, Phx 28, 9 Dec. 1941, both in PAC, RG 24, 4038, NS 1074-2-2, vol. 1
29 P. Elliott, *Allied Minesweeping in World War Two*, 49, 54–5
30 Ibid., 49
31 'Summary of Test on Canadian Hammer Box,' 20 Feb. 1942, DHist, Degaussing History Part 1, 1942–4 General; Summaries of Naval War Effort, 1942
32 Millard to CNES, 18 March 1942, PAC, RG 24, 4038, NS 1074-2-2, vol. 1
33 Middleton, *Physics*, 88
34 'Combined Acoustical and DG Channel Range at Halifax, NS,' 18 Dec. 1942, DHist, Degaussing History Part 1, 1940–1 General
35 Rose to Hibbard, 13 Nov. 1942, PAC, RG 24, 4039, NS 1074-3-1, vol. 1
36 Milner, *North Atlantic Run*, 273–4
37 Middleton, *Physics*, 90
38 Naval Staff Minutes 214, 13 Dec. 1942, NS Minutes 215, 20 Dec. 1943; G.H. Henderson to Chief of Staff C-in-C CNA, 23 Nov. 1943, DHist, 81/520, 1000-973, vol. 4
39 Master Card Files, Ship Files, Naval Historian's Files, DHist

CHAPTER EIGHT Exile and Dissent

1 The story of ONS 154 as well as the rest of the account on the withdrawal of the Canadian C groups from Mid-Ocean Escort Force is taken from Marc Milner, *North Atlantic Run*, 185–213, except where otherwise noted.
2 Hughes and Costello, *The Battle of the Atlantic*, 192–220
3 Milner, *North Atlantic Run*, 180
4 Ibid., 190
5 Secretary of State for Dominion Affairs to Secretary of State for External Affairs, 17 Dec. 1942, PAC, MG 26, J 1, vol. 334
6 SOA/s to DOD, 24 Dec. 1942, PAC, RG 24, 6796, NS 8375-4
7 Nelles to Macdonald, n.d. but attached to Nelles to Macdonald, 5 Jan. 1942, PAC, RG 24, 6796, NS 8437-4
8 Report of the Conference on Fuel Supply to UK and Africa and Related Escort Matters, Washington, 29–31 Dec. 1942, PAC, RG 24, 6796, NS 8375-4
9 Nelles to Macdonald, n.d. but attached to Nelles to Macdonald, 5 Jan. 1942, PAC, RG 24, 6796, NS 8437-4
10 Nelles to Macdonald, 5 Jan. 1942, PAC
11 Milner, 'Royal Canadian Navy Participation in the Battle of the Atlantic Crisis of 1943'
12 For a complete account of the RCN's struggle to regain operational control

in the North-West Atlantic see W.G.D. Lund, 'The Royal Canadian Navy's Quest for Autonomy in the Northwest Atlantic,' 138–57

13 Neither Lund nor Milner have realized that the RCN's efforts to regain operational control of the North-West Atlantic was likely done at the expense of improving the equipment situation. The crisis of late 1943 (see chapter 11) is rooted in the failure of Nelles to deal forcefully with the equipment issue. Writes Milner in *North Atlantic Run*, 212: 'Having faced the dual horror of being brought to book for performing badly and of risking the loss of the battle for recognition and independence in the Northwest Atlantic, the RCN clearly felt it had salvaged a strategic victory from a tactical defeat. *And so it had.*' (Note: emphasis added.) We should ask what the RCN had in fact won? It was in fact Nelles's personal victory and the navy's defeat, because by failing to deal forcefully with the equipment issue Canadian escorts continued to remain second rate in comparison to their RN counterparts.

14 Naval Order 2587 as quoted in 'Modernization of Armament and Equipment,' 18–19

15 Allied Anti-Submarine Survey Board to Nelles, 18 May 1943, PAC, RG 24, 3996

16 Secretary of the Naval Board, Memo on Naval Staff Reorganization, 1 June 1943, in G. Tucker, *The Naval Service*, 2: 542–4; see also 'Miscellaneous Papers,' Part VI, 'Naval Staff', 6.

17 Tucker, *Naval Service*, 2: 472

18 Nelles to Macdonald, 27 Nov. 1943, PANS, Macdonald Papers, F276/34

19 Ibid.

20 Captain (D), Newfoundland to FONF, 1 May 1943, PANS, Macdonald Papers

21 Piers, 'Comments on the Operations and Performance of HMC Ships, Establishments, and Personnel in the Battle of the Atlantic,' 1 June 1943, PAC, RG 24 3997, NS 1057-3-24

22 Bidwell to Murray, 22 June 1943, Murray to Secretary, Naval Board, 30 June 1943, PANS, Macdonald Papers, F276/13

23 Lay, *Memoirs of a Mariner*, 148

CHAPTER NINE The Ten-Centimetre Débâcle

1 Mackenzie Diary, 12 Nov. 1942, PAC

2 W.E.K. Middleton, *Radar Development in Canada*, 42–5

3 Smyth to Wallace, Mackenzie to Argyle, 31 Jan. 1942, PAC, RG 77, 173, NRC file 45-2-52, vol. 1

4 Warren as quoted by H.R. Smyth and K.C. Mann, 'Comments on Report

of J.R. Warren on visit to NRC re: RXC, July 23, 1942,' 1 Aug. 1942, PAC, RG 77, 173, file 45-2-52, vol. 1

5 H.R. Smyth and K.C. Mann, 'Comments on Report of J.R. Warren,' PAC

6 Wallace to Hackbusch, 18 Aug. 1942, PAC, RG 77, 173, file 45-2-52, vol. 1; see also Smyth and Mann, 'Comments,' 1 Aug. 1942, PAC.

7 Quote from Pounsett to Hackbusch, 18 Sept. 1942; also see Hackbusch to Wallace, 18 Sept. 1942, PAC, RG 77, 173, file 45-2-52, vol. 1

8 Middleton, *Radar*, 42–3

9 Report on the Meeting Held at REL, Leaside, 27 Nov. 1942, PAC, RG 77, 173, file 45-2-52, vol. 3

10 'Detailed Reply to Items Raised in the Honourable Mr. Ralston's Letter of April 28th, 1943,' undated but May 1943, Howe Papers, vol. 43, file 5-9-85-7 (85)

11 Notes on conversation at REL with Lt Carlisle and Mr F.H.R. Pounsett, PAC, RG 77, 173, file 45-2-52, vol. 1

12 Lt Campbell to DDSD, 6 April 1943, PAC, RG 24, 8086, NS 1272-24, vol. 2

13 Ibid.; secretary Naval Board to Mr C.L. Croll, Army-Navy Production Agency, Pentagon, 18 Feb. 1943, PAC, RG 24, 8086, NS 1272-24

14 Minutes of the meeting of the Co-Ordination and Management Committee, 8 Feb. 1943, NRC C3000-12-1; secretary Naval Board to Wallace, 8 Feb. 1943, PAC, RG 24, 11,580, NS D19-1-12

15 Hackbusch to Wallace, 1 April 1943, PAC, RG 77, 173, file 45-2-52, vol. 2

16 Campbell to DDSD, 6 April 1943, PAC, RG 24, 8086, NS 1272-24

17 Mackenzie to secretary, Chiefs of Staff Committee, 12 April 1943, PAC, RG 24, 5282, HQ534-7-2, vol. 3

18 Ralston to Howe, 28 April 1943; Mackenzie to secretary, Chiefs of Staff Committee, 12 April 1943; both in PAC, RG 24, 5282, HQ534-7-2, vol. 3

19 Phillips to Howe, 12 May 1943, Howe Papers. vol. 433, file 5-9-85-7 (1)

20 'Detailed Reply to Items Raised in the Honourable Mr. Ralston's Letter of April 28th, 1943,' undated but May 1943, Howe Papers, vol. 43, file 5-9-85-7 (1)

21 Howe to Ralston, 2 June 1943, Howe Papers, vol. 43, file 5-9-85-7 (1)

22 J.N. Kennedy, *A History of the Department of Munitions and Supply*, 1: 440

23 Worth to DES, 1 Sept. 1943, PAC, RG 24, 3982, NS 1052-1-1, vol. 2

24 Captain (D), Newfoundland to FONF, 1 May 1943, Macdonald Papers, PANS

25 FONF to secretary Naval Board, 13 May 1943, Macdonald Papers

26 T.J. Brown, Memorandum, 20 May 1943, Macdonald Papers

27 RDF Base Maintenance Officer, HMCS *Stadacona*, to Staff RDFO Officer, 11 June 1943, PAC, RG 24, 11579, NS DO 19-1-2

28 Captain (D), Halifax to C-in-C CNA, 10 June 1943, PAC, RG 24, 11570, NSD 019-1-2

29 Deputy secretary Naval Board to Naval Member Canadian Joint Staff, C-in-C CNA, FONF, COPC, 25 June 1943, PAC, RG 24, 11579, NSD 019-1-2

30 L.C. Marshall, 'Survey of ssv Radar Sets in Production and Design,' 1 July 1942, Records of Division 10, Radiation Laboratory, NA (Waltham), Box 1326

31 Radar Base Maintenance, HMC Dockyard, Halifax, 4 Sept. 1943, PAC, RG 77, 173, file 45-2-52, vol. 2

32 Smyth to N.B. Clark, Manager REL Radio Division, Oct. 1943, PAC, RG 77, 173 file 45-2-52 vol. 2; secretary Naval Board to Smyth, 13 July 1942, PAC, RG 77, 173, file 45-2-52

33 Minutes of the Second Meeting of the Radar Co-ordination Committee, 23 Aug. 1943, NRC file C3000-12-1; Worth to DES, RG 77, 174, file 45-7-52, vol. 3

34 Minutes of the Fifth Meeting of the Radar Co-ordination Committee, NRC file C3000-12-1; Worth to DWT, 19 July 1943, PAC, RG 24, 3982

35 RCN Monthly Radar and Loran Progress Report, 1 Feb. 1944, PAC, RG 24, 3982

36 Murray, C-in-C CNA to Commodore Superintendent, Halifax, 21 Jan. 1944; Prentice to C-in-C CNA, 25 Nov. 1943, both in PAC, RG 24, 11580, NSD 19-1-12

37 A/Lt Commander B.E. Miles, Report on the Radar Trials Carried Out in HMCS *Wallaceburg*, 20 Dec. 1943, PAC, RG 24, 11580, NSD 19-1-12

38 Murray to Captain (D), Halifax, 31 Jan. 1944. PAC, RG 24, 11580, NSD 19-1-12

39 Murray to secretary Naval Board, 1 Feb. 1944, PAC, RG 24, 11580, NSD 19-1-12

40 Secretary Naval Board to C-in-C CNA, 11 Feb. 1944, PAC, RG 24, 11580, NSD 19-1-12

41 Prentice to C-in-C CNA, 21 Feb. 1944; also see Commanding Officer, HMCS *Portage* to Captain (D), Halifax, 7 Feb. 1944, PAC, RG 24, 11580, NS D19-1-12

42 Secretary Naval Board to Wallace, 23 April 1944, PAC, RG 77, 174, file 45-2-52

43 W.M. Cameron, Report of RX/C Faults Aboard HMCS *Winnipeg*, 4–15 May 1944, PAC, RG 24, 11580 NSD 19-1-12

44 G.Tucker, *The Naval Service of Canada*, 2:297-8

45 Captain (D), Newfoundland, Draft Report on Radar Operators, December 1943, PAC, RG 24, 11986, Capt. (D), Newfoundland Radar file

46 'Instructions to Operators for Use with the RX/C and RX/C PPI Set,' 5 June 1944, PAC, RG 24, 11580, NSD 19-1-12

47 Tucker, *The Naval Service*, 2:290

48 Captain (D), Halifax to C-in-C CNA, 22 June 1944, PAC, RG 24, 11580, NSD 19-1-12
49 Extract of a report by Worth to DOP, D.Org, D/DSD, VCNS, 11 May 1943, Macdonald Papers, PANS; Tucker, 2:297
50 F.R. Park, 'Report on Operational and Maintenance Problems with RX/C Radar,' May 1944, PAC, RG 77, 174, file 45-2-52, vol. 3
51 'War History of the Radio Branch,' 28; Minutes of the Tenth Meeting of the Radar Coordination Committee, 12 April 1944, NRC file C3000-12-1
52 Electrical Lt R.A. Montgomery to Commanding Officer, HMCS *St Boniface*, 9 May 1944, PAC, RG 24, 11580, NSD 19-1-12
53 Naval Staff Minutes 240, 29 May 1944, DHist
54 Naval Board Minutes 155, 29 May 1944
55 Secretary Naval Board to C-in-C CNA, FONF, COPC, 5 June 1944, PAC, RG 24, 11580, NSD, 19-1-12
56 Naval Staff Minutes 146, 14 Jan. 1943, NS Minutes 147, 18 Jan. 1943, DHist
57 Naval Staff Minutes 188, 28 June 1943
58 'Report of Worth's Trip to the U.K., March–April 1943,' PAC, RG 24, 3804, NS 1008-33-25, vol. 1
59 Naval Staff Minutes 266, 21 Feb. 1944, DHist
60 Naval Staff Minutes 235, 24 April 1944

CHAPTER TEN One Step Behind

1 Banks to NSHQ, 26 Oct. 1943, SCNO (L) to NSHQ. 2 Nov. 1943, both in DHist, 81/520 1000-413 vol. 4
2 Naval Staff Minutes 204, 9 Nov. 1943, DHist
3 'Modernization of Armament and Equipment.' 16–17
4 'Modernization of Armament and Equipment.' 25–6
5 Admiralty to Pew, 21 April 1941, PAC, RG 24, 3963, NS 1046-1-1, vol. 1; Naval Staff Minutes 153, 17 Sept. 1942
6 W. Hackmann, *Seek and Strike*, 279
7 Naval Staff Minutes 175, 3 May 1943, 187, 21 June 1943, 192, 26 July 1943, DHist
8 Hackmann, *Seek and Strike*, 280, 309
9 Naval Staff Minutes 198, 6 Sept. 1943
10 Peter Elliott, *Allied Escort Ships of World War Two*, 213
11 Naval Staff Minutes 209, 9 Nov. 1943
12 Marc Milner, 'The RCN and the Offensive against the U-Boats, 1943–1945,' 20
13 Naval Staff Minutes 224, 7 Feb. 1944, DHist

14 Naval Staff Minutes 255, 11 Sept. 1944, 269, 18 Dec. 1944, 293, 4 June 1945
15 Naval Staff Minutes 255, 11 Sept. 1944, 258, 2 Oct. 1944
16 Milner, 'Offensive,' 14
17 Naval Staff Minutes 208, 1 Nov. 1943
18 Tucker's Asdic Tables, DHist, 81/520 1000-973; D/DWT to ACNS, 23 Sept. 1943 and 1 Oct. 1943; secretary Naval Board to C-in-C CNA, 12 April 1944, all in DHist, 81/520 1000-973 vol. 4
19 D/DWT to ACNS, 2 Nov. 1943, DHist, 81/1/520 1000-973 vol. 4
20 Naval Staff Minutes 254, 5 Sept. 1944; Summary of Naval War Effort, 1 April 1944 to 30 June 1944, 1 July 1944 to 31 Dec. 1944, DHist; Neale to DWT, 18 May 1944, DHist, 81/520 1000-973 vol. 4
21 A/S Materials Meeting, 17 Aug. 1943, DHist, 81/520 1000-973 vol. 4
22 Neale to DWT, 21 April 1944, DHist 81/520 1000-973 vol. 4
23 Tucker, *The Naval Service of Canada*, 2:458; 'Miscellaneous Papers on the History of the Royal Canadian Navy,' RCN-RN Relations, 17–18
24 Tucker, *Naval Service*, 2:458
25 Neale to DWT, 18 May 1944, DHist, 81/520 1000-973 vol. 4
26 NS Minutes 265, 20 Nov. 1944
27 For an operational account of these actions see Michael Hadley, *U-Boats against Canada: German Submarines in Canadian Waters.*
28 For a detailed study of coastal ASW in the RCN see Marc Milner, 'Inshore ASW: The Canadian Experience.'
29 Lt Col H.B. Hatchey and Lt E.L. MacVeigh, 'Asdic Ranging Conditions in the Halifax Approaches,' NRC Report PSA 1, PAC, RG 24, 11463, Bathermography General
30 NS Minutes 119, 17 Sept. 1942
31 W.E.K. Middleton, *Physics at the National Research Council of Canada*, 90–1
32 Ibid., 91; Milner, 'Inshore ASW,' 15–16
33 Milner, 'Inshore ASW,' 24; AORG to Commodore Superintendent, Halifax, PAC, RG 24, 11696, NSDH 1003-6-15
34 'Asdic Ranging Conditions in the Halifax Approaches,' NRC Report PSA 1, PAC
35 Hatchey, MacVeigh, Lt J.D. Barber, 'Asdic Ranging Conditions in the River and Gulf of St Lawrence in Late Summer,' NRC Report PSA 2, 17 Nov. 1944, PAC, RG 24, 11463, Bathermography General
36 Hatchey and MacVeigh, 'Bottom Sediments and their Effect on Shallow Water Echo Ranging Conditions,' NRC Report PRA 3, 30 Nov. 1944, PAC, RG 24, 11463, Bathermography General
37 Milner, 'Inshore ASW,' 15

38 NS Minutes 261, 23 Oct. 1944
39 Milner, 'Inshore ASW,' 26
40 Raymond as quoted in Milner, 'Inshore ASW,' 27

CHAPTER ELEVEN Confrontation and Dismissal

1 For an excellent account of the events from Aug. 1943 to Jan. 1944 from an operational perspective see Marc Milner, *North Atlantic Run*, 242–80.
2 C.P. Stacey, *Arms, Men and Government*, 316–17
3 Commanding Officer, HMCS *Assiniboine* to Captain (D), St. John's, 9 Aug. 1943, PAC, RG 24, 3997, NSS 105-7-3-24
4 Stacey, *Arms, Men and Government*, 316–17
5 Tucker, *The Naval Service of Canada*, 2:429
6 J.W. Pickersgill, *The Mackenzie-King Record*, 1:565
7 Stacey, *Arms, Men and Government*, 316; minister to Nelles, 21 Aug. 1943, PAC, RG 24, 3995, NSS 1057-1-27
8 Nelles to Macdonald, 1 Sept. 1943, DHist file M-11
9 Creery to Nelles, 30 Aug. 1943, DHist, Nelles Papers, B-13
10 Stacey, *Arms, Men and Government*, 316
11 'Canadian Naval Construction Program,' n.d. but fall 1943, PANS, Macdonald Papers, F276/45
12 Naval Staff Minutes 210, 15 Nov. 1943
13 Griffiths to Nelles, 16 Nov. 1943, PANS, Macdonald Papers, F276/26
14 Stephens to Nelles, 11 Nov. 1943, PANS, Macdonald Papers, F276/23
15 Jones to Nelles, 12 Nov. 1943, PANS, Macdonald Papers, F276/22
16 Johnstone to Nelles, 13 Nov. 1943, PANS, Macdonald Papers, F276/25
17 Griffiths to Nelles, 16 Nov. 1943, PANS, Macdonald Papers, F276/126
18 Milner, *North Atlantic Run*, 258
19 'Memorandum on the State of Equipment on RCN Ships,' n.d. but circa 20 Nov. 1943, PANS, Macdonald Papers, F276/3
20 Macdonald to Nelles, n.d. but 25 Nov. 1943, PANS, Macdonald Papers, F276/28
21 Nelles to Macdonald, 27 Nov. 1943, PANS, Macdonald Papers, F276/34
22 Hibbard to Naval Staff, 26 Nov. 1943, PANS, Macdonald Papers, F276/42; Stephens to Nelles, 26 Nov. 1943, PANS, Macdonald Papers, F276/37; Pressey to ACNS, CNS, 2 Dec. 1943, DHist, Nelles Papers, B-17
23 Nelles to Macdonald, 4 Dec. 1943, PANS, Macdonald Papers, F276/39. Emphasis added
24 Macdonald to Nelles, 4 Dec. 1943, PANS, Macdonald Papers, F276/39. Emphasis added

25 See assorted correspondence about this period in Nelles's life in the Nelles Papers, DHist, and on his retirement in the Macdonald Papers, PANS.
26 Milner, in *North Atlantic Run*, suggests that the equipment gap was diminishing by the time of Nelles's dismissal. Evidence presented here and in two of Milner's recently completed unpublished studies, 'Inshore ASW: The Canadian Experience' and 'The RCN and the Offensive against the U-Boat,' indicate that problems with equipment continued through to the end of the war.
27 'Summary and Comments on Paper Relating to Comparison of Relative Fighting Efficiency of RCN as against RN,' n.d. but spring of 1944, DHist, RN file, 1440/150
28 Nelles to Macdonald, 27 Nov. 1943, PANS, Macdonald Papers, F276/39
29 Canadian Confidential Naval Orders 271, 12 Feb. 1944, DHist; see also Forms S 2231 and Master Card Files in Ship Files, DHist.

CHAPTER TWELVE The Case of the Missing Scientists

1 Mackenzie Diary, 14 July 1945, PAC
2 R.W. Clarke, *The Rise of the Boffins*, 213–15
3 P.M.S. Blackett, 'Scientists at the Operational Level,' in *Studies of War*, 171
4 Clarke, *Boffins*, 215–17
5 D. Kevles, *The Physicists*, 313
6 Ibid., 314
7 Ibid. 313–15
8 Millard to D/DWT, ACNS, 22 July 1943, PAC, RG 24, 5590, NS 10-39-6
9 Mackenzie Diary, 24 Aug. 1942, 18 June 1943, 21 Sept. 1943; Mackenzie to secretary Naval Board, 26 July 1943, PAC, RG 24, 5590, NS 10-39-6; W.E.K. Middleton, *Physics at the National Research Council of Canada*, 98
10 Millard to D/DWT, ACNS, 22 July 1943, PAC, RG 24, 5590, NS 10-39-6
11 Secretary Naval Board to Mackenzie, 1 Sept. 1943, PAC, RG 24, 5590, NS 10-39-6
12 Mackenzie Diary, 24 Aug. 1942, 15 Feb. 1943, PAC
13 Mackenzie to Mills (Naval deputy minister), 19 Nov. 1943, PAC, RG 24, 4040, NS 1074-6-6, vol. 1
14 Mills to Mackenzie, 13 Jan. 1944, Mackenzie to Mills, 20 July 1944, PAC RG 24, 5590, NS 10-39-6
15 Millard to DWT, ACNS, DM, CNEC, 3 Dec. 1943, PAC, RG 24, 5590, NS 10-39-6
16 'Memorandum by the Director of Office Personnel,' 18 April 1944, PAC, RG 24, 8166, NS 1700-100/53, vol. 1

17 King to Raymond, 28 Sept. 1944, King to Raymond, 4 Oct. 1944, Raymond to King, n.d. but Oct. 1944, PAC, RG 24, 8166. NS 1700-100/53

18 Millard, marginal note dated 2 Dec. 1943 on Millard to DWT, ACNS, DM, CNEC, 22 July 1943, PAC, RG 24, 5590, NS 10-39-6

19 NSHQ to NMCS, 5 July 1943, PAC, RG 24, 11464. Personnel and Equipment file

20 'RCN Operational Research Report,' n.d. but Aug. 1943, PAC, RG 24, 11463, Reports file

21 'Memorandum on Visit of J.H.L. Johnstone to England to Study Operational Research Methods, August 4–September 4, 1943,' DHist 81/520, 1000/73 vol. 4

22 'Memorandum to the Editor of the Naval List,' 10 March 1944, PAC, RG 24, 11464, Personnel and Equipment file

23 Johnstone to Blackett, 26 Dec. 1944, PAC, RG 24, 11433, Correspondence file

24 See various OR reports in PAC, RG 24, 11464, Personnel and Equipment file.

25 Johnstone to Blackett, 26 Dec. 1944, PAC, RG 24, 11463, Correspondence file

26 Milner, *North Atlantic Run*, 264

27 Worth to Nelles, 22 Nov. 1943, DHist, Nelles Papers, file B-15

28 'Joint Communications Subcommittee, Item v.' 8 April 1944, PAC, RG 24, 8086, NS 1272-24, vol. 3

29 Worth to CNS, 20 April 1944, PAC, RG 24, 8086, NS 1272-24, vol. 3

30 Minutes of the Chiefs of Staff Meeting, 21 April 1944, Mackenzie to the secretary Chiefs of Staff Committee, 4 May 1944, both in PAC, RG 24, 8086, NS 1272-24, vol. 3

31 Mackenzie Diary, 15 May 1944, PAC

32 Minutes of the 36th, 37th, and 50th Meeting of the Radar Committee, 15 May 1944, 19 June 1944, 17 Sept. 1944; Worth to CNS, 13 March 1945, Worth to the secretary JCC, 3 July 1945, PAC, RG 24, 8086, NS 1072-24, vol. 3; Mackenzie Diary 15 May 1944, PAC; Minutes of the meeting of the Chiefs of Staff Committee, 22 March 1945, 8 Nov. 1945, DHist

33 J.J. Kirgon, L.B. Leppard, etc. to Worth, 22 July 1944, Worth to Director of Plans, DOD, DWT, ACNS, 4 Aug. 1944, Jones to deputy minister, 25 Sept. 1944, all in PAC, RG 24, 3982, NS 1052-1-5; Naval Staff Minutes 252, 21 Aug. 1944, DHist; N. Friedman, *Naval Radar*, 147–8, 154, 193–4

34 Howlett to Mackenzie, 30 Oct. 1941, PAC, RG 77, 174, file 45-2-59, vol. 1

35 Secretary Naval Board to Mackenzie, 27 May 1942; Vice-Admiral A.E. Evans

(BATM Chief) to Nelles, 2 May 1942; CNS to Evans, 5 May 1942; all in PAC, RG 77, 174, file 45-2-59, vol. 1
36 'History of the BATM,' 98
37 R.W. Brooking to Wallace, 5 June 1945, PAC, RG 77, 174, file 45-2-59, vol. 3; J.N. Kennedy, *A History of the Department of Munitions and Supply*, 1:434
38 Minutes of Radar-U-Committee, August 1944, PRO, RG 24, 8070
39 Minutes of Meeting on Application of Type 268 in RCN, 22 April 1944; 27 April 1944, PAC, RG 24, 174, file 45-2-59, vol. 2
40 Mackenzie to Howe, 20 March 1945, PAC, Howe Papers, vol. 43, S-9-85-7 (1). Emphasis added

EPILOGUE

1 W.A.B. Douglas, 'Conflict and Innovation in the Royal Canadian Navy'
2 D.J. Goodspeed, *A History of the Defence Research Board of Canada*, 38
3 Ibid., 78
4 S.M. Davis, 'The St Laurent Decision – Genesis of a Canadian Fleet,' 6
5 D.G. Brassington, 'The Canadian Development of VDS,' 45–65; W. Hackmann, *Seek and Strike*, 350–2
6 Goodspeed, *History of the Defence Research Board*, 212
7 Mackenzie as quoted in Thistle, ed., *The Mackenzie-McNaughton Wartime Letters*, 144, 148
8 Goodspeed, *History of the Defence Research Board*, 11
9 Mackenzie as quoted in *The Mackenzie-MacNaughton Wartime Letters*, 140
10 Goodspeed, *History of the Defence Research Board*, 11–54
11 For details of post-war industrial policy see R. Bothwell and W. Kilbourne, *C.D. Howe*, 180–206.
12 *Disposal and Peacetime Use of Crown Plant Buildings*, 20; see also 44.
13 'Annual Reports Canadian Defence Arsenals Limited,' nos. 1–18 (1946–65)
14 For an examination of the first original Canadian warship building effort see Davis, 'The St Laurent Decision.'

Bibliography

PRIMARY SOURCES

Public Archives of Canada
MG 26   W.L. Mackenzie King Papers
MG 27   C.D. Howe Papers
        J.L. Ralston Papers
MG 30   A.G.L. McNaughton Papers
MG 32   C.J. Mackenzie Diary and Papers
RG 2   War Cabinet Committee Papers and Minutes
RG 21   Department of Mines and Resources Papers
RG 24   Army Central Registry Files
        Naval Headquarters Registry Files
        Atlantic Command Files
        Pacific Command Files
        Canadian Naval Liaison Files
        Naval Directorate of Operations Research Files
        Naval Council Minutes
        Airforce Central Registry Files
RG 28   Records of the Department of Munitions and Supply
        Records of the Department of Reconstruction and Supply
RG 77   Records of the National Research Council
Henderson Papers   Note: Consulted at the National Research Council before
                   transfer to PAC

Directorate of History, National Defence Headquarters
Chiefs of Staff Minutes and Papers
Degaussing History (uncatalogued)

Modernization of Armament and Equipment
Naval Historian's Files
Naval Board Minutes
Naval Staff Minutes
Summaries of Naval War Efforts
P.W. Nelles Papers
Daily States

Public Archives of Nova Scotia
Angus L. Macdonald Papers

National Research Council of Canada
Central Registry Files
PRA and PRB Reports
Papers of the Head of the Division of Physics and Electrical Engineering
Heads of Groups Meeting Minutes
Co-ordinating and Management Committee Minutes

Public Records Office
ADM 1   General Subject Files
ADM 187   Pink Lists
ADM 189   Torpedo and Anti-Submarine School Reports
ADM 199   War History Cases
ADM 204   Admiralty Research Laboratory Reports
ADM 205   First Sea Lord's Papers
ADM 215   Records of the Admiralty Signals Establishment
ADM 217   Western Approaches Command Files
CAB 101   Historians Papers, Military
AVIA 7   Telecommunications Research Establishment Files
AVIA 8   Air Ministry's Research and Development Files
CAB 102   Historians Papers, Civil

Churchill College, Cambridge
J.D. Cockcroft Papers
Charles Goodeve Papers
S.V. Alexander Papers
S.W. Roskill Papers

National Archives, Washington
RG 277   Records of the Office of Scientific Research and Development

National Archives, Waltham
Records of Division 10 The Radiation Laboratory

SECONDARY SOURCES

Aitkens, H.G.J. *American Capital and Canadian Resources.* Cambridge: Harvard University Press 1961
Baxter, James Phinney, the 3rd. *Scientists against Time.* Boston: Atlantic / Little Brown 1946
Beyerchen, Alan D. *Scientists under Hitler.* New Haven: Yale University Press 1977
Blackett, P.M.S. *Studies of War.* London: Oliver and Boyd 1962
Bliss, Michael. 'A Candian Businessman and War.' in J.L. Granatstein and R.D. Cuff, ed., *War and Society in North America.* Toronto: T. Nelson and Sons 1971
– 'War Business as Usual,' in N.F. Dreiziger, ed., *Mobilization for Total War: The Canadian, American and British Experience, 1914–1918, 1939–1945.* Waterloo: Wilfrid Laurier University Press 1981
Bothwell, R., and W. Kilbourne. *C.D. Howe.* Toronto: McClelland and Stewart 1979
Boutilier, J.A., ed. *The RCN in Retrospect.* Vancouver: University of British Columbia Press 1982
Brassington, D.G. 'The Canadian Development of VDS,' in *Maritime Warfare Bulletin*, Commemorative Edition, 1985, 45–65
Brown, J.J. *Ideas in Exile.* Toronto: McClelland and Stewart 1967
Burton, E.F. *Canadian Naval Radar Officers.* Toronto: University of Toronto Press 1946
Bush, Vannevar. *Modern Arms and Free Men.* New York: Simon and Schuster 1949
– *Pieces of the Action.* New York: William Morrow and Co. 1970
Cameron, James M. *Murray: The Martyred Admiral.* Hantsport, NS: Lancelot Press 1981
Clark, R.W. *The Rise of the Boffins.* London: Phoenix House 1962
– *Tizard.* London: Methuen and Co. 1965
Conant, J.B. *My Several Lives.* New York: Harper and Row 1970
Cuff, R.D., and J.L. Granatstein, eds. *Ties that Bind.* Toronto: Samuel Stevens Hubbert 1977
Davis, S. Mathwin. 'The *St Laurent* Decision – Genesis of a Canadian Fleet.' Paper presented at the RCN's 75th Anniversary Conference, October 1985

Disposal and Peacetime Use of of Crown Plant Building. Ottawa: King's Printer 1948

Dönitz, Grand Admiral Karl. *Memoirs: Ten Years and Twenty Days,* trans R.H. Stevens. London: Weidenfeld and Nicolson 1959

Douglas, W.A.B. 'Conflict and Innovation in the Royal Canadian Navy,' in G. Jordon, ed., *Naval Warfare in the Twentieth Century.* New York: Crane Russak 1977

Douglas, W.A.B., and B. Greenhous. *Out of the Shadows.* Toronto: Oxford University Press 1977

Drury, Alfred T. 'War History of the Naval Research Laboratory.' Unpublished monograph, 6 Aug. 1948, Library, u.s. Naval Historical Division

Dupree, F. *Science in the Federal Government.* Cambridge: Harvard University Press 1957

Dziuban, Stanley. *Military Relations Between the United States and Canada, 1939–1945.* Washington: Office of the Chief of Military History 1959

Easton, Alan. *50 North: Canada's Atlantic Battleground.* Toronto: Ryerson Press 1964

Eayrs, James. *In Defence of Canada,* vol. 1. Toronto: University of Toronto Press 1964

Eggleston, Wilfrid. *National Research in Canada.* Toronto: Clarke, Irwin and Co. 1978

– *Scientists at War.* Toronto: Oxford University Press 1950

Elliott, Peter. *Allied Escort Ships of World War Two.* London: Macdonald Janes 1977

– *Allied Minesweeping in World War Two.* Cambridge: Patrick Stevens 1979

Forbes, Ernest. 'Consolidating Disparity: The Maritimes and the Industrialization of Canada during the Second World War,' *Acadiensis* 15, no. 2 (Spring 1986), 4–27

Friedman, Norman. *Naval Radar.* Annapolis: Naval Institute Press 1984

Garneau, Marc, and A. Ball. 'Technology and the Canadian Navy, 1953–1984.' Paper presented at the RCN's 75th Anniversary Conference, Halifax, October 1986

Gingras, Yves. 'Les physiciens canadiens: genealogie d'un groupe social, 1850–1950.' Thèse de doctorat, Université de Montréal 1984

Goodspeed, D.J. *A History of the Defence Research Board of Canada.* Ottawa: Queen's Printer 1958

Gowing, Margaret. *Britain and Atomic Energy, 1939–45.* London: Macmillan and Co. 1964

Granatstein, J.G.L. *Canada's War.* Toronto: Oxford University Press 1975

– *Mackenzie King: His Life and Work.* Toronto: McGraw-Hill Ryerson 1977

Granatstein, J.L., and R.D. Cuff, eds. *War and Society in North America*. Toronto: T. Nelson 1971

Hackmann, Willem. *Seek and Strike*. London: HMSO 1984

Hadley, Michael L. *U-Boats against Canada: German Submarines in Canadian Waters*. Kingston and Montreal: McGill-Queen's University Press 1985

Hall, H. Duncan. *North American Supply*. London: HMSO 1955

Henderson, John. 'Progress Report for the Period June 1939 to 1 January 1942.' Ottawa: NRC Radio Section May 1942

Hezlett, Arthur. *The Electron and Sea Power*. London: Peter Davies 1975

Hill, A.V. 'Science in War: Co-operation with Canada and the United States,' *Cambridge Review* May 1941

Hinsley, F. *British Intelligence in the Second World War*. vols. 1–3A. Cambridge: Cambridge University Press 1979–83

'History of the British Admiralty Technical Mission.' Unpublished monograph, 1946. Copies at PAC, PRO, and the Directorate of History

Hughes, Terry and John Costello. *The Battle of the Atlantic*. New York: Dial Press 1977

The Industrial Front. Ottawa: Department of Munitions and Supply 1944

Jay, K.E.B., and J.D. Scott. 'History of the Development and the Production of Radio and Radar.' Unpublished monograph. PRO, CAB 102/63–4

Jones, R.V. *Most Secret War*. London: Hamish Hamilton 1978

Kennedy, J.N. *A History of the Department of Munitions and Supply*. 2 vols. Ottawa: King's Printer 1950

Kevles, Daniel J. *The Physicists*. New York: Alfred A. Knopf 1978

Lay, H.N. *Memoirs of a Mariner*. Ottawa: Lowe-Martin Company 1982

Leir, Richard, ' "Big Ship Time": The Formative Years of RCN Officers serving in RN Capitol Ships,' in J.A. Boutilier, ed., *The RCN in Retrospect*. Vancouver: University of British Columbia Press 1982

Lund, W.G. 'The Royal Canadian Navy's Quest for Autonomy in the Northwest Atlantic,' in J.A. Boutilier, ed., *The RCN in Retrospect*.

MacIntyre, Donald. *The Battle of the Atlantic*. London: B.T. Batsford 1961

– *U-Boat Killers*. London: Weidenfeld and Nicolson 1956

Macpherson, K., and J. Burgess. *The Ships of Canada's Naval Forces, 1910–1981*. Toronto: Collins 1981

Mellor, D.P. *The Role of Science and Industry*. Canberra: Australian War Memorial 1958

Middleton, W.E.K. *Mechanical Engineering at the National Research Council of Canada, 1929–1951*. Waterloo: Wilfrid Laurier University Press 1984

– *Physics at the National Research Council of Canada, 1929–1952*. Waterloo: Wilfrid Laurier University Press 1979

– *Radar Development in Canada: The Radio Branch of the National Research Council of Canada, 1939–1946.* Waterloo: Wilfrid Laurier University Press 1981
Milner, Marc. 'Canada's Naval War.' *Acadiensis* 12, no. 2 (Spring 1983)
– 'Convoy Escorts: Tactics Technology and Innovation in the Royal Canadian Navy, 1939–43,' *Military Affairs* 48, no. 1 (January 1984)
– 'Inshore ASW: The Canadian Experience.' Paper presented at the RCN's Seventy-Fifth Anniversary Conference, Halifax, October 1985
– *North Atlantic Run.* Toronto: University of Toronto Press 1985
– 'The RCN and the Offensive against the U-Boats, 1943–1945.' Unpublished monograph, June 1986, Directorate of History
– 'Royal Canadian Navy Participation in the Battle of the Atlantic Crisis of 1943,' in J.A. Boutilier, ed, *RCN in Retrospect.* Vancouver: University of British Columbia Press 1982
'Miscellaneous Papers on the History of the Royal Canadian Navy, 1939–1945.' Ottawa: unpublished manuscript of the Naval Historical Section, 1960, DHist 85/115
'Modernization of Armament and Equipment.' Unpublished monograph, n.d., DHist 8060
Morison, S.E. *The History of U.S. Naval Operations in the Second World War,* vols 1 and 10. Boston: Little Brown and Co. 1947 and 1962
Morton, Desmond. *Canada and War: A Military and Political History.* Toronto: Butterworths 1981
– *A Military History of Canada.* Edmonton: Hurtig 1985
Phillipson, D.J.C. *International Scientific Liaison and the National Research Council of Canada, 1916–74.* Ottawa: NRC 1985, 26–30
Pickersgill, J.W. *The Mackenzie King Record.* 4 vols. Toronto: University of Toronto Press 1960–70
Porten, Edward P. Von der. *The German Navy in World War II.* New York: Thomas Crowell Co. 1969
Postan, M.M. *British War Production.* London: HMSO 1964
Postan, M.M., D. Hay, and J.D. Scott. *The Design and Development of Weapons.* London: HMSO, 1964
Preston, A. and A. Raven. *Flower Class Corvettes,* ensign no. 3. London: Bivouac Books 1973
Purcell, Carrol W. Jr., 'Science Agencies in World War II: The OSRD and Its Challengers,' in Nathan Reingold, ed., *The Sciences in the American Context: New Perspectives.* Washington: Smithsonian Institution 1979, 359–78
Research and Scientific Activity: Canadian Federal Expenditures, 1938–1946. Ottawa: King's Printer 1947

Rohwer, J. *The Critical Convoy Battles of March 1943*. Annapolis, Md: U.S. Naval Institute Press 1977

Roskill, S.W. *Churchill and the Admirals*. London: Collins 1977

– *Naval Policy Between the Wars*. 2 vols. London: Collins 1968–77

– *The War at Sea, 1939–1945*. 3 vols. London: HMSO 1954–61

Schull, J. *The Far Distant Ships*. Ottawa: The Queen's Printer 1952

Snow, C.P. *Science and Government*. Cambridge: Harvard University Press 1961

Stacey, C.P. *Arms, Men and Government*. Ottawa: Department of National Defence 1970

Stewart, Irvin. *Organizing Scientific Research for War*. Boston: Little Brown and Co 1948

Swettenham, John. *McNaughton*, vol. 1. Toronto: Ryerson Press 1968

Swords, Sean S. *A Technical History of the Beginnings of Radar*. Dublin: Trinity College 1983

Thistle, Mel. *The Inner Ring*. Toronto: University of Toronto Press 1966

Thistle, Mel, ed. *The Mackenzie-McNaughton Wartime Letters*. Toronto: University of Toronto Press 1978

Tucker, Gilbert. *The Naval Service of Canada*. 2 vols. Ottawa: The King's Printer 1952

Waddington, C.H. *O.R. in World War 2: Operational Research against the U-Boat*. London: Elek Science 1973

'War History of the Associate Committee of the Radio Branch.' Ottawa: NRC n.d.

'War History of the Division of Physics and Electrical Engineering.' Ottawa: NRC 1949

'War History of the Radio Branch.' Ottawa: NRC 1948

Watts, A. *The U-Boat Hunters*. London: Macdonald Janes 1976

Wrigley, C.G. *Studies of Overseas Supply*. London: Her Majesty's Stationary Office 1956

Zimmerman, David. 'Northern Waves: Science, Technology and the Royal Canadian Navy, 1939–45.' Doctoral dissertation, University of New Brunswick 1988

– 'Organizing Science for War: The Management of Canadian Radar Development, 1939–45,' *Scientia Canadiensis* 10, no. 2 (Autumn-Winter 1986), 93–108

– 'Radar and Research Enterprises: A Case Study of Wartime Industrial Failure,' *Ontario History*, June 1988, 203-21

– 'The Royal Canadian Navy and the National Research Council, 1939–45,' *Canadian Historical Review*, June 1988, 121-42

Picture Credits

Index

ABC 1 and 22 104–5

Acoustics: and bathythermography 132–4, 161; research 94–7

Adams, K.F. 107, 128–9; report 135–6, 140–1

Admiralty: asdic production 29; and exile of MOEF groups 99–103; relations with RCN 9, 65–6, 79–80, 82–4, 91–3, 99–103, 122, 129–31, 138–9, 141–2, 151, 166; 268 radar 159–60. *See also* Admiralty research establishments; BATM; NRC; NSHQ; RCN

Admiralty research establishments: Admiralty Research Laboratory 92; Admiralty Signals Establishment 39, 41–2, 68, 72–3; HMS *Fairlie* 88; HMS *Osprey* 30–1; HMS *Vernon* 27; Miscellaneous Weapon Development Department 68, 88

Alberta, University of 121

Alexander, A.V. 100, 104

Allied Anti-Submarine Survey Board 106–7

Anglo-Canadian co-operation 20–1, 66–9. *See also* Admiralty; NRC; NSHQ; RCN

Angus, F.W.R. 31, 36

Anti-submarine weapons: hedgehog 88–90, 92, 109, 125, 127–8, 135–6, 137–9, 145; squid 127–30, 145

Anti-U-boat Committee 99, 149

Appleton, Sir Edward 16

Argyle, J.V. 42–3, 45–6, 60, 74, 76–80, 165

Asdic: compasses 86, 89, 137–8; dismissal of Nelles 137–9, 145; fitting 7, 86–90, 126–7; myth 9–10, 23; production 29–32, 85–6, 93, 127; Q device 126–7, 129–30, 136; research 94; T device 131; training 10, 87; variable depth sonar 162. *See also* Acoustics

Asdic sets: 123A 86, 90, 108, 136, 145, 164; 123D 89–90, 92; 124 87, 136; 127 86–7, 89, 145; 127D 130; 127DV 89, 92; 128 86–7, 126; 128A 126; 144 88–90, 126, 129–30, 136; 144Q 127–8; 145 88–90, 92, 109, 126, 130, 136, 145; 145Q 127; 147 127–31; 147F 131

Atlantic and West Indies Squadron 10, 66
Atlantic, Battle of 4, 104; situation 1942 99
Atlantic Convoy Conference 105
Atlantic Oceanography Research Group, St Andrews, New Brunswick 132–4

Ballard, B.G. 28
Banks, C.A. 125
Bangor-class. See Minesweepers
Beaverbrook, Lord 35, 66
Bell, J.F. 39
Bennett, R.B. 7, 12, 14
Bidwell, R.E.S. 41, 79, 109–10, 140, 157
Biggar, O.M. 59
Blackett, P.M.S. 148–9, 152, 156, 167
Bliss, P.M. 101
Borden, Sir Robert 12
Boyle, R.W. 13, 17, 19, 36, 61–2, 94
Brainard, A.M. 99, 105
Brand, E.S. 11
Bren gun scandal 21–2
Bristol, A.L. 105
British Admiralty Repair Mission 47
British Admiralty Technical Mission 65, 93; and asdic 30, 85–6, 127
British Central (Commonwealth) Scientific Office 70–1
British Purchasing Mission 31
Brodeur, V.G. 102
Brown, T.J. 114, 117
Burton, E.F. 62
Bush, Vannevar 56, 68, 149–50, 167

Campbell, C.B. 114

Canadian Arsenals Limited 163
Canadian North-West Atlantic 105
Carlisle, J. 75
Carmichael, H.J. 115–16
CAT. See Acoustics
Cathode-ray direction finder. See McNaughton; Steel; Henderson, John
Chiefs of Staff Committee 9, 59, 157
Churchill, Sir Winston 4, 99–101, 136, 141, 149
Cockcroft, J.D. 35
Connolly, J.J. 136–41, 157
Convoys: ON 115 81; ONS 18 96; ONS 100 81; ONS 102 81; ONS 122 82; ONS 127 99; ONS 144 99; ONS 154 98–9; SC 42 38; SC 94 81; SC 104 99; SC 107 99
Corvettes 84, 118; Castle-class 127–8, 145; modernization of 90–3, 125–6, 138–9; ordering and design of 25, 91
Cossette, J.O. 37, 75
Creery, W.B. 107, 137
Croil, G.M. 19
Currie, Sir Arthur 15

Dalhousie University 28, 154, 162
Davis, Henry H. 22
Defence Purchasing Board 22, 31
Defence Research Board 162
Degaussing. See Mines
De Marbois, J.M.B.D. 80–1
Depression, 1929–39 7, 9, 12
Destroyers: River-class destroyers, fitting policy 78–9, 81–3, 87, 165; Town-class 25–6, 126–7
DeWolf, H.G. 102–3, 148, 158
Dominion Observatory 155
Dyer, K.L. 100

Easton, Alan 3
Equipment, comparison between RN
  and RCN 80, 101, 106, 108–9,
  137–8, 140–2, 145; crisis of 1942
  98–105; crisis of 1943 135–47.
  See also Antisubmarine weapons;
  Asdic; HF/DF; Radar
Equipment Division. *See* Asdic
  production
Esquimalt 8, 87
Escort groups: A 3 81; B 6 82, 99;
  C 1 81, 99, 135–6; C 3 81; C 4 99;
  E 9 96; W 4 122

Field, G.S. 68; and acoustics 94–6;
  and bathythermography 132–4;
  post-war 162
First World War 6–7, 11
Flood, E.A. 15
Fowler, R.H. 67–8, 70–1
Frigates; Loch-class 128, 145; River-
  class 84, 118, 128, 145; 164; St
  Laurent-class 164
Furer, Julius 150

Goodeve, Charles 88, 167
Gretton, Peter 135
Griffiths, G.L. 139, 142

Hackbusch, R.A. 62–3; confrontation
  with Wallace 111; relations with
  NRC 111–16; resignation 116
Halifax, Nova Scotia 8, 33, 55, 73,
  81, 91, 93, 107, 110, 117, 118–19;
  naval research station 27–8, 58–9,
  95–6, 152–3, 155, 161–2; training
  42–3, 87, 120
Hatchey, H.B. 132–3
Heakes, F.V. 18

Hedgehog. *See* Anti-submarine
  weapons
Henderson, G.H. 33–4, 58, 67, 161;
  begins work for navy 28; SWIC 40;
  operational research 154–5
Henderson, John T. 32, 167; early
  career 16; examines British
  radar 18–19; leaves NRC 60–1;
  work with CRDF 16; work on
  SWIC 40–1; work on RX/C 74–5
Hibbard, G.M. 59, 107
High-frequency direction finding:
  DAQ 124, 163; FH3 80–2, 97, 124,
  136; FH4 108, 124; FH5 124;
  policy 80–1, 83–4, 108–9, 123–4
Hill, A.V. 33–4
Horton, C.E. 159
Horton, Sir Max 99, 109, 138
Hose, Walter 7, 9
Houghton, F.L. 26, 33, 40–2
Howe, C.D. 160, 165; appointment
  to DMS 32; economic discrimination
  of the Maritimes 91; formation
  of the radar committee 59–60; in-
  tervenes with Beaverbrook 66;
  NRC-REL relations 62–3, 114–15;
  post-war industrial policy 163
Howlett, L.E. 69, 74, 95

Identify Friend or Foe (IFF) 48
Imperial Conference 1937 20
Industry: pre-war preparedness
  19–22; early war policy 29;
  post-war policy 163. *See also* asdic;
  radar; REL
Interservice Electrical Methods of
  Fire Control Committee. *See* Radar
  Committees

John Inglis Inc. 21

Johnston, J.H.L. 58, 161; begins work for navy 28; operational research 154–6
Johnstone, E. 139, 142
Joint Communications Committee 157
Jones, G.C. 55, 142, 157; appointment as CNS 144; conspires against Nelles 110; post-war policy on science 161; reaction to criticism of NSHQ 139

Kauffman, J.L. 106–7
King, E.J. 149–50
King, R.O. 154
King, William Lyon Mackenzie 32, 59, 100, 163, 166; demands independent navy 24–5; economic discrimination of the Maritimes 90; post-war policy 161; pre-war attitudes to navy 7–8; shapes Macdonald's attitude to the equipment crisis 136
Laurier, Sir Wilfrid 6
Law, E.G. 131
Lay, H.N. 82–3
Lend-Lease Act 30
Lowe, Francis 150

Macdonald, Angus L. 91, 164–5; appointment as naval minister 24; dismissal of Nelles 136–8, 140–6, 157; and the exile of mid-Atlantic escorts 103–4; relations with NSHQ 52–3, 110
McGill University 11, 28
McGregor, D.E. 94
McIntyre, Gordon 37
Mckellar, Andrew 155
Mackenzie, C.J. 30, 166–7; appoint-

ment to NRC 26; international liaison 66–71, 95, 160; post-war 162–3; and REL 111–12, 115–16; relation with navy 36, 56–8, 77, 148, 150–2, 156–8; and radar committee 59–60; and Radio Branch 61–3; 268 radar 160
McKinley, D.W.R. 43–4
Mckinley, J.G. 102
Maclachlan, K.S. 30, 36
McMaster, H. 107
McNaughton, A.G.L. 68; attempts to cut naval budget 7; CRDF 15–17; leaves NRC 26; president of NRC 14–19, 26
Mainguy, E.R. 82
'Major Hoople' 100
Mann, K.C. 112–13
Mansfield, J.M. 102–3, 106–7
Maritime provinces: economic discrimination of 28–9, 90–1
Marshall, L.C. 118
Mid-Ocean Escort Force 99, 101, 106
Millard, J.R. 37, 57, 161; as DTR 151–4; proposals for scientific organization 63–4
Millar, A.W. 31
Milles, E.E. 119
Mines: magnetic 23, 27; measures against 27–8, 95
Mines and Resources, Department of 93
Minesweepers: Algerine-class 84, 90, 118, 164; Bangor-class 25, 84, 86, 91; Fundy-class 20
Montgomery, R.A. 122–3
Montreal, University of 57
Moyls, B.N. 155
Munitions and Supply, Department of 56, 79, 85, 91, 114, 129, 142;

creation of 30; and REL and NRC
114–16; Reconstruction and
Supply 163
Murray, L.W. 38, 82, 109, 133; and
C-in-C CNA 104–5; and RX/C
119–20
Musgrave, F.M. 36

National Defence Research
Committee 56, 70
Nationalism 24–5
National Research Council of Canada: Acoustics Section 13, 94–7,
132–4; Ballistics Section 15; and
asdic 30, 94–4; DND, relations
with 13–15, 17, 19; division of
Physics and Electrical Engineering 13; expansion 57; field
station, Metcalfe Road 57, 81;
formation 11–12; liaison with
British 66–71, 79; liaison with the
Americans 70–1; post-war 162–3;
pre-war 12–17; radar research
and development at 32–4, 43–4,
73–6, 114, 118, 159–60; Radio
Branch 26, 40, 43, 60–3, 73, 75–6;
Radio Section, formation 13; REL,
relations with 62–3, 111–16; RCN,
relations with 10–11, 36–7, 47, 50,
56–8, 73–6, 94–7, 148, 150–2,
156–60
Naval Order 2587 106, 108–9
Naval Research Laboratory 55, 95
Naval Service Headquarters: asdic
policy 86–93, 125–31; and bathythermography 132–4; criticism of
108–10, 116–17; dismissal of Nelles
137–47; exile of mid-Atlantic
escorts 101–4; formation of Naval
Staff and Council 24; HF/DF policy

80–1, 83–4, 108–9, 123–4; internal
dissent 110; and operational control of North Atlantic 104–5; post-
war attitudes to science 161–2;
pre-war 8–9; radar policy 38–42,
77–80, 82–3, 113–14, 117, 119–20,
123, 156–9; relations with NRC
10–11, 36–7, 47, 50, 56–8, 94–7,
148, 150–2, 156–60; reorganization, 1942 50–6; reorganization,
1943 106–7, 147, 150–6; and
scientific directorates 150–6. See
also RCN
Naval Staff. See Naval Service Headquarters
Navy, Army and Air Supply Committee 21
Neale, G.M. 130–1
Nelles, Percy W. 24–5, 82, 91, 123,
156, 164–6; conspiracy against
110; dismissal 137–46; early
career 9; and exile of mid-Atlantic escorts 101–4; relations with
naval minister 52–3
New Brunswick, University of 121
Newfoundland Escort Force 38
Noble, Sir Percy 99
Northern Electric Company 42, 74

Oceanography. See Acoustics
Ontario, elections, 1943 136
Operational research 129; in Canada 154–6; in Great Britain
148–9; in the United States
149–50

Park, F.R. 122
Petrie, O.M. 155
Pew, A.E.H. 36, 93; asdic produc-
tion 30–2, 85–6

Phillips, W.E. 59–60, 165; conflict with NRC 111, 113, 115–16
Piers, D.W. 108
Pounsett, F.H.R. 113
Prentice, J.D. 45–6, 117, 119–21
Pressey, A.R. 60, 76, 79–80, 89, 131–2, 165; and naval radar policy 40–2, 44

Quebec Conference 136

Radar 17, 24; British disclosure to Canada 17; Committees 39, 43, 58–60, 115–16, 156–8; dismissal of Nelles 137; early attitudes to 11, 26; fitting on ships 47–8, 84, 116, 145; magnetron 35, 41, 72, 74; naval policy 38–42; PPI 45 n.3, 114, 120; RDF Officer and Branch 42–3, 46, 50, 73; research 34–6; training 42, 120–2; and the United States 76–7, 158–9. See also NRC; NSHQ; REL
Radar sets: ASV 32, 34, 39–41, 44, 61; CD 32; GL Mark I 34; GLC Mark III 61, 74; Night Watchman 33–4, 40; 972 160; RX/C 73–7, 79, 81–4, 112–15, 118–23, 142, 157, 160, 164; RX/U 77, 79, 112, 114, 117–18, 119, 146, 157; SG 76, 158; SG2C 73–6, 81; SJ 76–7, 114, 117–18; SSV 76; SU 158, 160, 163; SW1C 43–9, 61, 72–3, 75; SW2C 48–9, 75, 77; SW3C 48; 268 159–60, 166; 271 54, 72–5, 78–84, 97, 108, 116, 118–19, 122; 271P 116, 118–19, 135–6; 271P 116, 118–19, 135–6; 271Q 116, 119; 277 158; 286 39, 43, 46–7, 78–9, 135–6, 158; 290 78
Radiation Laboratory, Massachusetts Institute of Technology 73, 116

Ralston, J.L. 14, 59, 91, 115
Raymond, D.L. 134, 154
Renfrew, Ontario 93
Research Enterprises Limited: dismantling of 163; NRC, relations with 62–3, 111–16; and the navy 63, 113–4, 143; and radar committee 58–60; radar production at 35–6, 74, 79, 81, 111–16, 118, 159–60; and SW1C 41, 44. See also NRC
Reid, H.E. 36, 41, 82, 108, 116–17, 165; asdic production 29; establishes Halifax Station 28
Roosevelt, F.D.R. 136
Rose, D.C. 9, 15, 37, 152
Rowland, J.M. 108, 116–17, 140
Royal Canadian Air Force 7, 14, 16, 44, 61, 106
Royal Canadian Navy; pre-war organization 6–11; relations with NRC 56–8, 73–6; relations with RN 10, 24–5, 65–6, 82–3, 122, 130–1, 157. See also NSHQ

St Hyacinthe, Quebec 120–1
Saint John, New Brunswick 91
St John's, Newfoundland 47, 56, 110, 116–17
Science. See Acoustics, Asdic, Operational research, NRC, Radar
Shenstone, A.G. 70
Ships: Athenia 23; Target 98
Signals, Directorate. See Worth
Smith, A.H.R. 68–9
Smyth, H.R. 16, 43–4, 62, 76, 81, 112–13
Somerville, James 88
Sonar. See Asdic
Sperry Corporation 86
Stephens, G.L. 139, 142

Strange, William 135–7, 140
Steel, W.A. 13, 15, 16

Task Force 24 105
Taylor, E.P. 59
Telecommunications Research
Establishment 72
Tizard mission 34, 61, 70, 72
Torch, Operation 93
Toronto, University of 11, 28, 87,
155
Tory, H.M. 12–14
Turnbull, A.D. 152

U-boats: U29 23; U30 24; U356 97
United States: HF/DF 124, 163;
Navy 95, 104, 106, 123; radar
76–7, 79–80, 158–9; scientific
liaison with 69–71

Wallace, F.C. and NRC 61–3; and
REL 111, 113–14, 116
Walsh, H.L. 155
Warships
– Allied: O-15 45–6
– British: Celandine 136; Courageous
23; Duncan 135; Fidelity 98;
Forester 136; Itchen 96, 136; Orchis
72–3; Polyanthus 96
– Canadian: Agassiz 136;
Assiniboine 135; Battleford 98;

Beaver 47; Calgary 126;
Chambly 38, 45, 72; Chilliwack 98;
Edmonston 93, 116, 125–6;
Galt 136; Kenogami 98; Moose
Jaw 38; Naponee 98; Portage 122;
Port Arthur 81, 83, 112;
Restigouche 55, 80, 83, 108;
Sackville 48, 136; Saguenay 7, 82;
St Boniface 122; St Croix 96; St
Laurent 98, 135; Shediac 97;
Skeena 7, 82, 100; Standard
Coaster 95; Wallaceburg 119;
Winnipeg 120
– German: Graf Spee 23
Warren, J.A. 112–13
War Supply Board 31
Welsy-Everard, P.H.E. 159
Westdale Technical School 87
Western Escort Force 121
Western Ontario, University of 42
Wilson, Carol 70–1
Windeyer, Guy 97
Woods Hole Oceanographic
Institute 132
Worth, G.A. 79–80, 82–4, 166;
appointment as DSD 53; confronta-
tion with Mackenzie 156–8; and
RX/C 122–3; and RX/U 117
Wylie, F.J. 83

Zimmerman, A.H. 116